DELIVERING A CLIMATE NEUTRAL EUROPE

Delivering a Climate Neutral Europe summarises the achievements of 25 years of EU Climate Policy, with the emphasis on what has been achieved under the Green Deal. It also highlights climate issues on the table of policy makers in the next European policy cycle 2024–2029.

Curated by Jos Delbeke, one of the foremost experts in this field, the chapters are all written by responsible officials of the EU Commission services, who were deeply involved in the negotiations related to the legislation they prepared. They explain how ambitious targets were prepared for 2030 and 2050 in view of implementing the commitments taken in 2015 under the Paris Agreement and present the overall architecture of the policy to counter the idea that an avalanche of legislative action is being developed without much structure. In particular, this book examines the carbon pricing tool that Europe implemented under the EU Emissions Trading System (EU ETS), the differentiated targets Member States have to deliver and climate-relevant EU legislation in the fields of energy, transport, industry, finance and agriculture and forestry. The authors also discuss the upcoming headwinds in the form of a growing scepticism in public opinion, and the impact of the wars in the close neighbourhood of the European continent.

Written as a follow-up to previous publications *EU Climate Policy Explained* and *Towards a Climate-Neutral Europe*, this new volume will be a vital resource for students, scholars and policy makers alike who are researching and working in the areas of climate change, environmental governance and EU policy more broadly.

Jos Delbeke holds the first EIB Chair on Climate Policy and International Carbon Markets and was previously Director-General of the European Commission's DG for Climate Action (2010–2018). Delbeke was involved in setting the EU's climate and energy targets for 2020 and 2030 and in developing EU legislation on the Emissions Trading System (ETS), cars and fuels, air quality, emissions from big industrial installations and chemicals (REACH). He developed Europe's International Climate Change strategy and was the European Commission's chief negotiator at the UNFCCC Conference of the Parties, playing a key role in the EU's implementation of the Kyoto Protocol and in negotiations on the Paris Agreement.

DELIVERING A CLIMATE NEUTRAL EUROPE

Edited by
Jos Delbeke

Routledge
Taylor & Francis Group
LONDON AND NEW YORK

earthscan
from Routledge

Designed cover image: Getty

First published 2024
by Routledge
4 Park Square, Milton Park, Abingdon, Oxon OX14 4RN

and by Routledge
605 Third Avenue, New York, NY 10158

Routledge is an imprint of the Taylor & Francis Group, an informa business

British Library Cataloguing-in-Publication Data
A catalogue record for this book is available from the British Library

ISBN: 978-1-032-79760-1 (hbk)
ISBN: 978-1-032-79761-8 (pbk)
ISBN: 978-1-003-49373-0 (ebk)

DOI: 10.4324/9781003493730

Typeset in Times New Roman
by codeMantra

CONTENTS

List of Illustrations   *xv*
List of Contributors   *xix*
Foreword   *xxv*
Introduction   *xxvii*

PART 1
Climate Action in the EU and the World   **1**

1   EU Climate Policy After 25 Years: Looking Back,
    Looking Ahead   3
    Jos Delbeke

    Introduction 3
    1.1   Climate Change Is Happening 3
    1.2   EU Greenhouse Gas Emissions Reduced by
    *   32.5% between 1990 and 2022 7*
    1.3   Building Further on the Cornerstones of EU
    *   Climate Policy 11*
    *   1.3.1   The Politics: A Vision Endorsed by the*
    *   Highest Political Level 11*
    *   1.3.2   The Economics: Putting an Explicit*
    *   Price on Carbon 14*
    *   1.3.3   The Technicalities: Designing Policies*
    *   Based on Solid Preparation 18*
    1.4   Anchoring Climate into a Strengthened
    *   Geopolitical EU Strategy 23*
    *   1.4.1   The Climate Transition as Part of an*
    *   EU Geopolitical Industrial Strategy 23*

1.4.2   *Investing in Social and Regional Cohesion 25*

1.4.3   *Investing in Removals 27*

1.4.4   *Raising Much More Sustainable Finance 28*

1.4.5   *Addressing Adaptation 29*

Conclusion 31

2   The Paris Agreement   35

Jacob Werksman and Jos Delbeke

Introduction 35

2.1   *The UN Framework Convention on Climate Change and the Kyoto Protocol 35*

2.2   *From the Failure of Copenhagen (2009) to the Success of the Paris Agreement (2015) 38*

2.3   *Essential Features of the Paris Agreement 42*

    2.3.1   *Applicable to All Parties 42*

    2.3.2   *Ambitious Collective Goals 43*

    2.3.3   *Dynamic Five Year Ambition Cycles 44*

    2.3.4   *Transparency and Accountability 45*

    2.3.5   *Increasing Resilience to and Responding to the Adverse Effects of Climate Change 46*

    2.3.6   *Fostering Cooperation and Financial Flows 47*

2.4   *Are Global Emissions Peaking? 48*

2.5   *The International Dimensions of the European Green Deal 49*

    2.5.1   *Sharing Lessons on the Climate and Energy Transition 50*

    2.5.2   *Trade-related Climate Measures 50*

    2.5.3   *Mobilising Sustainable Finance 51*

Conclusion 52

PART 2

The EU Emissions Trading System   57

3   The EU Emissions Trading System   59

Damien Meadows, Mette Quinn, and Beatriz Yordi

Introduction 59
3.1 *How Does the EU Emissions Trading System Work? 59*
3.2 *Price and Emissions Development 61*
3.3 *The Creation of the Market Stability Reserve 64*
3.4 *A Strengthening of the Emissions Cap 2024–2030 67*
3.5 *The Creation of ETS2 for Road Transport, Buildings, and Smaller Industry 70*
    3.5.1 *Defining the ETS2 Cap Trajectory 71*
    3.5.2 *The Market Stability Reserve for ETS2 71*
    3.5.3 *Gradual Implementation and Safeguards for a Smooth Start 72*
3.6 *The Growing Importance of EU ETS Revenues 73*
    3.6.1 *Raising Revenue through Auctioning of Allowances 73*
    3.6.2 *EU Solidarity and the Use of Auctioning Revenue 75*
    3.6.3 *The Social Climate Fund 77*
Conclusion 77

4   Addressing Carbon Leakage under the EU ETS   83
    Damien Meadows, Beatriz Yordi and Peter Vis

Introduction 83
4.1 *The Problem of Carbon Leakage 83*
4.2 *The EU Approach to Free Allocation 84*
    4.2.1 *Benchmarks 85*
    4.2.2 *Carbon Leakage List 88*
    4.2.3 *Seizing the Benefit of Technological Progress 89*
    4.2.4 *The Correction Factor 90*
    4.2.5 *The State Aid Provisions and the New Entrants Reserve 91*
4.3 *The Creation of a Carbon Border Adjustment Mechanism (CBAM) 92*
    4.3.1 *The CBAM Design 92*
    4.3.2 *Defining the CBAM Liability 92*

    4.3.3   *Reduction for a Carbon Price Paid 95*
    4.3.4   *Monitoring the Introduction of*
             CBAM 96
    4.3.5   *CBAM as an Impetus for More*
             Intensive Policy Cooperation 97
  Conclusion 99

5   The International Dimension of the EU ETS   104
    Damien Meadows and Beatriz Yordi

  Introduction 104
  5.1 *International Cooperation on Carbon*
      Markets 104
  5.2 *Experience with International Credits 108*
  5.3 *Aviation Emissions 109*
    5.3.1   *The International Governance for*
             Aviation Emissions 109
    5.3.2   *The EU ETS Includes Aviation within*
             Europe 112
    5.3.3   *The 2023 EU ETS Review 114*
    5.3.4   *Sustainable Aviation Fuels 116*
    5.3.5   *Development of CORSIA within*
             ICAO 117
  5.4 *Maritime Emissions 121*
    5.4.1   *The International Governance of*
             Shipping Emissions 121
    5.4.2   *Extension of EU ETS to Maritime*
             Emissions 123
    5.4.3   *Developments in the IMO 127*
  Conclusion 129

PART 3
Climate Action by Member States and
Economic Sectors   **137**

6   The Effort Sharing Regulation   139
    Cecile Hanoune

  Introduction 139
  6.1 *Emissions from the Effort Sharing Sectors 139*
  6.2 *Effort Sharing 2013–2020 142*
    6.2.1   *Setting Differentiated Targets 142*

6.2.2   *Developing More Elements of Redistribution 142*

6.2.3   *Experience to Date 145*

6.2.4   *Flexible Provisions 145*

6.3   *Differentiation and Flexibilities Allowed for 2021–2030 147*

6.3.1   *Continuation of the Differentiated Target Approach 147*

6.3.2   *More Differentiation among Member States 149*

6.3.3   *Towards More Convergence among Member States by 2030 151*

6.3.4   *Starting Point and Trajectories 152*

6.3.5   *Flexibility with the Emissions Trading System 154*

6.3.6   *Flexibility to Land Use Change and Forestry Sectors 156*

6.3.7   *Flexibility Linked to Earlier Over-Achievement 157*

6.3.8   *The 2030 Targets as Adopted 158*

6.4   *An Energy and Climate Governance System 158*

6.4.1   *Integrated Energy and Climate Governance and the Climate Law 158*

6.4.2   *National Climate and Energy Plans 160*

Conclusion 162

7   Climate-Related Regulations in the Field of Energy, Transport, F-gases and Methane   166

Edoardo Turano and Tom Van Ierland

Introduction 166

7.1   *Renewable Energy 167*

7.1.1   *A Binding EU-Wide Target 167*

7.1.2   *Biomass 169*

7.2   *Electricity and Gas Market Integration and Climate Policy 171*

7.2.1   *The Challenge of Integrating Renewable Energy 171*

7.2.2   *The Combined Effects of Electricity Market Reform and Carbon Pricing 173*

7.2.3   *Strengthened Role for Consumers 174*

7.3   Energy Efficiency 175
    7.3.1   Energy Dependence, the Import Bill
           and Barriers to Energy Efficiency 175
    7.3.2   The EU's Bottom-up Approach and the
           Energy Efficiency Directive 176
    7.3.3   Regulating the Energy Use and
           Labelling of Products and Devices 177
    7.3.4   Addressing the Energy Efficiency of
           Buildings 178
7.4   Emissions from Road Transport 179
    7.4.1   Biofuels and Renewable Energy in the
           Transport Sector 180
    7.4.2   Regulating Zero CO_2 Emissions from
           Cars and Vans by 2035 182
    7.4.3   Emissions from Heavy-Duty Vehicles
           (HDV), such as Lorries and Buses 184
7.5   Phasing Down the Use of Fluorinated Gases 188
    7.5.1   Addressing the Hole in the Ozone Layer
           Internationally 188
    7.5.2   EU legislation Implementing the
           Montreal Protocol and the Kigali
           Amendment 188
7.6   The EU Methane Strategy 190
Conclusion 193

8   Removals and Emissions from Agriculture and Forestry   198
    Christian Holzleitner, Artur Runge-Metzger
    and Sevim Aktas

Introduction 198
8.1   The Role of the Land Use Sector in Mitigating
      and Removing Greenhouse Gas Emissions 199
8.2   The LULUCF Carbon Sink in the EU 201
    8.2.1   Evolution of LULUCF: From Kyoto
           Protocol to Ambitious EU Targets 202
    8.2.2   Building Further on the 2018 LULUCF
           Regulation 203
8.3   Scaling Up Carbon Removals and Ensuring
      Credibility 208
8.4   An Enabling Environment for Climate Action
      in Forestry and Agriculture 208
Conclusion 211

9   Accelerating the Greening of EU Industry   214
    Stefaan Vergote and Christian Egenhofer

    Introduction 214
    9.1   The New Policy Context 214
    9.2   The Innovation Fund 218
    9.3   The Battery Alliance 221
    *9.4   The Role of State Aid: The Temporary Crisis
          and Transition Framework (TCTF) 223*
    *9.5   The Hydrogen Bank and EU-Level Auctioning
          under the Innovation Fund 224*
    9.6   Towards a European Net-Zero Industry 227
          9.6.1   Net-Zero Industry Act (NZIA) 228
          9.6.2   Critical Raw Materials Act 229
          *9.6.3   Strategic Technologies for Europe
                  Platform (STEP) 230*
    Conclusion 231

10 The Greening of EU Finance   235
    Laura Iozzelli and Yvon Slingenberg

    Introduction 235
    10.1 The EU Sustainable Finance Strategy 235
          10.1.1   The EU Taxonomy 236
          10.1.2   Disclosure Rules 238
          10.1.3   Benchmarks and Green Bonds 239
          *10.1.4   The EU and the International
                   Approach to Sustainable Finance 240*
    10.2 Mainstreaming Climate in the EU Budget 243
          *10.2.1   The Climate Mainstreaming
                   Target 243*
          10.2.2   The Specific Programme Targets 244
    10.3 The EIB becomes the EU's Climate Bank 249
    Conclusion 251

11 Conclusion   255
    Jos Delbeke

Index   *259*

ILLUSTRATIONS

Figures

1.1 Increase of global temperature compared to 1850–1900 levels 4
1.2 Increase of global emissions resulting from human activities 5
1.3 From Holocene to Anthropocene 7
1.4 EU emissions and removals by sector, past trends, and required reductions 8
1.5 EU: Decoupling economic growth from CO_2 emissions 1990–2022 10
1.6 Global *per capita* greenhouse gas emissions 1850–2021 11
1.7 Pathway to climate neutrality in the EU 19
1.8 The structure of EU climate policy 21
2.1 Fossil CO_2 emissions of the major economies, 1970–2021 (in Gt) 39
3.1 Price trends for allowances under the EU ETS and EU ETS eligible international credits (CERs) under the Kyoto Protocol (€/tonne) 62
3.2 Emissions cap in the EU ETS compared with verified emissions, 2005–2030 63
3.3 Surplus of EU ETS allowances with cumulative number of international UNFCCC credits used in EU ETS up to 2022 65
3.4 Outlook on the estimated supply and demand of allowances until 2030 69
3.5 Revenues from EU ETS and their reported use in 2013–2022 74
4.1 Share of free allocation (%) in 2021–2023 85
5.1 Carbon pricing initiatives in place or in development 106
5.2 Average annual per capita jet fuel use in litres, 2019 110
5.3 Domestic and international shipping emissions [1990–2021] ($MtCO_2$-eq) 122
6.1 Main greenhouse gas emitting Effort Sharing sectors in 2021 140

6.2 2020 national effort sharing targets compared to 2005
resulting from the methodology in relation to 2005 GDP
per capita   143

6.3 Distribution of costs of the 2020 climate and energy
package, comparing impacts of cost efficient distribution
of non-ETS and renewable energy target with
re-distributed targets and auctioning revenue based on
relative income levels   144

6.4 Difference between Member States' 2020 target under
the Effort Sharing Decision and emissions in the
Effort Sharing sectors in 2020 (in % of 2005 base year
emissions). Positive and negative values, respectively,
indicate over-delivery and shortfall   146

6.5 Comparison between 2020 targets and 2030 targets
applying updated methodology   148

6.6 Gap between GDP-based 2030 targets and cost-efficient
emission reductions for high income Member States
(as a % of 2005 emissions)   150

6.7 *Per capita* emissions in the Effort Sharing sectors in
2005 and projected *per capita* allowed emissions in the
Effort Sharing sectors by 2030   152

6.8 Stylised representation of possible extreme options to
set the starting point in 2021 for the Annual Emissions
Allocation and the subsequent linear target trajectory to
the 2030 target   153

6.9 Representation of the updated linear target trajectory to
the 2030 target under different scenarios   155

6.10 Member States 2030 reduction targets in the non-ETS
sectors as well as maximum amount of EU ETS flexiblity
and LULUCF credit flexibility *per* Member State   159

7.1 Global weighted average levelised cost of electricity
(2010–2021)   169

7.2 Energy efficiency trends and the 2030 targets   176

7.3 Evolution of EU greenhouse gas emissions from
transport, 1990–2021   179

7.4 Average emission standards for new passenger cars   185

7.5 Methane emissions in EU 1990–2021 and projections
until 2030 ($MtCO_2eq$)   191

8.1 Land use and agriculture in EU climate policies   200

8.2 LULUCF emissions and removals by source and emissions   201

8.3 Net removal targets for EU Member States   204

9.1   Regional shares of manufacturing capacity for selected
       clean technologies   217
9.2   The Innovation Fund as part of the innovation value chain 219
9.3   The role of the Member States in the EU hydrogen auction 227
10.1   The pillars of the EU sustainable finance framework   237
10.2   ERDF, CF and Interreg EU climate amounts by policy area 246
10.3   Main pillars of the EIB climate strategy   250

Tables

4.1   Initial benchmark values for 2013–2020 (tonne CO_2 per
       1000 tonnes of output produced), and the benchmark
       values that apply for 2021–2025   86
4.2   Reductions of transitional ETS free allocations over 2026–2034   94
5.1   Aircraft operators – verified emissions, free allocation and
       allowances auctioned   113
6.1   2030 targets compared to 2005 emission levels for ESR
       sectors *per* Member State   151
6.2   Maximum allowed LULUCF credits for potential use to
       comply with effort sharing targets; million tonnes of CO_2
       equivalent   157
8.1   LULUCF regulation   206
9.1   Innovation fund supported production capacities
       contributing to NZIA objectives   228

CONTRIBUTORS

Sevim Aktas is a policy officer at the European Commission's Directorate-General for Climate Action, where she works in the unit for Land Economy and Carbon Removals. Before joining the DG CLIMA, Sevim worked in the energy market unit in DG ENER. Preceding her involvement in public service, she worked in the private sector at Knauf Energy Solutions. Sevim holds a degree in Energy Systems from the University of Oxford and a degree in Engineering from the University of Twente.

Jos Delbeke holds the first EIB Chair on Climate Policy and International Carbon Markets and was previously Director-General of the European Commission's DG for Climate Action (2010–2018). Delbeke was involved in setting the EU's climate and energy targets for 2020 and 2030, and in developing EU legislation on the Emissions Trading System (ETS), cars and fuels, air quality, emissions from big industrial installations and chemicals (REACH). He developed Europe's International Climate Change strategy and was the European Commission's chief negotiator at the UNFCCC Conference of the Parties, playing a key role in the EU's implementation of the Kyoto Protocol and in negotiations on the Paris Agreement.

Christian Egenhofer is Senior Research Associate at the Florence School of Transnational Governance at the European University Institute (EUI) in Florence, Italy. Prior to this, from 2000 to 2019, he was Head of the Energy, Climate and Resources programme at the Centre for European Policy Studies (CEPS) in Brussels. He is also Visiting Professor at the Paris School of International Affairs at SciencesPo in Paris and at the College of Europe in Natolin. Throughout his career, he has published eight books and written more than 160 articles, book chapters or policy reports. Selected articles and book chapters have been translated into ten languages. He holds a Master in Business Administration from the University of Konstanz, Germany, and LLM (Public Law Degree, A-grade; qualifying exam for civil service).

Cecile Hanoune is heading the unit responsible for Climate Governance, Plans and Mainstreaming in the European Commission's Directorate-General for Climate Action. Previously she held various positions in the same Directorate-General, focusing on policy development and implementation of the EU Emission Trading System and on the EU overall climate action strategies and the economic analysis underpinning them, as well as in the Directorate-General for Communications Networks, Content and Technology. Before joining the Commission in 2005, she worked for the French Ministry of Environment. She holds academic degrees in political sciences (IEP – Strasbourg) and local environmental management (ESSEC business school – Cergy-Pontoise).

Christian Holzleitner is the head of Unit for Land Economy and Carbon Removals at the European Commission, responsible for the revision of the LULUCF Regulation, the new Framework for the Certification of Carbon Removals and Carbon Farming and the Commission proposal for Forest Monitoring. Before, Christian played a pivotal role as the head of Unit in developing and implementing the EU's Innovation Fund, a financial instrument designed to support innovative low-carbon technologies. He has been with the European Commission for over 19 years and has held a variety of positions in the Directorate-General for Climate Action and Directorate-General for Competition. He holds a PhD in economics from the University of Linz.

Laura Iozzelli is a research fellow at the European University Institute's Florence School of Transnational Governance. Her research focuses primarily on the EU sustainable finance agenda and sustainability reporting rules. Laura is also a senior associate researcher at the Brussels School of Governance Centre for Environment, Economy and Energy. Prior to joining the EUI, she was Lecturer in EU politics and international relations at the UCLouvain Saint-Louis Bruxelles. She holds a joint PhD in political science from the Vrije Universiteit Brussel and the UCLouvain Saint-Louis Bruxelles.

Damien Meadows is the advisor on European and International Carbon Markets at the European Commission's Directorate-General for Climate Action. He has been involved in developing market-based responses to climate change since 2000, including as Head of the European Commission's unit for the International Carbon Market, Aviation and Maritime, and as Deputy Head of the unit responsible for the EU ETS from 2006 to 2010. He has worked on the drafting, negotiation and implementation of the EU ETS, ratification of the Kyoto Protocol and other climate-related legislation. He also worked on the negotiation and adoption of the REACH law that comprehensively reformed

EU chemicals regulation. Before joining the European Commission, he was a solicitor in the UK, working for the UK government and in private practice, as well as for the UNFCCC Secretariat at COP4.

Mette Quinn has been the head of Unit for ETS Coordination and International Carbon Markets in the European Commission's Directorate-General for Climate Action since January 2022. Before that she was Head of the Directorate-General's Unit for ETS Implementation. She has also worked on innovation policy, climate finance and mainstreaming and took part in the Paris Agreement negotiations. She is an economist and worked in Denmark's Representation to NATO and in the Danish Ministry of Foreign Affairs before joining the European Commission in 2004.

Artur Runge-Metzger is currently a fellow at the Mercator Research Institute on Global Commons and Climate Change, Berlin, and a member of the boards of AGORA and Germanwatch, and the sustainability advisory council of Novo Nordisk, Copenhagen. Until his retirement in early 2021, he was Director at the European Commission in charge of developing climate neutrality strategies and the governance of EU climate policy, regulating emissions from non-ETS sectors and supporting innovation in the EU's energy and industrial sectors (e.g. Innovation and Modernisation Fund). He served on the Boards of the European Environment Agency and the European Fund for Strategic Investments. From 2003 until the conclusion of the Paris Agreement in 2015, he led on international climate negotiations for the EU. He co-chaired the working group preparing the Paris Agreement in 2013–2014 and was a member of the UNFCCC Bureau from 2010 to 2012. Between 1993 and 2003, he worked as European Commission Official in Sarajevo, Brussels and Harare. Until 1993, he conducted research in West Africa and lectured at the University of Göttingen. He holds a doctoral degree in agricultural economics.

Yvon Slingenberg is Acting Deputy Director General of DG CLIMA and Director in DG CLIMA for "Strategy, Analysis & Planning" since June 2023 and January 2022, respectively. Before then, she was Director responsible for Climate strategy, Governance and Emissions from Non-Trading Sectors, i.e. in charge of different parts of the "Fit for 55" package of proposals, as well as DG CLIMA's contribution to the Recovery and Resilience Facility.

From end 2016 to end 2020, she was Director responsible for international climate negotiations, cooperation with third countries on the implementation of the Paris Agreement, EU Action on adaptation and resilience and mainstreaming of climate issues in EU policies. During the first two years of the Juncker Commission (2015–2016), she was Senior Adviser in the Cabinet of Commissioner Arias Cañete for Climate Action and Energy, where she steered the work on the legislative framework to achieve the 2030 climate and energy targets. From 2007 to 2014, she was DG CLIMA Head of Unit in charge of implementing the EU Emissions Trading System. From 2003 to 2007, Yvon was in charge of the chemicals policy unit and negotiated the new chemicals legislation (REACH) in DG Environment. She has also worked in the Cabinet of Commissioner Wallström on environment and climate issues (2002–2003), for the European Commission's Task-force for the World Summit on Sustainable Development in 2002 (Johannesburg), in the international climate negotiations (1998–2002) and in the "Waste Management Policy" Unit. Yvon is a lawyer of Dutch nationality with a degree in international law (specialisation in environmental law) from the University of Amsterdam. She speaks Dutch (mother tongue), English, French, German and Spanish.

Edoardo Turano is an engineer and currently Head of Unit for road mobility in the European Commission's Directorate-General for Climate Action, where he was also previously Deputy Head of Unit. Before this, he worked as Policy Officer in the European Commission in different climate-related files, including the EU ETS, Governance of the Energy Union and Climate Action, Monitoring, Reporting and Verification of GHG emissions at domestic and international level.

Tom Van Ierland joined the Commission in 2006. Within DG Climate Action he is Head of Unit C1 "Low carbon solutions (I): Montreal Protocol, clean cooling & heating, twin transitions". This unit is leading on policies related to F-gases and ozone-depleting substances and looks into the interconnections of the policy fields of climate, energy, digitalisation and standardisation. He has been closely involved in the development of the overall climate change policy framework both at the EU and international level and the economic modelling underpinning it. He started his career at the Belgian's Federal Planning Bureau in 1999 where he focused on emission trading. He was a member of Cabinet of the Belgian Federal Minister for the Environment. He worked two years as Consultant for PricewaterhouseCoopers. He has a broad experience both in the international negotiations on climate change as well as in the development of EU Climate Change policies. He holds academic degrees in Applied Economics, Environmental Economics and Computer Sciences from the University of Leuven and University College London.

Stefaan Vergote is the advisor for low carbon innovation in the European Commission's Directorate-General for Climate Action. He has previously held positions as Head of Unit for "Research & Low Carbon Solutions" and for "Strategy and Economic Analysis" in the Directorate-General for Climate Action, as well as Head of Unit for "Economic Analysis and Financial Instruments" in Directorate-General for Energy. He holds a degree in electro-mechanical engineering and a postgraduate degree in environmental management from the University of Leuven.

Peter Vis is a senior research associate at the Florence School of Transnational Governance at the European University Institute. He also works part time for Rud Pedersen Public Affairs in Brussels. He is a former official of the European Commission (1990–2019), where he worked on climate, energy, transport and taxation policies. From 2010–2014, he was Chief of Staff to the European Commissioner for Climate Action, Connie Hedegaard. He also worked in the Private Office of Andris Piebalgs, European Commissioner for Energy, from 2007 to 2010. He has an MA (History) from the University of Cambridge, UK.

Jacob Werksman has, since 2012, served as Principal Adviser to Directorate-General for Climate Action in the European Commission, where his work focuses on the international aspects of European climate policy. He is Head of Delegation for the European Union to the Paris Agreement and the UN Framework Convention on Climate Change, and advises the Commission with regard to international partnerships to reduce greenhouse gas emissions. He supports the Commission Executive Vice President for the European Green Deal and the European External Action Service in strengthening bilateral relationships between the EU and major economies, including the United States, India and other international partners.

Werksman is an international lawyer, specialising in international environmental law and international economic law. Prior to joining the Commission, he provided legal and policy advice to developed and developing country governments, NGOs and international institutions in the context of the multilateral negotiations on climate change, biosafety and trade. He has taught and published widely on the international legal dimensions of climate policy, including on the design of compliance mechanisms, climate finance and on the relationship between carbon markets and international trade and investment agreements.

Werksman is currently Visiting Professor at the Fletcher School of Law and Diplomacy, and has lectured in international environmental and economic law at the master's level at New York University Law School, Georgetown University Law Center, and at the School of Oriental and African Studies and University College at the University of London. Prior to joining the Commission, he held posts at the World Resources Institute, the Rockefeller Foundation, United Nations Development Programme and the Foundation for International Environmental Law and Development (FIELD) in London. Werksman holds degrees from Columbia University (AB), the University of Michigan (JD) and the University of London (LLM).

Beatriz Yordi is Director in DG Climate Action, responsible for the EU Emissions Trading System (ETS) and international cooperation on carbon markets, a pillar of the Fit for 55 European Commission package, as well as for the promotion of clean mobility on roads, air, water and rail. Notable examples include CO_2 standards for cars and vans with the 2035 target, and the current heavy duty vehicles dossier. She negotiated the reform of carbon markets, with increasing ambition in aviation and the inclusion of the maritime sector in the ETS, as well as the creation of the new Emissions trading system in Roads and Buildings (ETS II). She has been the director responsible for designing and negotiating the Social Climate Fund, which is key for a fair green transition.

She has been a pioneer in renewable energy policies, joining the European Commission in 1994, working on Eco-innovation, Green businesses and in different Commission Departments in DG Energy, DG Environment and EASME. She has been leading CLIMA negotiations in the EU-UK Trade agreement. Her career began at the Research Centre CIEMAT and this was followed by the role as young Chief Engineer in Endesa-RWE and Naturgy's joint venture designing and constructing the first European solar PV plant. She specialised in Fundamental Physics at the University of Santiago de Compostela.

FOREWORD

Climate change is and will remain with us. It is the challenge of a generation. Currently, we see its impacts increasing wherever we look. Copernicus just reported that 2023 has been the hottest year ever recorded, with temperatures already getting very close to 1.5°C. Floods, droughts and forest fires are becoming the "new normal", in Europe and for the world at large. Some vulnerable countries already face prohibitive climate costs and small island states risk disappearing altogether.

This book explains wonderfully how EU climate action developed over more than two decades. It gives great insights into how politicians, policymakers and stakeholders continued the course to a greener future while constantly fine-tuning the climate policy toolbox. It also gives important pointers to where the opportunities and pitfalls for future climate action may lie.

We are on the right track to fight climate change. Yet, a lot more needs to be done. The agreement at COP28 to transition away from fossil fuels needs to be put into action sooner rather than later.

In the EU, work is underway to become climate neutral by 2050 and reduce greenhouse gas emissions by at least 55% by 2030. With improvements in energy efficiency and a rapid build-up of renewable energy, the EU's energy mix has already profoundly changed.

But this is only a start. The European Green Deal represents a comprehensive package of measures covering all economic sectors, from energy, transport and industry to environment, agriculture and circular economy. The legislation to achieve the 2030 climate goals is now adopted and being implemented. This is our main framework to shape the green transition for the benefit of citizens and industries.

For the success of this transition, we need a massive shift towards investments in net zero technology. Getting the right economic incentives in place, combined with regulatory predictability, is key. The EU Emission Trading Scheme (ETS) plays a crucial role in this regard. It makes the polluter pay for their emissions and has become the engine of continued reductions.

The ETS creates a business case to reduce emissions at the lowest cost, it triggers and rewards low-carbon innovation and through its revenues it allows Member States to support regions and different societal groups in their transition. More and more countries in the world are embracing carbon pricing, and the Carbon Border Adjustment Mechanism that the EU is implementing can be a helpful instrument.

Climate change is a global crisis. Russia's brutal invasion of Ukraine and the conflict in the Middle East are clear wake-up calls and underline the need for all countries to manage their dependencies including in energy and raw materials. Diversifying value chains, investing in the build-up of the circular economy and restoring nature and biodiversity will be essential foundations for the future.

Cooperation across countries and continents can strengthen the climate transition while demonstrating the continued strength of multilateralism. The EU is determined to take leadership in this endeavour by implementing the European Green Deal and its objectives in an ambitious and cooperative manner, taking along citizens, businesses and international partners.

Wopke Hoekstra
European Commissioner for Climate Action

INTRODUCTION

This is the third book in what became *de facto* a series that started in 2015[1] about how EU Climate Policy developed over the last 25 years. The first one described the planting of the seeds, the second is its growing up to adolescence, and this third one is about its coming to maturity. It started as a review of the previous edition but ended up as a self-standing new book capturing the major and multiple policy changes that happened under the Green Deal up to 1 January 2024.

This does not suggest that EU Climate Policy will not develop further, as new challenges are looming around the corner. For instance, climate neutrality will not be achieved by 2050 unless carbon removals are developed at scale. Moreover, the changing geopolitical context, notably with two wars at the doorstep of Europe, will undoubtedly influence many policies, including on climate.

More fundamentally, climate change is far from being solved. The global temperature keeps increasing, and the increasingly intense impacts in terms of floods, droughts and forest fires, just to mention a few, are becoming visible to every citizen. Sadly, emissions of greenhouse gases are still increasing even if these are expected to peak in a not-too-distant future. Europe has shown leadership and reduced its emissions by 32.5% since 1990 without harming its economic growth. Per head emissions have been steadily reduced from 12 to 7 tonnes. EU policies have been crucial to deliver this reduction, and the emphasis should now shift towards intensifying cooperation with the world based on the best elements of this experience.

Most chapters of this book have been written by my former colleagues and friends at the European Commission. I am very grateful to all of them, not least because they spared precious time out of their busy work schedules. They played a crucial role in the legislation they were writing about as most of them were literally holding the pen. They oversaw not only the early beginnings of each piece of legislation but were also involved in the complex negotiation between the European Parliament and the Council, and the finalisation of the legal texts.

I would like to thank the EIB Institute for their support in creating the first EIB Chair in Climate Change Policy and International Carbon Markets at the European University Institute (EUI). I am grateful to the climate team of the School of Transnational Governance at EUI led by Barry O'Connell for the many comments and invaluable assistance in editing this book.

This book has three parts and focuses on the reduction of greenhouse gas emissions, more than on adaptation to climate change. The first part gives an overview of the targets and policies the EU has been adopting within the context of the Paris Agreement. The opening chapter is to some extent an introduction and conclusion combined. It also raises policy issues that are likely to land on the table of the incoming members of the European Parliament and the Commission later in 2024. The second part deals with the EU ETS, the emissions trading system which was fundamentally reviewed and strengthened. A Carbon Border Adjustment Mechanism and an adjacent trading system covering transport and heating fuels have been added, while the international dimension of carbon pricing is steadily growing. In the third part, critical pieces of climate-related legislation are reviewed in the sectors of energy, transport, industry, agriculture and finance. A governance system is monitoring the implementation of the targets of each Member State.

To some extent this is also a personal book. It covers my involvement in EU climate policy since the late 1990s, when I started the journey as a young official at the European Commission. I had the pleasure to oversee the birth of many pieces of legislation for two decades. More recently, I followed the development of the different parts of the legislation under the Green Deal with some more distance, as a professor at the European University Institute in Florence. I was able to observe from the first row the learning-by-doing process that started following the entry into force of the Kyoto Protocol and developed into comprehensive policy designed to deliver climate neutrality by 2050 as part of the EU Green Deal. I feel privileged for having been part of a fascinating journey that has hopefully contributed to solving the determinant problem of our time that global climate change represents.

Note

1 Delbeke, J. and Vis, P. (Eds.) (2015) *EU Climate Policy Explained.* Routledge, 136p.; Delbeke, J. and Vis, P. (Eds.) (2019) *Towards a Climate-Neutral Europe.* London: Routledge, 223p.

PART 1

Climate Action in the EU and the World

1

EU CLIMATE POLICY AFTER 25 YEARS

Looking Back, Looking Ahead

Jos Delbeke[1]

Introduction

Climate change policy at EU level first gathered momentum in the early 2000s when the ratification of the Kyoto Protocol needed to be rescued following the US decision not to ratify it. Member States realized that pooling their resources maximized their influence in multilateral negotiations and created opportunities in designing climate policies in the context of the single market. The Paris Agreement of 2015 replaced the Kyoto Protocol and received universal participation even if Parties still need to do a lot more to fully implement their commitments. The fight against climate change is not won yet, but the world is still in a position to avoid its catastrophic consequences.

This chapter looks back at what has been achieved in EU Climate Policy over the last 25 years and sketches out what could and probably should be done over the next decade. It starts with a review of some basic facts and highlights the significant emission reductions realized in the EU and the key elements that led to that result. The European Green Deal[2] developed over the last five years created a significant boost both in terms of increased ambition and involvement of more sectors and policy domains. Many detailed implementation issues still need to be sorted out and new challenges appear on the horizon. But a point of no return has been reached.

1.1 Climate Change Is Happening

Climate change is here, and the consequences are already felt over the entire world including the EU. The World Meteorological Organization (WMO) declared 2023 the warmest year ever recorded, both on land and in the oceans.[3] Frequent droughts, floods, and forest fires mark a clear manifestation of

DOI: 10.4324/9781003493730-2

what happens when global warming reaches 'only' some 1.2°C above pre-industrial levels. Worries about climate tipping points have far from receded, with, for instance, new scientific findings pointing to a potential weakening of the Gulf Stream system. Overall, weather patterns changed more profoundly and much earlier than anticipated.

The impact of climate change leads to adverse impacts for humans, the economy, and natural systems in different ways all over the globe. The extent of sea level rise may be limited to date, but the forecasts project that a complete melting of the Greenland ice sheet – even if occurring over a long period – could make sea levels rise by up to seven meters.[4] The consequences of expanded desertification in the Mediterranean and Africa will burden economic development, which could further boost migration pressures. The consequences of climate change are more acute in vulnerable developing countries, and several small island states notably in the Pacific are about to disappear.

Scientific evidence has been consistently offered by the Intergovernmental Panel on Climate Change (IPCC), based on peer-reviewed contributions from an overwhelming number of scientists from all over the world. The latest report[5] concludes that it is unequivocal that the planet is warming at an unprecedented speed, compared to past decades, centuries, and even millennia (Figure 1.1).

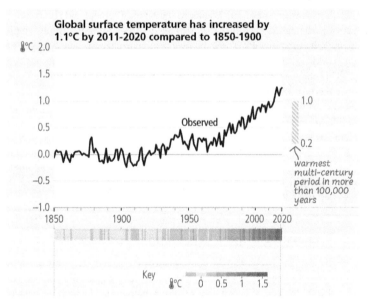

FIGURE 1.1 Increase of global temperature compared to 1850–1900 levels

Source: IPCC (2023)[6]

Humans are the cause of this global warming, mainly due to the emissions from the burning of fossil fuels. The world has not yet reached a peak in those emissions, although research indicates that this may finally happen in the coming years. The IPCC has concluded that the worst impacts of climate change can be avoided if global temperature increase is limited, in particular when kept below 1.5°C compared to pre-industrial times (Figure 1.2).[7]

The IPCC also calculated a "carbon budget" related to the 2°C temperature limit and indicated that about two-thirds has already been used mostly due to emissions originating from the industrialized countries from the Northern Hemisphere. A basic feature of the global understanding on how to tackle greenhouse gas emissions is that all developed and emerging economies must reduce their emissions as soon as possible, with the former achieving a faster rate of reductions to create space for countries that started their economic development much more recently.

Since 1992, when the UN Framework Convention on Climate Change (UNFCCC) was adopted, the world has changed profoundly as a new wave of industrialization occurred. It was, therefore, important that the Paris Agreement of 2015 agreed by consensus to step up economy-wide action in all countries. This will be necessary to reach its main goal to limit global average temperature rises as compared to pre-industrial levels to "well below 2°C" while "pursuing efforts to limit such a rise to 1.5°C". The latter

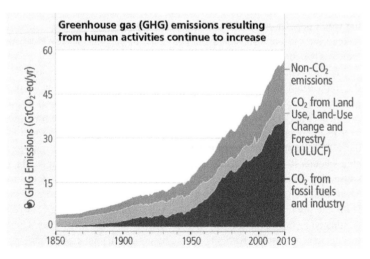

FIGURE 1.2   Increase of global emissions resulting from human activities

Source: IPCC (2023)[8]

figures endorse the scientific findings of the IPCC and represent a major challenge. The 1.5°C warming limit may already be crossed for a single year in the coming decade and quite likely for a longer period later this century. Ensuring only a very limited overshoot and bringing global warming back to levels of 1.5°C warming should, therefore, serve as the long-term objective. This will require a significantly larger role for carbon removals compared to what is needed to compensate for the few remaining emissions of greenhouse gases.

Countries and continents have very different emission profiles when it comes to greenhouse gases. In Europe as in most parts of the industrialized world, the main contributor is CO_2 emissions from fossil fuel use while in some other countries the major concern is deforestation or methane emissions from cattle. Not only do emissions differ significantly, income and wealth are also unevenly distributed across the globe. This variation pleads in favor of a policy approach allowing for considerable flexibility. The "bottom-up" approach as enshrined in the Paris Agreement through policy pledges made by Parties in their "Nationally Determined Contributions" captures the need for such flexibility.

Many observers wonder why more significant reductions of greenhouse gases have not been achieved in view of the compelling scientific evidence and the visible changes in the world's climate. The root cause lies in the fact that the use of fossil fuels – be it coal, oil, or gas – has permeated directly or indirectly into almost all features of modern society not least through consumption and production patterns as well as energy use in transport and heating. This makes daily life easy and comfortable but difficult to change. Moreover, the world population is still growing and developing countries are aspiring income and welfare levels comparable to those of the developed world. This indicates the complexity and magnitude of the task ahead.

Tackling climate change seems to require a revolution comparable to the 'Industrial Revolution' of the 18th century. Its essence will consist of a generalized use of low-carbon technology combined with a profound shift in human behavior. As Europe showed the way then, it can also now pioneer this new paradigm shift. The low-carbon revolution will require a lot more time compared to what is commonly assumed. It is even questionable whether it will be possible to bring climate change to a complete halt, so limiting its extent as much as possible seems a more realistic scenario. Meanwhile, scientists have started to refer to the geological cycle of the Holocene giving way to a new one, the Anthropocene, "a geological cycle dominated by man". Such a profound change would imply that we are about to enter new unknown territory triggered by the global temperature increase, accompanied by environmental pollution and an unprecedented loss of biodiversity (Figure 1.3).

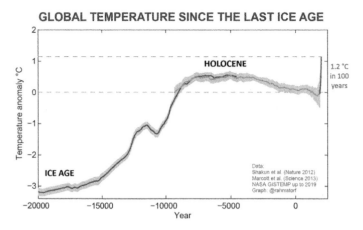

GLOBAL TEMPERATURE SINCE THE LAST ICE AGE

FIGURE 1.3   From Holocene to Anthropocene

Source: Stefan Rahmstorf (2020)[9]

Conclusion: Man-made emissions of greenhouse gases have been accumulating in the atmosphere since the Industrial Revolution, mainly because of increasing fossil fuel use. The world adopted the Paris Agreement in 2015 and agreed to limit global average temperature increase to "well below 2°C and pursuing efforts to 1.5°C". Parties submitted 'Nationally Determined Contributions' but implementation remains a challenge.

1.2   EU Greenhouse Gas Emissions Reduced by 32.5% between 1990 and 2022

Since 1990, the base year of the UNFCCC, the EU reduced its net emissions by 32.5% from 4.7 to 3.1 billion tons annually (Figure 1.4). Its share of global emissions has been falling continuously to around 7%, partly thanks to its policies but also because other parts of the world, especially the emerging economies, have been emitting more. The EU decided to accelerate the downward path toward climate neutrality by 2050 as part of the European Green Deal and to reduce net emissions by 2030 by at least 55% compared to 1990 levels. This makes the operational target clear and indicates a straightforward long-term perspective. It will require a significant increase in efforts to go from the 53 million tons CO_2eq that was reduced on average each year between 1990 and 2020 to 97 million tons needed for the period until 2030.

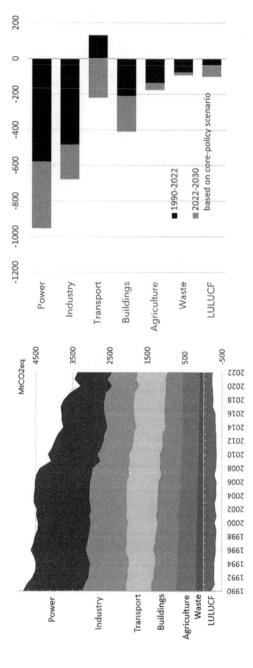

FIGURE 1.4 EU emissions and removals by sector, past trends, and required reductions

Source: European Commission (2023)[10]

In the EU, CO_2 represents more than 80% of total greenhouse gas emissions and these are mainly related to the use of fossil fuels in power generation, industry, transport, and heating. Renewable energy surpassed fossil fuels as the largest electricity source and represented 43.6% of power generation in 2023.[11] The other greenhouse gases are methane (CH_4), nitrous oxide (N_2O), and fluorinated gases (F-gases). They originate mainly from the agricultural, chemical, and waste sectors. The non-CO_2 gases are produced in much smaller volumes but are more potent global warming gases, so have a correspondingly larger impact on the climate system.

The most important emissions reductions were realized in power generation through fuel switching away from coal and toward natural gas and more recently renewables, while the share of nuclear was rather stable or slightly declining. Natural gas is the least carbon intensive fossil fuel and was available in huge quantities and at relative low cost through pipelines from Russia. This created some unease in 2014 with the annexation of Crimea by Russia, but it became a real geopolitical challenge when Russia invaded Ukraine again in 2022. The availability of cheap natural gas disappeared, coal was again used, albeit in limited quantities and only temporarily, but the advantage of a smooth fuel switch disappeared. Emissions from manufacturing industry decreased only slightly, contrary to the marked increase from the transport sector and in particular aviation, thereby neutralizing some of the progress made elsewhere.

The amount of carbon stored in the forest, soil, and vegetation of the EU, the so-called carbon "sink", was estimated to be around 230 million tons of CO_2-equivalent in 2021.[12] Since 1990, the sink has been growing but then declined because of ageing forests as well as harvesting. For the future it is becoming increasingly important to fix more carbon in forests, in the soil, in products, and in the underground.[13] The EU's targets are now expressed in "net" terms which implies that the tons stored in the carbon "sink" – and any stored removals from captured CO_2 – are being subtracted from the emissions incurred in the sectors of the economy.

The EU has decoupled its emissions from economic growth. Over the period 1990–2022, GDP increased by around 65% while at the same time emissions were reduced by 32.5%. This is illustrated in Figure 1.5 for CO_2 emissions. It is sometimes claimed that this decoupling is unduly flattered by the accounting methodology based on the "direct" emissions approach, as adopted by the UNFCCC. This makes all countries directly responsible for the emissions emitted on their territory and the universal participation of the Paris Agreement makes this approach globally inclusive. To some extent the EU is importing more carbon-intensive products, but this is counterbalanced by the fact that its exports are relatively efficient in terms of carbon content. A correction for consumption confirms that decoupling happened, and that climate policy has not been undermining economic growth in the EU.

Change in CO₂ emissions and GDP, European Union (27)

Consumption-based emissions¹ are national emissions that have been adjusted for trade. This measures fossil fuel and industry emissions² . Land use change is not included.

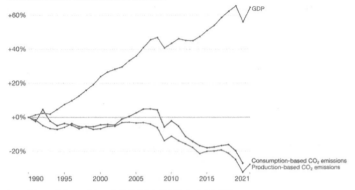

Source: Data compiled from multiple sources by World Bank, Global Carbon Budget (2022)
Note: Gross Domestic Product (GDP) figures are adjusted for inflation.
OurWorldInData.org/co2-and-greenhouse-gas-emissions • CC BY

---

1. Consumption-based emissions: Consumption-based emissions are national or regional emissions that have been adjusted for trade. They are calculated as domestic (or 'production-based' emissions) emissions minus the emissions generated in the production of goods and services that are exported to other countries or regions, plus emissions from the production of goods and services that are imported. Consumption-based emissions = Production-based – Exported + Imported emissions

2. Fossil emissions: Fossil emissions measure the quantity of carbon dioxide (CO₂) emitted from the burning of fossil fuels, and directly from industrial processes such as cement and steel production. Fossil CO₂ includes emissions from coal, oil, gas, flaring, cement, steel, and other industrial processes. Fossil emissions do not include land use change, deforestation, soils, or vegetation.

FIGURE 1.5   EU: Decoupling economic growth from CO_2 emissions 1990–2022

Source: Ritchie (2021), Our World in Data[14]

In 2021, greenhouse gas emissions *per capita* in the world were at 6.9 tons. The EU, with 7.6 tons *per capita*, is close to the average and down from more than 12.6 tons in 1980 (see Figure 1.6). At the same time, China's emissions *per capita* have risen very significantly since 2002, surpassing those of the EU. Although declining, *per capita* greenhouse gas emissions of the US are high compared to the global average and amount to more than twice those of the EU. If distributed evenly across the world's population, every citizen would not be allowed to emit more than approximately 2.3 tons per year to be compatible with the 2°C goal of the Paris Agreement.

> Conclusion: The EU has reduced its net emissions in 2022 by 32.5% since 1990, while economic growth increased by 65%. Major factors were the use of low-carbon technology and fuel switching away from coal toward natural gas and renewable energy sources. Emissions per head are steadily going down.

Per capita greenhouse gas emissions

Greenhouse gas emissions¹ include carbon dioxide, methane and nitrous oxide from all sources, including land-use change. They are measured in tonnes of carbon dioxide-equivalents² over a 100-year timescale.

Data source: Jones et al. (2023); Population based on various sources (2023)
Note: Land-use change emissions can be negative.
OurWorldInData.org/co2-and-greenhouse-gas-emissions | CC BY

1. **Greenhouse gas emissions:** A greenhouse gas (GHG) is a gas that causes the atmosphere to warm by absorbing and emitting radiant energy. Greenhouse gases absorb radiation that is radiated by Earth, preventing this heat from escaping to space. Carbon dioxide (CO_2) is the most well-known greenhouse gas, but there are others including methane, nitrous oxide, and in fact, water vapor. Human-made emissions of greenhouse gases from fossil fuels, industry, and agriculture are the leading cause of global climate change. Greenhouse gas emissions measure the total amount of all greenhouse gases that are emitted. These are often quantified in carbon dioxide equivalents (CO_2eq) which take account of the amount of warming that each molecule of different gases creates.

2. **Carbon dioxide equivalents (CO_2eq):** Carbon dioxide is the most important greenhouse gas, but not the only one. To capture all greenhouse gas emissions, researchers express them in "carbon dioxide equivalents" (CO_2eq). This takes all greenhouse gases into account, not just CO_2. To express all greenhouse gases in carbon dioxide equivalents (CO_2eq), each one is weighted by its global warming potential (GWP) value. GWP measures the amount of warming a gas creates compared to CO_2. CO_2 is given a GWP value of one. If a gas had a GWP of 10 then one kilogram of that gas would generate ten times the warming effect as one kilogram of CO_2. Carbon dioxide equivalents are calculated for each gas by multiplying the mass of emissions of a specific greenhouse gas by its GWP factor. This warming can be stated over different timescales. To calculate CO_2eq over 100 years, we'd multiply each gas by its GWP over a 100-year timescale (GWP100). Total greenhouse gas emissions - measured in CO_2eq - are then calculated by summing each gas' CO_2eq value.

FIGURE 1.6   Global *per capita* greenhouse gas emissions 1850–2021

Source: Global Carbon Budget (2023); Population based on various sources (2023) – with major processing by Our World in Data[15]

1.3   Building Further on the Cornerstones of EU Climate Policy

The EU has currently 27 sovereign Member States with highly diverse characteristics in terms of wealth, income, industrial performance, and natural endowment. Yet, the EU developed a common climate policy. It was key to ensure that all Member States felt their specific concerns were adequately addressed in the policy architecture. Three key elements played out decisively in the EU's performance: the politics, the economics, and the policy preparation.

1.3.1   *The Politics: A Vision Endorsed by the Highest Political Level*

It was imperative for the EU to embed its emerging climate policy firmly into the multilateral context of the UNFCCC. Europe recognized its significant historical contribution to the greenhouse gases accumulated in the atmosphere. However, it was equally important to search for a maximum emission reduction at reasonable cost as it would be of utmost importance to preserve the collective "willingness to pay" for climate policy. Even if the long-term benefits of the policy are clear, there are also considerable transition efforts to be delivered in the short term. This inevitably raises political questions, even by those who accept the need to act.

A clear endorsement at the highest levels of a long-term policy vision turned out to be critical. In 2007, the European Council – comprising of the EU's Heads of State and Government – agreed on an "independent commitment to achieve at least 20% reduction of greenhouse gas emissions by 2020 compared to 1990" as EU's contribution to COP9 in Copenhagen.[16] They even offered to increase this commitment to 30% by 2020 if other developed countries would commit themselves to a comparable emission reduction. This was a clear invitation to the US to join in the overall efforts. The climate commitment was accompanied by specific energy objectives also to be delivered by 2020, including a binding target to increase the share of renewable energy in final energy consumption to 20% (from about 8.5% in 2005) and an indicative target to reduce energy consumption by 20%.[17]

Seven years later, in 2014, a similar approach was followed by the European Council that formally decided on an "at least 40% greenhouse gas reduction" to be achieved by 2030. This decision constituted the EU's contribution in the run-up to the Paris UNFCCC Conference in 2015 and had a critical influence on the ambition set out by the US and China shortly thereafter. During the European policy cycle 2019–2024, the European Green Deal was launched as a comprehensive economic policy with the climate targets at its center. A new European Climate Law created legally binding targets of climate neutrality by 2050 and a net emission reduction of at least 55% by 2030 compared to 1990. These developments set in motion an international dynamic to define long-term targets and today 169 countries including all G20 members have formulated net-zero climate targets for 2050–2070.

1.3.1.1 Looking Ahead

Dealing with political headwinds for climate policy looks to be a key issue in the coming years.

1 So far leaders supporting ambitious climate policies have been enjoying broad popular support, not least thanks to actions by the young and the massive mobilization of people concerned about the future of their children and grandchildren. However, pressure from those opposing climate action on the political right is likely to become more prevalent.

Standard ingredients will undoubtedly include more finger pointing at other countries that renege on their net zero commitments or worse will have conspiracy theories at their center.

Keeping the implementation of so many decisions taken in the past on track will continue to require political skill. Policymakers too will need to think about their priorities. It is a question whether much political energy needs to be spent on discussing a further strengthening of the climate targets in respect of 2040 as the implementation of what has been agreed is likely to bring the EU closely on the path to climate neutrality by 2050. It will instead be critical to include sectors largely unaddressed so far, not least agriculture, forestry as well as carbon removals in general to compensate for remaining emissions. Moreover, a debate is starting on whether Europe should not pay more attention to its industrial sector in view of the changed security context in the world. These are important new elements that need to be addressed in view of delivering a credible pathway to climate neutrality by 2050.

2   Never let a good crisis go to waste. There are always crises along the way and policymakers should anticipate them as far as possible. The 2008 banking crisis delayed tangible climate action and postponed the breakthrough of promising climate technologies, but it also led to more international cooperation within the G20, for example, which facilitated the conclusion of the Paris Agreement. The COVID pandemic led to a break-up of global trust but also created new habits such as virtual meetings, reducing the reliance on traveling, or the need for office space. The EU also assured a significant greening of the new Resilience and Recovery Fund. The Russian invasions of Ukraine in 2014 and 2022 have been severe blows to the world order but also gave a significant boost to renewable energy and energy savings. Politics should be aware that major unexpected events are likely to happen also in the coming decades and that dealing with them can offer unforeseen opportunities to foster rather than stall climate action. The EU should also use its influence to keep climate on top of the global agenda in the current re-balancing of the world order.

3   Finally, the political debate related to climate should not merely dwell on 'angst' about the damaging impacts climate change is causing. All too frequently this leads either to despair, or worse gives space to climate fatalism. Politicians should avoid polarizing the climate debate but rather concentrate on pragmatic action-oriented steps. Policies that have worked well in the past consist of creating economic incentives and business cases and addressing potential social imbalances. It should be better explained that many of the low-carbon technologies needed in the future may – apart from helping the climate problem – also bring other benefits such as improved air quality, greater resource efficiency, new economic

opportunities, less dependence on imports of energy and raw materials, or increase the general comfort levels of consumers, as the use of electric bikes or building refurbishment and heat pumps is showing.

Conclusion: Climate neutrality by 2050 and an emissions reduction target of at least 55% by 2030 compared to 1990 levels has been put into law. This triggered a process in which all G20 members representing 80% of global emissions committed to long-term contributions. Political leadership was crucial and will also be necessary in the elaboration of critical implementation issues. A gradual, pragmatic, and non-polarized approach has proven to be successful.

1.3.2 The Economics: Putting an Explicit Price on Carbon

In the wake of the reports of the Club of Rome (1972) and based on theoretical work such as from Pigou, Hardin, and Coase, economists launched a debate on how to put into practice the pricing of economic externalities such as on climate change. Prices are a very effective way of transmitting information through the economy and influencing behavior, right down to the levels of individual producers and consumers. This can be achieved through taxes, or alternatively, through the setting of overall limits to pollution levels ("a cap") and allow for trading among participants. The EU opted for carbon pricing that is based on the principle that the polluter should pay, as enshrined in the EU Treaty.

Another challenge was to focus on policies that are best placed at the European level in view of avoiding distortions of competition within the Single Market. It was decided to act in a harmonized manner in the fields of energy-intensive and manufacturing industry, electricity, and heat production. The production of electricity, which traditionally has been characterized by closed national markets, was increasingly opened and subject to market forces. This enabled the harnessing of economies of scale provided by a market of 450 million consumers.

The initial proposals at EU level were for pricing through taxes. Under the EU Treaty, this required unanimity which is challenging. After almost a decade of difficult negotiations, the tax approach was abandoned, and the debate on economic instruments shifted to cap setting and emissions trading. Based on its successful schemes on Sulphur and NO_x emissions, the US pushed successfully for a 'cap-and-trade' approach in the Kyoto Protocol, against the wishes of the Europeans and others. However, it was the EU that subsequently put this into practice, while the US repeatedly failed to do so at a federal level.

Following an extensive consultation exercise with stakeholders from civil society, the business sector, and national authorities, the EU adopted legislation for emissions trading, with decisions to be made through qualified majority voting in Council. In 2005, the EU Emissions Trading System (EU ETS) included all major actors in the field of power and manufacturing. Today some 10,000 industrial installations and airlines operating across Europe are covered by one EU-wide cap on emissions, that is steadily declining. The EU-wide approach has effectively ensured that abatement is achieved where the costs are the lowest.

By 2022, the emissions in the ETS-covered sectors had declined by 37.3% since 2005, which is significantly more than the average reductions made across the EU. The price for one EU allowance is currently hovering in the range between €75 and €90. Significant revenues have been raised through auctioning. In 2022, the EU ETS auctions generated a total of €38.8 billion.[18] These revenues are spent on enhancing climate policies, including technological innovation and mitigating social impacts. Moreover, as of 2026, a Social Climate Fund will be established addressing social barriers to the climate transition, financed from the adjacent ETS system, also known as "ETS2", which as of 2027 will include road transport and heating fuels. By 2030, carbon pricing should cover some 70% of the EU's emissions.

Addressing carbon leakage and maintaining the international competitiveness of manufacturing industry has been a key issue since the start of the EU ETS. A system of free allocation has addressed these concerns so far but will be gradually replaced by a Carbon Border Adjustment Mechanism (CBAM). This is a major policy change. The CBAM Regulation has the potential of reinforcing climate policies around the globe, not least on carbon pricing. But it also contains the risk of diversion of trade flows through exports of green commodities to the EU while containing the higher carbon content versions of the same products for local or other export markets. Although CBAM remains the subject of discussion, it is important that a world leading trading partner has put to the fore market incentives for low-carbon goods.

1.3.2.1 Looking Ahead

The EU ETS faces several critical deadlines related to the implementation of the changes agreed in the 2023 revision of the legislation.

1 CBAM is a most critical one. CBAM will start with payments as of 2026 following an introductory phase that will focus on data collection. Before 2030, free allocation in the covered sectors will remain significant

and hence CBAM will be implemented very gradually. The Commission specified how to calculate and report the embedded carbon of imports and adopted default values for the concerned products. The EU now needs to engage pro-actively with its trading partners as some acrimony continues to exist about the perceived unilateral nature of the imposed CBAM regime. Finally, an important provision is made on how local carbon prices paid by importers can lead to a reduction of their CBAM payments, but the way to compare different emissions trading systems still needs clarification.

2 ETS2 covering road transport and heating fuels will also require further implementation decisions. Obtaining a political agreement on ETS2 was made more difficult after the high price increases for fuels over the last few years. More detailed elaboration is still needed, not least in relation to the Effort Sharing Regulation defining the mandatory targets for the Member States. Similarly, the relation with the Energy Tax Directive needs to be clarified as some minimum excise duties for transport and heating fuels have been defined according to carbon content. Member States can also opt out from ETS2 in favor of their own pricing or taxing measures. Finally, it is commonly known that the marginal cost of abatement is high in the newly covered sectors. To ease a possible price pressure in ETS2, it is foreseen that more allowances could be auctioned but the quantities defined are not substantial.

3 The EU ETS is being extended to emissions from the maritime and aviation sectors. While technically the ground is well prepared for the maritime sector, a critical deadline emerges on international aviation. ICAO developed the offset instrument CORSIA that is meant to be mandatory for China and other large countries as of 2027. It will be critical to assess the real emissions reductions CORSIA is able to deliver and how international participation is expanding. By that same date the Commission will have to make a proposal on whether and how long-distance flights should contribute more to climate action. Several options are still on the table, such as lifting the excise duties exemption on kerosene as foreseen in the pending proposal on the Energy Tax Directive, or the broadening of the EU ETS to include departing flights. By 2027, the EU will have waited for two decades for meaningful multilateral measures to deal with emissions from international aviation, so far without much success. Public opinion is very aware of the rapidly growing climate impact aviation represents, and the need for long distance flights to contribute.

4 As the market gets much tighter in view of the 2030 and 2050 targets, liquidity issues in the EU ETS will need to be addressed. While the Market

Stability Reserve functioned well to prevent the carbon price returning to its low level following the banking crisis of 2008, something similar does not exist for upward price movements. Moreover, the declining cap as agreed under the 2023 ETS review implies that significantly fewer allowances will be issued as of the second half of the next decade. By then the power sector should be almost fully decarbonized, thanks to a continued expansion of renewable energy. Solutions may also have to be agreed to avoid market volatility and to improve liquidity while maintaining the overall climate ambition. Possible key elements that need careful consideration is the merger between ETS and ETS2 or access to industrial carbon removals that can be provided by biomass and CCS. For the period before 2030, the enlargement of the EU ETS to candidate countries raises opportunities to revisit arrangements related to the overall cap. Others have been raising the perspective of allowing high-quality land-based removals credits or even credits from outside the EU as part of a cost containment strategy. These options may fit together with the creation of a European central carbon bank that would closely monitor the key elements of the newly decided changes such as on ETS2, CBAM, aviation, carbon removals, and possibly other offsets within the boundaries of the targets set out in the Climate Law.

5   The EU needs an international strategy on how to develop its carbon pricing in a global context. In part thanks to CBAM, many countries are developing compliance markets. In the context of the so-called "Florence Process", the different design features of existing compliance markets are being debated in view of closer cooperation over time.[19] However, international initiatives are developing in which the EU may want to consider more active participation. The EU was a major market for international credits generated under the Clean Development Mechanism (CDM) but this was discontinued due to integrity concerns. Various forms of carbon credits are being created by Voluntary Carbon Markets (VCM), although without robust regulation successive scams have been reported that have undermined the credibility of VCM despite there also being some very useful initiatives. In addition, under the Paris Agreement the operationalization of Article 6 is still underway. Continents such as Africa have expressed interest to engage with the EU. However, the EU's Climate Law excludes the use of international carbon credits, which limits possible action to Member States and companies that are willing to go beyond the EU targets. An interesting perspective is the Call for Action for Paris Aligned Carbon Markets as well as the repeated calls by the World Bank and the International Monetary Fund to reinforce global action on carbon markets.[20]

Conclusion: The EU ETS is a successful carbon pricing system that reduced emissions, gained the trust of economic operators, and is central for delivering climate neutrality by 2050. It is being extended to cover some 70% of the EU's emissions. Continued policy development is required regarding issues such as the implementation of the Carbon Border Adjustment Mechanism, ensuring market liquidity, and engagement in existing and new international initiatives.

1.3.3 The Technicalities: Designing Policies Based on Solid Preparation

EU climate policy was, from the start, prepared on the basis of extensive economic and policy analysis, known as "impact assessment". Several policy options were investigated for their capacity to bring down emissions but also according to a series of other questions related to the impact on adjacent policy areas such as energy and transport and on macro-economic issues including on industrial competitiveness, innovation, required investment, employment, and social impacts. A series of environmental, technical, and economic models were linked in that respect. At the same time, extensive consultation with stakeholders from the private sector and the NGO community as well as from the Member States revealed early in the process particular sensitivities. This policy preparation and consultation allowed to address policy barriers well on time.

The impact analysis[21] in preparation of the EU Climate Law resulted in the adoption of ambitious targets. The pathway summarized in Figure 1.7 indicates that the main source of emissions reduction in the current decade would come from the power sector, which would be largely decarbonized by 2030. The sectors of industry and transport would deliver most of their emission reductions after 2030. It illustrates how much of the EU's strategy was built on natural gas as a transition fuel. Since the war in Ukraine, the original timetable for renewable energy and energy efficiency deployment has been brought forward by a decade and this requires frontloading an immense amount of low-carbon investments, in particular in the sectors of transport and industry.[22]

The impact analysis also showed that a combination of several policy instruments is necessary to deliver the emissions reductions. Economists have been influential in advocating carbon pricing as a key instrument but struggled with the issue of double regulation. Others have pointed out that

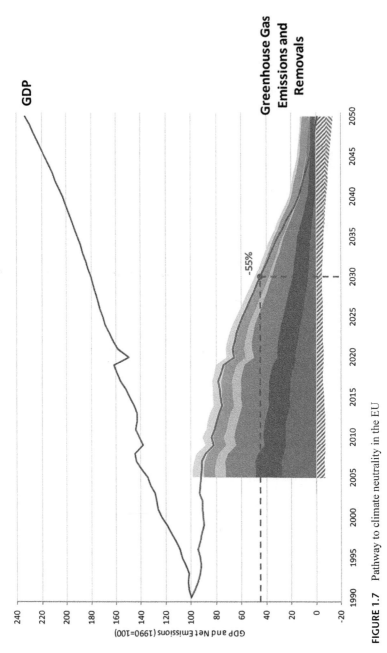

FIGURE 1.7 Pathway to climate neutrality in the EU

Source: COM(2020) 562 final[23]

markets work with imperfect information or suffer from too high discount rates to make economic optimal decisions. Unlike theoretical models, the real world is always subject to multiple regulations, and some of them may partially overlap. The critical issue is to make sure that these regulations work in synergy or at least do not counteract one another. The EU ETS has been a solid instrument to realize low-cost emission reductions complementing legislation on scaling up renewable energy technologies that were at the early stage of technological development and hence had much higher implicit carbon prices. Similarly, the ETS 2 will benefit from interaction with strengthened policies such as those relating to CO_2 emissions of new cars or those related to the energy performance requirements of the EU's building stock.

While the EU ETS covers some 40% of emissions, many small emitters such as households, transport users, and agriculture generate the remaining 60%. Managing these emissions require primarily policies at national or even local level, such as city and transport planning, and therefore these are shared between the Member States in the form of legally binding targets under the Effort Sharing Regulation (ESR). The overall EU target also accounts for emissions originating from the agriculture and forestry sectors, often called the "Land Use, Land Use Change and Forestry", or "LULUCF" sectors. The economic modeling calculated a cost-effective reduction pathway. Based on this, the political negotiation resulted in an agreement that the emissions under the EU ETS will be reduced by 62% in 2030 compared to 2005, which is much more than the collective reduction target of 40% for the sectors covered by the ESR.

EU climate policy is comprehensive as it covers the totality of greenhouse gases according to three emerging pillars: the EU ETS containing power, industry, intra-EU aviation, and shipping; the Effort Sharing Regulation covering road transport, heating, agriculture, and waste; and the LULUCF Regulation (see Figure 1.8). There are only very limited gateways of flexibility allowed between those three pillars.

An emissions accounting system and an integrated energy and climate governance system tracks progress in the different Member States. While the targets under the EU ETS are being delivered 'automatically' as part of the compliance with the legislation, the delivery of the Effort Sharing targets depends on the Member States and many policy decisions they make in the fields of housing, infrastructure, urbanization, traffic management, etc. Moreover, the creation of the adjacent ETS2 system for transport and heating fuels will deliver a significant part of the commitments the Member States are responsible for.

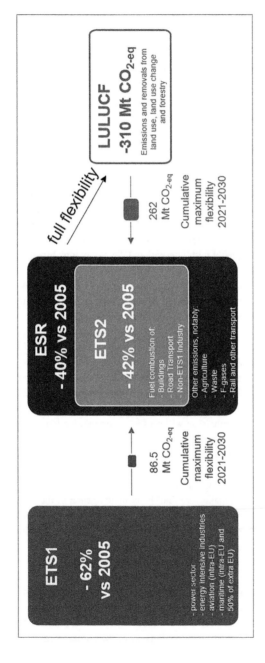

FIGURE 1.8 The structure of EU climate policy

Source: European Commission

1.3.3.1 Looking Ahead

Cost-effectiveness combined with a fair distribution of the burden needs to be brought back as the central pillar of future climate policy. More climate ambition implies measures that are higher on the cost curve, and these should not be made even more expensive through suboptimal policy design.

1 The methodological rigor in preparing climate and climate-related policies is of capital importance for a well-informed policy debate as well as for solid implementation. The impact assessment should remain meaningful and not fall into the trap of a box-ticking exercise. The policy debates on the Nature Protection Law and the Farm to Fork strategy demonstrated that insufficient quantification and analysis easily trigger heated policy discussions. The increase of the 2030 target from 50 to 55% could also have benefited from more economic analysis. Close attention is required for prior consultation of stakeholders, coordination with other pieces of regulation, or for more alignment with international developments. Finally, an important number of sub-targets of very different nature have been adopted in various regulations, some of which may not contribute to a cost-effective delivery of the overriding climate objectives. Most of these regulations include regular reviews, and these could be an opportunity for well-prepared improvements.

2 Internationally, the Dubai COP28 has gone through the first global stock-take and the sobering outcome is that the world is not yet on track to deliver the Paris objectives. Parties need to prepare the next round of Nationally Determined Contributions (NDCs) running up to 2035 which should be submitted well ahead of COP30 taking place in Brazil in 2025. The European Commission will present a communication and impact assessment on the EU's post-2030 climate policy. It is an opportunity to revisit the proven method of cost-effectiveness combined with fairness, to prepare for a solid debate on carbon removals as well as to consider opening the EU's climate agenda to more international cooperation. It is also a major occasion to make sure that the climate agenda of the future is well embedded into the new geopolitical strategy the EU is developing.

3 The Effort Sharing Regulation is now covering the larger share of the emissions, but the performance is lagging in many Member States. The integrated energy and climate governance system must be further strengthened to become a pro-active and forward-looking monitoring of policies planned by Member States. The execution of the plans has been supported by the Resilience and Recovery Fund, indicating that even more finance may have to be channeled at EU level after its end in 2026. Such funds need to be made conditional on delivery of the climate targets.

Conclusion: The EU has developed a comprehensive policy approach whereby the EU ETS is complemented with targets for the Member States. The principles of cost-effectiveness and fairness have been central and should guide the review of several pieces of legislation. A more pro-active governance system should facilitate the delivery of the massive low-carbon investment needs, also in view of addressing the EU's external energy dependence.

1.4 Anchoring Climate into a Strengthened Geopolitical EU Strategy

1.4.1 The Climate Transition as Part of an EU Geopolitical Industrial Strategy

The international community at COP28 finally recognized that the transition away from fossil fuel use is the only way forward. Europe used coal as a key element fueling its industrial revolution and the exploitation of oil and gas facilitated later waves of industrialization. Nuclear energy emerged from the energy crises of the 1970s and raised hope that Europe would place itself again at the center of providing abundant and clean energy.

The reality today is that Europe is weakly placed in the global energy landscape. The war in Ukraine, the sanctions toward Russia and the disappearance of cheap supplies of natural gas and minerals, demonstrated its vulnerability. The EU has built up a steadily increasing import dependency on oil and gas, not least from states having a doubtful record on democracy and human rights. Since the disasters of Chernobyl and Fukushima, most of the nuclear hopes have evaporated, also because the import of uranium is coming from Russia or countries often having unstable regimes while the problems related to waste and security remain largely unsolved. Europe realizes it has much to win from phasing out fossil fuels but also from leading the way in developing renewable energy sources and using energy more efficiently and these are facilitated through more electrification. Moreover, a world that wants to fight climate change will ultimately have to follow this path as well.

The newly emerging geopolitical reality leaves no other choice to Europe but to fundamentally review its industrial strategy. Apart from becoming more independent from Russia, this should also encompass a common approach toward China and the US. The EU will continue to depend on the integration into the world market but with due regard for a diversification of its imports and with special attention to its neighborhood in the Mediterranean, the Western Balkans, Türkiye, and in the future, Ukraine. The EU will have to rely more on its single market, develop strategies to reverse the de-industrialization trend, and address its energy vulnerability within the context of a strengthened cooperation on defense and foreign policy. These questions will undoubtedly figure prominently in the forthcoming reports being prepared by former Italian Prime Ministers Mario Draghi and Enrico Letta.

By opting for carbon pricing as a major policy instrument, the EU has incentivized demand for low-carbon products by making these cheaper compared to more polluting alternatives. This strategy needs an addition at the production side, since the US enacted the Inflation Reduction Act offering generous subsidies targeted at key industries, not least the production of batteries, hydrogen, and carbon dioxide removal technologies. The EU responded to this supply-driven approach by the US with the Green Deal Industrial Plan comprising the Critical Raw Materials Act as well as the Net Zero Industry Act (NZIA).

Most attention of NZIA goes to supporting strategic technologies in the energy sector, on which a successful net-zero transition depends. Affordable low-carbon electricity should be massively available, but its development is currently hampered by lengthy permitting procedures, lack of electricity grids, including cross-border ones. The EU should invest in keeping what it has (wind) and recover some lost ground (PV, batteries), but be realistic in accepting that imports of critical components of these value chains will be needed for years to come.

Key manufacturing sectors such as steel and chemicals are currently absent from NZIA, while in these sectors considerations related to the entire value chain are even more important. These sectors should continue to have an important industrial base in Europe, also because of security considerations, but they should develop their own climate transition pathway. A major point of attention will have to be the circular economy. As in the beginning recycling of waste will not be sufficient, Europe will have to consider opening new mining activity under sustainable conditions and find pragmatic solutions to "NIMBY" considerations.

The EU has been providing generous funds to support the climate and energy transition, but a more focused approach now seems necessary. The EU's tradition of CAPEX support has worked well for solar and wind deployment – which have comparatively low operational costs – but is far less effective for other sectors such as hydrogen or low-carbon industrial products. State aid provisions have been reluctant to encourage OPEX support, and this may need to be reconsidered. The Innovation Fund is addressing some of these issues and is reviewing its procedures for support for scaling up low-carbon technologies, including with the innovative use of EU-wide auction procedures.

The Member States, receiving most of the revenues of the EU ETS, could use these much more strategically, for example, through co-funding of projects successfully selected by Innovation Fund. EU ETS revenues are expected to be mounting to more than €500 billion over the next decade.

A major issue emerging globally is the strong technological competition on the new energy carrier hydrogen. Consensus is growing that hydrogen will be used primarily in a rather limited number of industrial sectors such as steel, fertilizers, or oil refineries, in which the potential of electrification is rather limited, as well as a precursor for synthetic fuels and chemicals. The real question, however, is the sustainable production of hydrogen. A fierce competition is emerging between blue and green hydrogen, produced, respectively, on the basis of natural gas with carbon capture and storage, or renewable electricity. The EU is putting a lot of emphasis on the latter, while blue hydrogen is likely to emerge more from gas-rich areas such as the Gulf region or the US. The CBAM Regulation includes hydrogen, and this represents a useful opportunity to check the carbon embedded in hydrogen imports.

> Conclusion: The low-carbon transition represents a core element of a new geopolitical industrial strategy. The single market should be central to the scaling up of innovations, to focus the use of State aid, to diversify imports of energy and raw materials, and to deliver the massive investment needs.

1.4.2 Investing in Social and Regional Cohesion

From the start the EU's policy has been guided by the principle of cost-effectiveness corrected for distributive impacts. If targets were to be distributed purely based on cost-effectiveness, lower-income Member States, notably in Central and Eastern Europe, would face higher additional investments in relative terms because of their higher energy- and carbon-intensity and their lower GDP. As the *per capita* income disparity between the EU's poorest and richest Member States is still around 1–10, the EU has been ensuring that fairness is a central concept in its climate policy.

The emissions targets of each Member State under the Effort Sharing Regulation is varied according to national *per capita* income.[24] Similarly, on renewable energy for 2020, national targets were formulated in such a way as to promote a fair distribution between Member States. Finally, the EU ETS design foresees that 10% of allowances for auctioning are redistributed in favor of lower income Member States, while its Modernization Fund provides important financial support for the energy sector in these Member States. The Social Climate Fund provides a larger share of resources for the lower income Member States.

Considering the uncertainties related to future economic development and the need to enhance cost-effective achievement of targets, flexibility is allowed for Member States to transfer emission rights between themselves. In this way, countries with higher national costs could achieve their target more cheaply, and countries that over-achieve their target could benefit financially. The obligations are set in such a way as to give benefit to the relatively poorer Member States. There is clearly, therefore, a link between flexibility and fairness, as the flexibilities allow for the transfer of obligations in exchange for revenue.

Addressing social issues at the level of individual households will become crucial in the coming years as was signaled by the *gilets jaunes* protest movement that erupted in France in 2018. Many of them are concentrated in regions where the old fossil-fuel based industries flourished in the past. Especially in the areas of buildings and transport, poorer households will require special support to be able to keep the energy bills affordable through, for example, the modernization of heating systems away from fossil fuels, using electric cars or having better access to decarbonized public transport. As of 2026, a dedicated Social Climate Fund will help focus on low and lower middle-income households as well as investments, such as in social housing.

The EU has developed regional and social policies successfully and a good start has been made in turning them toward alignment with the climate goals. Regional policy represents the EU's second largest budget line. Infrastructure investments are capable of re-orienting carbon-intensive regions toward more diversified economic activities, and housing and public services are priority areas. The EU's experience in creating alternative employment in former coal mining regions in the Benelux countries, Germany, France, and Spain has paid off in setting up appropriate policies in the more recent Member States. This policy is now being reinforced in the Commission's Coal and Carbon-Intensive Regions in Transition Initiative[25] and in the context of the Just Transition Fund.

Furthermore, the climate and energy transition embodied in new low-carbon technologies such as heat pumps and electric vehicles require a complete new set of skills that go beyond traditional education programs. Similarly, a significant amount of construction workers needs to be retrained in view of performing well in the highly technical requirements to build passive and highly energy efficient buildings. The employment initiatives through the EU Social Fund have started to address these issues.

Conclusion: Fairness considerations have been and should remain at the core of EU's climate policy. Targets are differentiated according to GDP *per capita*, and lower-income Member States receive additional revenues through the EU ETS. A Social Climate Fund is starting in 2026 and climate considerations are increasingly included in the use of regional and social funds.

1.4.3 Investing in Removals

Scientific research has indicated that to limit the impacts of climate change increasing amounts of CO_2 will have to be removed from the atmosphere. Such carbon removals will have to compensate any remaining emissions but also temperature overshoots when global warming goes beyond 1.5°C. Land-based activities, such as forest, agricultural, or soil management, have the potential to remove and/or store significant amounts of carbon. Equally, there are technological ways of removing greenhouse gases from activities in the energy and manufacturing industry. Such technology is known as Carbon Capture and Storage when the carbon is stored in the underground, or as Carbon Capture and Use in case it is fixed in products.

The EU will need carbon removals to reach its goal of climate neutrality by 2050, as not all economic activities will be carbon-free by then. The order of magnitude by 2050 is estimated to be around 10% of today's emissions. Activities related to LULUCF are emerging as a separate pillar with the aim of increasing the EU's natural sink to 310 million tons CO_2eq by 2030. This will require pro-active policies in the field of forestry and agriculture, such as on carbon farming. A reflection is needed in the context of the Common Agricultural Policy (CAP), as farmers will have to be rewarded for their removal activities. Another option is to open the EU ETS and/or ESR legislation to removals, or to create a dedicated emissions trading system for emissions and removals from agriculture, forestry, and land use.

The NGO community should reconsider their long-held reservation on carbon removal policies. These are unlikely to weaken the case and urgency for reducing emissions but rather help in delivering climate neutrality. A well-functioning crediting system for land-based carbon removals should address the concerns around the measurability and the non-permanence of natural carbon sinks, with related risks of 'greenwashing' due to reversals, leakages, and double-counting. The EU has started work on a voluntary EU-wide CO_2 removals certification system that will in a first phase focus on areas where high-quality monitoring capability already exists, such as afforestation, reforestation, and agro-forestry. It may be useful to open these discussions for international participants from countries with considerable removal capacity such as in Africa.

The Innovation Fund started to invest in industrial CO_2 capture and use technologies. Several of these technologies still need to be brought to the market and be tested before scaling up the most promising ones. In view of a wider deployment, it will be equally important to secure an economic incentive for such industrial CO_2 removal activities.

Conclusion: The EU must urgently intensify and reward activities on carbon removals as climate neutrality by 2050 is likely to require a compensation for remaining emissions. A LULUCF target of 310m tons has been agreed for 2030 and a carbon removal certification system is being developed. Industrial removal technologies need to be brought urgently to the market at scale.

1.4.4 Raising Much More Sustainable Finance

The implementation of the European Green Deal and the climate targets requires an annual investment of approximately 2% of GDP, which is a daunting figure.[26] The EU has been progressively integrating climate and sustainability considerations in its budget and its financial policy. However, much more is needed, also in view of improving the resilience of the EU economy in terms of energy and industry and the related infrastructural requirements. These are productive long-term investments for which also the fiscal rules inside the euro area could be made more supportive.

The EU currently spends a third of its budget on climate-related matters while for the remaining part the principle of "do-no-significant-harm" (DNSH) was introduced, which implies that no EU funding should go against or undermine climate or environmental objectives. These are fundamental steps that should be reinforced in the debate on the future budget of the EU. A critical question is how to blend its expenditure with a maximum amount of other sources of money in view of maximizing the overall sustainable impact. As the EU budget only accounts for roughly 1% of the EU's GDP, applying these principles, targets, and blending mechanisms as soon as possible also to Member States' use of public budgets would make a significant leap forward in mainstreaming.

The EU has put in place a comprehensive policy framework to improve transparency around the climate and sustainability risks incurred by the private sector.[27] A central element is the EU Taxonomy, a common classification of economic activities contributing in a substantial way to environmental objectives. In addition, an extensive disclosure regime for both financial and non-financial companies has been introduced, such as the Sustainable Finance Disclosure Regulation (SFRD), the Corporate Sustainability Reporting Directive (CSRD), and the proposed Green Claims Regulation. Rules for Environmental, Social and Governance rating providers were developed[28] and efforts are underway to simplify the reporting burdens for companies.[29] Along with disclosure rules, the EU has created a range of tools for financial actors such as companies and financial intermediaries to develop sustainable investment solutions, including the launch of a European Green Bond Standard.

The speed of adoption and the elaboration of the reporting rules since 2018 has been impressive. The implementation in the first reporting periods is now starting and will have to focus on maximum impact and avoid the tendency of box ticking the legal requirements. A wealth of new data will become available and new questions will arise. One of these is about how to create an optimal transition from the old economy in which many companies still have considerable capital equipment toward the new low-carbon economy. Another issue will be to align the European legislation with initiatives in other parts of the world to maximize reporting efficiency and impact.

> Conclusion: In the preparation of its next multi-annual budget, the EU should continue to mainstream climate considerations into its overall budget and to commit to the 'do no significant harm principle'. The EU taxonomy and the related disclosure regulations should strengthen funding for the climate transition by the private sector.

1.4.5 Addressing Adaptation

The Paris Agreement recognizes adaptation as a major issue and includes it within the regular stocktakes.[30] So far, most policy efforts have gone toward mitigation, while climate emergencies forced local authorities to deal with the sudden and unexpected impacts of climate change. In the past, many in the NGO community feared that too much attention given to adaptation would weaken the case for mitigation. Today, they support efforts to integrate the adaptation dimension into climate policy.

The economic losses related to climate change are increasing globally but also in Europe. Between 1980 and 2021 weather- and climate-related extremes have cost some €560 billion in the EU. The most expensive hazards include the 2021 flooding in Germany and Belgium, representing almost €50 billion. Europe, like other parts of the world, has no other option than to develop policies to deal with the economic, environmental, and social costs of climate change. Well-planned and early adaptation action can save money and lives later.

The local level is the bedrock of adaptation efforts and the stark distinction with mitigation policies is helpfully disappearing. The EU supports local initiatives and guidelines were adopted for the preparation of national adaptation strategies and plans including the development of stress tests as the basis for the climate risk and vulnerability assessments. Mainstreaming of adaptation in a broad spectrum of policy areas is encouraged, including in infrastructure, water management, disaster risk reduction, transport, agriculture, and biodiversity. One of the keys for successful adaptation action is the full integration into land use planning legislation and in the way local authorities develop their disasters policies.

A European Climate Risk Assessment is being prepared by the European Environment Agency. It should help defining the priorities for more resources to be made available in the EU budget as well as for the adaptation financing of the European Investment Bank. Climate proofing applies to infrastructure and buildings funded by the EU budget, for instance, by InvestEU, the Connecting Europe Facility, and regional and cohesion funds. A Horizon Europe Mission has been launched on adaptation to climate change and counts now more than 300 regions participating. Climate Resilience Dialogues[31] are bringing together policymakers, insurers, risk managers, consumers, cities, and other stakeholders.

Conclusion: The costs related to the impact of climate change are increasing. The EU should continue to support the regional and local level as the bedrock of adaptation efforts and mainstream climate resilience into a wide range of policies such as on environment, agriculture, or cohesion. In 2024, the European Environment Agency is presenting a Climate Risk Assessment for the EU.

Conclusion

Climate change is happening faster than anticipated. The world is united in its decision to manage the problem, but this is a gigantic task. The use of fossil fuels has permeated all facets of modern society, directly or indirectly. The continued growth of population, even if it is slowing down, constitutes an additional dimension. The emissions of greenhouse gases keep increasing at global level, even if there is some hope that the peak may be reached soon. The EU accepted its historical responsibility and reduced its greenhouse gas emissions by 32.5% compared to 1990. Also, emissions per head steadily decreased from more than 12 to around 7 tons today. This was achieved without sacrifices in terms of economic growth or jobs. The structure of the energy sector changed through a significant decline in the use of coal combined with a spectacular rise in renewable energy and steady improvements in energy efficiency. New economic activities have been created and low-carbon innovations continue to be brought to the market. EU climate policy has reached a point of no return.

The EU's climate policy experience is based on a gradual tightening of overall and specific policy objectives. It was necessary to learn from experience, for example, how to handle free allocation better under the EU ETS, or how to rely more on intermittent wind and solar to decarbonize the energy system. The learning-by-doing was invaluable and reinforced the confidence that more results lie within reach. As the EU targets are now aligned with the Paris Agreement, policy efforts should concentrate on implementing the many policies adopted under the European Green Deal.

Paying attention to the collective 'willingness to pay' remains crucial. Hence the search for policy options at the lowest cost possible must continue, combined with a due regard to fairness. The EU's 27 Member States are widely different economically, politically, and geographically. It has been of critical importance to take account of national and regional differences and to build in social corrections. In the coming years, addressing social issues at the level of individual households will become equally crucial. The European Continent has been and can remain a laboratory for an efficient and fair implementation of climate policies.

At the heart of its policy, the EU has successfully established a system of carbon pricing. In the sectors covered, emissions were reduced the most. Having the economic incentives right and making the polluter pay have proven to be solid policy principles. It also raises significant revenue that can be used to reinforce climate action or address distributive effects. Carbon leakage has been prevented through a system of free allocation that is gradually being replaced by a Carbon Border Adjustment Mechanism. Based on its internal EU success, it is now time to develop an outward-looking strategy. A start has been made by the Call for Paris aligned Carbon Markets in Paris. Several critical deadlines on detailed implementation are approaching, not least on CBAM and addressing emissions from international aviation. Discussions on Article 6 of the Paris Agreement also require active engagement by the EU.

While the shift toward renewables is gaining ground, fossil fuels still account for a high share of the energy mix, and this continues to make the continent heavily dependent on energy imports. At the same time, a delicate geopolitical re-balancing of the world is taking place. The EU should accelerate the energy and climate transition and turn the ongoing challenges into an opportunity for the continent. It should build further on its tradition of defending international trade and open markets but be more careful than in the past to diversify its risk and avoid dependencies in strategic sectors.

Finally, establishing a solid and comprehensive climate policy in the EU has been a tough job as much new ground needed to be covered. It is high time for Europe to become deeply engaged in the climate and energy transition that many countries in the world are starting. Plurilateral forms of cooperation on issues such as on carbon pricing and low-carbon technology can help to create confidence in view of demonstrating by 2025 that the world will be able to collectively meet the goals of the Paris Agreement while ensuring economic and social prosperity.

Notes

1 The author is solely responsible for the content of this chapter but is very grateful for the comments received by Jan Cornillie, Christian Egenhofer, Laura Iozelli, Elena Marro, Damien Meadows, Artur Runge-Metzger, Yvon Slingenberg, Sarah Tegas, Kurt Vandenberghe, Tom Van Ierland, Stefaan Vergote, and Peter Vis.
2 European Commission Communication (2019) *The European Green Deal*, dated 11.12.2019 reference: COM (2019) 640 final.
3 World Meteorological Organization (2023) *Provisional State of the Global Climate Report*, Dubai.
4 NASA. Global Climate Change. Available at: https://shorturl.at/mpAC2.
5 IPCC's 6th Assessment Report. Available at: https://www.ipcc.ch/assessment-report/ar6/.
6 IPCC (2023) *Climate Change 2023: Synthesis Report. A Report of the Intergovernmental Panel on Climate Change. Contribution of Working Groups I, II and III to the Sixth Assessment Report of the Intergovernmental Panel on Climate Change*, edited by Core Writing Team, H. Lee and J. Romero. Geneva, Switzerland: IPCC, p. 43.
7 There were clear indications of the benefits to limit warming to 1.5°C in the IPCC's Special Report (October 2018) *Global Warming of 1.5°C*.

8 IPCC (2023) *Climate Change 2023: Synthesis Report. A Report of the Intergovern-mental Panel on Climate Change. Contribution of Working Groups I, II and III to the Sixth Assessment Report of the Intergovernmental Panel on Climate Change*, edited by Core Writing Team, H. Lee and J. Romero. Geneva, Switzerland: IPCC, p. 44.

9 Rahmstorf, S. [@rahmstorf] (2020) "Global Temperature Since the Last Ice Age" [Tweet]. Twitter. https://twitter.com/rahmstorf/status/1220699044181368838.

10 European Commission (2023) *Progress Report 2023: Climate Action*, p. 9. Available at: https://climate.ec.europa.eu/document/download/60a04592-cf1f-4e31-865b-2b5b51b9d09f_en.

11 EUROSTAT (2023) Preliminary data for energy show mixed trends. Available at: https://ec.europa.eu/eurostat/web/products-eurostat-news/w/ddn-20230705-2

12 European Parliament (2022) Available at: https://www.europarl.europa.eu/news/en/press-room/20221107IPR49206/fit-for-55-deal-on-carbon-sinks-goal-will-increase-eu-2030-climate-target.

13 European Parliament (2022) Available at: https://www.europarl.europa.eu/news/en/press-room/20221107IPR49206/fit-for-55-deal-on-carbon-sinks-goal-will-increase-eu-2030-climate-target.

14 Ritchie, H. (2021) "Many countries have decoupled economic growth from CO2 emissions, even if we take offshored production into account", Published online at OurWorldInData.org. Available at: https://ourworldindata.org/co2-gdp-decoupling [Online Resource].

15 "Data page: Per capita CO_2 emissions", part of the following publication: Ritchie, H., Rosado, P., and Roser, M. (2023) "CO_2 and greenhouse gas emissions". Data adapted from Global Carbon Project, Various sources. Available at: https://ourworldindata.org/grapher/co-emissions-per-capita [Online Resource].

16 Brussels European Council (8/9 March 2007).

17 Compared to the EU's projected energy consumption in 2020, as established in the 2007 baseline scenario of the Impact Assessment for the 2020 climate and energy package (see Capros, Pantelis & Mantzos, L & Papandreou, V & Tasios, Nikos. (2008). Model based Analysis of the 2008 EU Policy Package on Climate Change and Renewables: Primes Model.).

18 COM (2023) 654 final.

19 The Florence process is an annual gathering organized by the European Commission in Florence since 2016, bringing together representatives of constituencies having established a compliance carbon market.

20 *Summit for a New Global Financing Pact*, Paris, 22–23 June 2023.

21 SWD (2020) 176 final.

22 *IEA Russia's War on Ukraine. Available at: https://www.iea.org/topics/russias-war-on-ukraine#*

23 Communication from the Commission to the European Parliament, The Council, The European Economic and Social Committee and the Committee of the Regions Stepping up Europe's 2030 Climate Ambition Investing in a Climate-Neutral Future for the Benefit of Our People, COM/2020/562 final (2020), p. 27. Available at: https://eur-lex.europa.eu/legal-content/EN/TXT/?uri=CELEX%3A52020DC0562&qid=1704881330252.

24 This principle was also partially used in the definition of the renewable energy 2020 targets for each Member State. For 2030 EU Member States do not have individual Renewable Energy targets but must rather make National Climate and Energy Plans (see Chapter 6 for more details of the Energy Union Governance Regulation).

25 Coal – including both hard coal and lignite – is currently mined in 12 EU countries and is an important source of economic activity in coal mining regions. The coal

sector provides jobs to about 240,000 people: about 180,000 in the mining of coal and lignite and about 60,000 in coal- and lignite-fired power plants. For more details see: https://ec.europa.eu/energy/sites/ener/files/crit_tor_fin.pdf

26 See Pisani-Ferry, J. (2021) "Climate policy is macroeconomic policy, and the implications will be significant", Peterson Institute for International Economics, *Policy Brief*, No. 21-20, p. 8.

27 https://finance.ec.europa.eu/sustainable-finance/overview-sustainable-finance_en.

28 See https://ec.europa.eu/commission/presscorner/detail/en/ip_23_3192.

29 See https://finance.ec.europa.eu/publications/2024-commission-work-programme_en.

30 Article 7(1) of the Paris Agreement.

31 Climate Resilience Dialogue (europa.eu), see https://climate.ec.europa.eu/eu-action/adaptation-climate-change/climate-resilience-dialogue_en.

2

THE PARIS AGREEMENT

Jacob Werksman and Jos Delbeke[1]

Introduction

Since their emergence from the Second World War, the Member States of the European Union have consistently supported a multilateral approach to global problems. From the first Earth Summit in 1972 in Stockholm, Europeans have been calling on the world to act together to halt and reverse environmental degradation. Climate change has emerged as the greatest of these challenges, for which there is no solution without international cooperation. For these reasons, European countries have worked hard to find coordinated solutions through the UN, including most recently through the Paris Agreement.

This chapter describes the origin, content and essential features of the 2015 Paris Agreement and explains why it has commanded near universal support and participation from the international community. We describe how the Paris Agreement's ambitious goals can only be achieved through a combination of leadership from each of its Parties and their active cooperation. Political leadership in setting ambitious climate policy has enabled the EU to be a reliable international partner, even as the commitment of some of the EU's most important partners has wavered with changes in administrations. Stability is essential to turning the commitments made under the Paris Agreement into policies and action on the ground. This is particularly the case for emerging economies, as their action on their rapidly growing emissions will significantly determine the climate change impacts of the future.

2.1 The UN Framework Convention on Climate Change and the Kyoto Protocol

The Paris Agreement is the third generation of international treaties designed to respond to the challenge of climate change. The first, adopted in 1992 just prior to the United Nations Conference on Environment and Development in Rio de Janeiro, is the UN Framework Convention on Climate Change

DOI: 10.4324/9781003493730-3

(UNFCCC).[2] The Convention contains an important objective namely to stabilise greenhouse gas concentrations in the atmosphere at safe levels. It established the principal institutions necessary for the UN's climate regime to function, including the UNFCCC Secretariat and its governing body – the annual Conference of the Parties (COP).

Most significantly, the UNFCCC created the first international system for the national reporting of inventories of greenhouse gases and for communicating policies and measures that Parties have put in place to manage their emissions and adapt to the impacts of climate change. In compliance with its obligations under the UNFCCC, the European Union developed and submitted its first greenhouse gas inventory to the UNFCCC Secretariat in June 1996, as part of its first National Communication.

The Convention also sets out key principles intended to guide international cooperation on climate policy, including an expression of the precautionary principle which calls on governments to act when faced with threats of serious or irreversible damage, even if there is a lack of full scientific certainty about the nature of those threats. It is also stated that measures to address climate change should promote sustainable development, be appropriate to the conditions of each Party, and not constitute a means of arbitrary or unjustifiable discrimination or a disguised restriction on international trade.

Importantly, the Convention calls on Parties to address climate change *"on the basis of equity and in accordance with their common but differentiated responsibilities and respective capabilities"*. Accordingly, the Convention states that developed country Parties (like the EU and its Member States) should take the lead in combating climate change and the effects thereof. Annex I of the Convention listed the industrialised Parties considered to be "developed" in 1992 and were therefore expected to stabilise their emissions of greenhouse gases at 1990 levels by 2000. The richest of these (the then members of the Organization for Economic Cooperation and Development [OECD]) were also included in Annex II and were expected to provide finance to support developing countries in implementing the Convention. Central and Eastern European Countries and those of the former Soviet Union were understood to be "economies in transition" and were not included in Annex II and were accorded some flexibility. The remaining Non-Annex I Parties were considered "developing" countries. This division of responsibility was essential in 1992 to forge a global treaty to act on climate change.

The UNFCCC has since achieved near universal participation, with 198 Parties. However, the Convention remains a framework instrument without Party-specific and enforceable targets. Recognising this weakness, in 1997 its Parties adopted the Kyoto Protocol. The Protocol entered into force in 2005 and contains legally binding commitments for developed countries to reduce their collective greenhouse gas emissions by 5% over the period of

2008–2012, compared to 1990. Individual targets were negotiated and agreed, ranging from cuts of 8% (including by the EU and its Member States) to growth caps of 10% as compared to 1990 levels. For some Parties these represented significant reductions against business-as-usual emissions trends, for others, particularly in Eastern Europe and Russia, the targets eventually turned out to be "surpluses" well-above existing emissions levels. These targets were harmonised internationally to the extent that they constituted broad, quantitative emissions limitation or reduction targets set against a common base year[3] and within a common timeframe.

To back up these internationally agreed and legally binding targets and timetables, the Kyoto Protocol Parties developed detailed and rigorous reporting requirements, as well as accounting rules and tracking systems necessary to check on Parties' compliance with their targets.[4] Developed country Parties' targets were converted into individual carbon budgets (denominated in "Assigned Amount Units" – each Unit corresponding to a metric-tonne of CO_2-equivalent). A Party could trade Assigned Amount Units it didn't need to another Party that needed them to remain within its budget – an arrangement referred to in the Protocol as "emissions trading". The Protocol also established the Clean Development Mechanism, the first international mechanism for certifying carbon offsets generated by projects in developing countries that could be used by developed country Parties to remain within their budgets. These "flexibility mechanisms" were essential to bringing the US and other countries on board that planned to meet their targets in part by acquiring the predicted surpluses in Assigned Amount Units from the Economies in Transition. The EU was concerned that these trades would significantly reduce the environmental effectiveness of the targets.

Compliance with the Kyoto targets and its carbon market rules is overseen by the Enforcement Branch of its Compliance Committee, which has the authority to suspend the right to trade Assigned Amount Units and to penalise Parties for failing to remain within their budgets. As designed, under the Kyoto compliance system, a Party found to have exceeded its carbon budget, or "assigned amount", during the first commitment period of the Kyoto Protocol must deduct that excess of emissions from its "assigned amount" in the subsequent commitment period at a penalty rate of 1.3.

The EU and its Member States ratified the Kyoto Protocol in April 2002. By that time, however, the US had decided not to follow up its signature of the Protocol by ratification. This was a considerable blow to the newly emerging multilateral approach. In the absence of the US, the ratification by Russia was necessary to trigger the emissions-based threshold for entry into force. Thanks to intensive diplomatic efforts by the EU, Russia finally submitted its ratification instrument and the Kyoto Protocol entered into force on 16 February 2005.

The rescuing of the Kyoto Protocol was important for the world's efforts on climate action, but also for Europe. Preparing for and implementing the Kyoto Protocol directly shaped the design of the EU's domestic targets, its rules for monitoring, reporting, and verifying emissions and, very significantly, the EU's Emissions Trading System. These policies contributed to the EU over-achieving its target of an 8% reduction below 1990 levels by three percentage points by the end of the Protocol's first commitment period in 2012.

Conclusion: The EU has consistently pursued the goal of tackling global environmental problems through UN institutions. EU climate policy has both shaped and been shaped by the Kyoto Protocol, which entered into force in 2005 following intensive diplomatic efforts by the EU.

2.2 From the Failure of Copenhagen (2009) to the Success of the Paris Agreement (2015)

In the 1990s, it was somewhat easier to describe the world as divided between "developed" and "developing" nations and this was reflected both in the Framework Convention on Climate Change and the Kyoto Protocol. Three decades later, due to the impressive rise of new emerging economies, the EU and other "developed" countries represent a far smaller share of the global economy than when the negotiations began. While more than 1 billion people have moved out of extreme poverty since 1990, in 2020, over 700 million people in the developing world still lived on less than $1.90 a day, the international line the World Bank defined for extreme poverty. At the same time, more than 20 Parties considered to be "developing" under the UNFCCC have *per capita* incomes higher than that of the EU's poorest Member State.

These profound economic changes were reflected, as one would expect, in the emissions pattern of the countries concerned. Figure 2.1 sketches out developments since 1970. The dramatic increase of China's greenhouse gas emissions is striking, representing roughly a doubling during the first decade of this century, which coincides with the early years of the entry into force of the Kyoto Protocol. Since then, China's emissions kept rising and represent today approximately a third of global emissions.

This rapidly changing context led to an intense debate on the kind of international climate change regime that should be in place after the Kyoto Protocol's first commitment period ended, in 2012. The Europeans preferred to extend the Kyoto Protocol and were prepared to continue taking the lead by signing up to a second commitment period of legally binding emissions

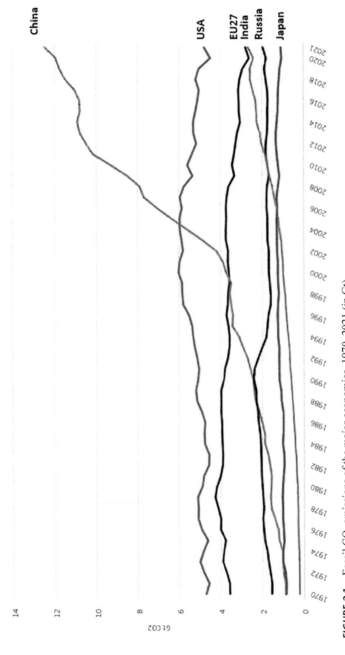

FIGURE 2.1 Fossil CO_2 emissions of the major economies, 1970–2021 (in Gt)

Source: JRC/IEA/PBL (2022)[5]

reduction targets, with the understanding that appropriate criteria and parameters should be agreed to include emerging economies in taking on quantitative obligations over time. The US, always sceptical about legally binding commitments and increasingly concerned about its competitive relationship with China, was interested in a more voluntary, "bottom-up" approach that would treat all countries in the same manner. While the views of developing countries were increasingly divided, the major economies within the G77 were unwilling to contemplate binding commitments under the Kyoto Protocol, but still wanted to capture as many developed countries as possible in a second commitment period.

In 2005, it was decided to start negotiations on a two-track approach to designing the post-2012 regime. Under the Kyoto Protocol the EU led a process to negotiate by 2009, new, binding commitments, even if many realised that this effort would unlikely capture the United States and other major emitters. Under a second track, UNFCCC Parties would, within the same timeframe, negotiate an "outcome" of an undefined legal character that would represent "long-term cooperative action" and that would include the identification of "nationally appropriate mitigation actions" for all countries.

This vague, lopsided mandate and the tensions between the different groups of countries came to a head at COP15 in Copenhagen in 2009. By then it was clear that despite its strong rules, innovative market, and compliance mechanisms, the Kyoto Protocol, and its exclusive focus on developed country targets, would not provide a long-term model. No alternative model for a legally binding agreement to replace the Kyoto Protocol gained consensus. In its place, the US vision for a more "bottom-up", less binding approach received the support of the emerging economies. The EU found itself isolated, despite strong support from the NGO community.

In the final days of the Copenhagen COP, the formal negotiating tracks broke down and were overtaken by an *ad hoc* group of 28 government leaders that produced the "Copenhagen Accord". The Accord proposed a system of "pledge and review" whereby all Annex I (developed) Parties would commit to implement individually or jointly, quantified economy wide emissions targets for 2020, whereas Non-Annex I (developing country) Parties to the Convention would implement "mitigation actions". These pledges of developed and developing countries would be compiled by the UNFCCC Secretariat in separate documents and be subject to distinct review processes. Under the Accord, developed countries would commit to a goal of jointly mobilising US$100 billion dollars a year by 2020 to address the needs of developing countries, and that a significant portion of such funding should flow through a newly established Green Climate Fund. The unorthodox way in which the Accord was negotiated and presented led to opposition from many countries and the COP ended in confusion and acrimony.

The UN process was brought back on track a year later by the COP16 in Cancun. By then, more than 90 countries, including the EU and its Member States, and all major economies, submitted voluntary 2020 emission reduction pledges. In fact, Parties agreed to the essential elements of the Copenhagen Accord, namely a common but differentiated system of "pledge and review", which called on all Parties to participate in emission reductions, but retained the "bifurcated", or differentiated, categories of the Convention Annexes. This, along with the US$100 billion pledge from developed countries, became the backbone of the international climate regime for the eight years 2013–2020.

After Copenhagen, the EU and its closest negotiating partners, including an increasingly engaged US administration under President Obama, recognised that neither an extension of the Kyoto Protocol to a larger group of Parties, nor a purely voluntary system of pledge and review, that continued to differentiate responsibilities between developed and emerging economies, was a sufficient response to the urgency of climate change.

In 2011, at COP17 in Durban, the EU together with the most vulnerable developing countries led a "progressive alliance" of developed and developing countries to win acceptance of a new mandate to negotiate *"a Protocol, another legal instrument or an agreed outcome with legal force under the Convention applicable to all Parties, which is to be completed no later than 2015"* and with the expectation that this new agreement would take over in 2020, when the Cancun/Copenhagen pledges ended.

To secure this outcome, the EU and its Member States also agreed to include their pledges as a new set of binding targets under an amendment to the Kyoto Protocol, adopted in Doha in 2012. The "Doha Amendment" would run from 2012 to 2020. This was possible in large part because the EU had already put in place all the key elements of its regional and national climate policies up to 2020. Meanwhile, Canada formally withdrew from the Kyoto Protocol while Japan, Russia, and several other industrialised countries declared their intention not to enter a second commitment period under the Kyoto Protocol. Ultimately, the Doha amendment reached the threshold of ratifications necessary to bring it into force in 2020, but by then the Paris Agreement had already become operational, thereby making the Kyoto Protocol irrelevant.

In November 2015, 23 years after the adoption of the Convention in 1992, the text of the Paris Agreement was adopted by "acclamation".[6] Drawing on lessons from experience of the UNFCCC and the Kyoto Protocol, the Paris Agreement combines ambitious goals, nationally determined emissions reductions and robust systems of transparency and accountability that is applicable to all Parties. More than 150 Heads of State and Government attended the Paris Conference to express their support for global action on climate change. While the US left the Paris Agreement during the Trump Administration, it re-joined shortly after Joe Biden entered the White House. This leaves the Paris Agreement with 195 Parties at near universal membership, with Iran, Libya, and Yemen as the only UNFCCC Parties that have yet to join.

> Conclusion: The Paris Agreement is the new multilateral structure for global action on climate change. It has achieved near universal membership and requires action by all countries.

2.3   Essential Features of the Paris Agreement

The Paris Agreement breaks new ground in the climate change regime. It combines several "top-down" and "bottom-up" elements in a way that sets collective goals while allowing for much more differentiation in Parties' commitments. It is a legally binding treaty, but its core obligations are procedural rather than substantive. It is a landmark agreement that has been designed to last decades, to be strengthened over time by the individual actions of its Parties rather than through additional legal agreements such as amendments or protocols.

2.3.1   Applicable to All Parties

The Paris Agreement sets ambitious collective goals, allows each Party to determine its own targets and timetables, and demands transparency and accountability from its Parties. It is the first international climate agreement that is in this way "applicable to all" Parties. It provides flexibility for developing countries based on differences in their national capacities and circumstances rather than the defined categories of developed and developing countries set under the UNFCCC and perpetuated under the Kyoto Protocol.

The Paris Agreement has now replaced the pre-2020 twin track approach of the Kyoto Protocol's binding targets and the voluntary pledges initiated in Copenhagen. Under Paris, all Parties must prepare, communicate, and maintain domestic mitigation targets, but the form and content of these "contributions" are "nationally determined" by each Party ("Nationally Determined Contributions" or "NDCs"). Nonetheless, each Party's NDC must reflect the "highest ambition possible" in the context of the Paris Agreement's goals of limiting global average temperature rise and achieving net zero global emissions. Developed country Parties (which are not defined in the Paris Agreement) are expected to continue to "take the lead" through emissions reduction targets that are absolute and economy wide. Developing country Parties (also not defined in the Paris Agreement) are expected to move over time to economy-wide targets as well.[7] The Paris Agreement thus combines both "bottom-up" and "top-down" elements, reflecting the principle of "common but differentiated responsibilities and respective capabilities", while doing so in "the light of different national circumstances" rather than through agreed categories of Parties.

While Europeans strongly support the Paris Agreement as an outcome of multilateralism, the EU and its progressive allies had hoped instead for a treaty with legally binding targets expressed in a common format of specific emissions reductions. The first round of NDCs which for most Parties will run from 2020 to 2030 are of variable quality, in both form and content. They range from absolute, economy-wide emissions reduction targets, like the one of the EU, to the most general description of policies and measures. To succeed as an urgent driver of policy change, the Paris Agreement process will need to generate strong diplomatic and political pressure on Parties to strengthen and implement their NDCs through increased transparency and regular reviews.

2.3.2 Ambitious Collective Goals

The Paris Agreement builds on the guidance offered by the International Panel on Climate Change (IPCC) and the Convention's objective of limiting concentrations of greenhouse gases in the atmosphere to levels that would prevent dangerous climate change. It clarifies that global average temperature rises as compared to pre-industrial levels must stay "well below 2°C" while "pursuing efforts to limit such a rise to 1.5°C". These "temperature goals" help to define what the international community considers to be dangerous climate change and set an overall ambitious direction for the development of Parties' individual and collective efforts.

The Paris Agreement also seeks to achieve a balance between sources and sinks of emissions in the second half of this century. In other words, it describes as its purpose a profound and global transformation over the next decades from an economy primarily dependent on fossil fuels to one that has reached a steady state in which global emissions are at "net zero" and atmospheric concentrations of greenhouse gases have balanced out at levels consistent with the temperature goals.

Considering increasingly urgent messages of the IPCC, Parties to the Paris Agreement have since recognised that the impacts of climate change will be much lower at the temperature increase of 1.5°C compared with 2°C and have resolved to pursue efforts to limit the temperature increase to 1.5°C. At COP26, in Glasgow, Parties also recognised that "limiting global warming to 1.5°C requires rapid, deep, and sustained reductions in global greenhouse gas emissions, including reducing global carbon dioxide emissions by 45% by 2030 relative to the 2010 level and to net zero around mid-century, as well as deep reductions in other greenhouse gases".

The Paris Agreement goals address global emissions and thus have the potential to cover all sources of emissions that contribute to anthropogenic climate change, including those originating from international aviation and maritime operations.[8] Both international transport sectors show rapidly increasing emissions, and these will have to be addressed, respectively, in the context of the International Civil Aviation Organisation (ICAO) and the International Maritime Organisation (IMO) if the ambitious goals of the Paris Agreement are to be achieved.

2.3.3 Dynamic Five Year Ambition Cycles

Under the Paris Agreement, each Party commits to "prepare, communicate and maintain successive Nationally Determined Contributions that it intends to achieve" every five years.[9] Each successive contribution will represent a progression over the previous one and shall be informed by a global stocktake of Parties' collective progress towards the Agreement's long-term goals. As a result of diplomatic efforts at every COP since 2015, an impressive 169 Parties, including the EU, have communicated new or updated NDCs that have substantially raised ambition. Although the ambition, form, and content of Parties' targets and contributions will remain nationally determined, the Paris Agreement puts in place rules and processes that will encourage their harmonisation, quantification, and comparability over time. Parties agreed to continue negotiations on common features that will be applicable to future rounds of targets.

The first global stocktake took place at COP28 in Dubai and concluded that the likely impact of Parties current, pre-2030 NDCs would, if fully implemented, still lead to an estimate global average temperature rise of 2.1°C–2.8°C by 2100. Parties recognised that

> limiting global warming to 1.5°C with no or limited overshoot requires deep, rapid and sustained reductions in global greenhouse gas emissions of 43 per cent by 2030 and 60 per cent by 2035 relative to the 2019 level, and reaching net zero carbon dioxide emissions by 2050.

In this context, COP28 called on all Parties to contribute to a set of new energy-related goals, focused on "transitioning away from fossil fuels in energy systems, in a just, orderly and equitable manner, accelerating action in this critical decade, so as to achieve net zero by 2050". These goals include "tripling renewable energy capacity globally and doubling the global average annual rate of energy efficiency improvements by 2030", "accelerating and substantially reducing non-carbon-dioxide emissions globally, including in particular methane emissions by 2030", and "accelerating efforts towards the phase-down of unabated coal power".[10]

COP28 builds significantly on the Paris Agreement by encouraging all Parties to come forward with their next NDCs with an end date of 2035 by 2025 (COP30), and to include in these NDCs "ambitious, economy-wide emission reduction targets, covering all greenhouse gases, sectors and categories and aligned with limiting global warming to 1.5°C". Together with the new goals on the decarbonisation of the energy sector, this guidance provides the clearest "top down" and "undifferentiated" expectations thus far of what Parties must do collectively and individually to reach the goals of the Paris Agreement.

2.3.4 Transparency and Accountability

The Paris Agreement establishes a robust, legally binding transparency and accountability framework that is applicable to all Parties. It sets out rules, institutions, and procedures for the measurement, reporting, and verification of information provided by Parties through national inventories of emissions and the policies they have put in place to achieve their targets. This will enable the tracking of progress of each Party towards its target, as well as an understanding of collective progress towards the Agreement's goals. The previous split approach between developed and developing countries operating under the Convention and the Kyoto Protocol, which required very little of Parties classified as developing countries, will be phased out after the submission of reports regarding data for the year 2020.

The transparency framework makes it clear that all Parties must report, at least bi-annually, greenhouse gas inventories and information necessary to track progress with the mitigation contributions in accordance with agreed methodologies and common metrics. Only the Least Developed Countries (LDCs) and the Small Island Developing States (SIDS) enjoy flexibility regarding the frequency of reporting.

The Agreement also includes an obligation on each Party to account for anthropogenic emissions and removals relating to their targets in a way that promotes environmental integrity, transparency, accuracy, completeness, comparability, and consistency and to ensure that any double counting arising from the use of carbon markets is avoided. These common rules known as the "Rulebook" are essential to promote trust in the international process. Each Party's report shall undergo a technical expert review and each Party shall participate in a facilitative multilateral consideration of its performance.

The Rulebook also elaborates on how the transparency system will provide flexibility for those developing countries that need it considering their capacity. These flexibilities were negotiated on a case-by-case basis to allow, for example, developing countries to report their national inventories less frequently or regarding fewer greenhouse gases. These countries must concisely clarify the capacity constraints they are facing and indicate estimated timeframes for overcoming these constraints.

The transparency system will be supported by a Committee on Implementation and Compliance, designed to both help and hold accountable countries experiencing challenges with the implementation of and compliance with the mandatory provisions of the Agreement and the rulebook. While this Committee is facilitative, non-adversarial, and non-punitive in nature, it can engage individual Parties regarding their performance and provide advice, recommendations to the Agreement's finance institutions, assist in the development of implementation plans, and in certain circumstances issue findings of fact. This will bring public and political attention to the challenge of implementation.

The EU's new Energy Union Governance Regulation[11] meets the requirements of this transparency and accountability framework and several features were updated, such as the alignment with the overall Paris ambition cycle. While a work programme has been launched to develop common accounting rules, including for land, these will not apply to Parties' first mitigation target under the Paris Agreement. The EU will work closely with other Parties to ensure any internationally agreed approaches including the accounting for emissions from land are consistent with EU approaches.

The framework will also provide for the transparency of the Agreement's provisions on adaptation and on climate finance, capacity building, and technology transfer, as discussed below.

2.3.5   Increasing Resilience to and Responding to the Adverse Effects of Climate Change

The Paris Agreement establishes, for the first time, a global goal on adaptation with the aim to enhance capacity, climate resilience and reduce climate vulnerability. Internationally, it encourages greater cooperation among Parties to share scientific knowledge on adaptation as well as information on practices and policies. As part of this international cooperation, developed country Parties must also continue to provide, as part of their commitments on climate finance, resources to developing country Parties to support their adaptation efforts.

All Parties' efforts to promote adaptation must "represent a progression over time" and the first global stocktake at COP28 provided significant additional guidance to Parties on how to plan for and track progress towards achieving the global goal on adaptation. This guidance includes a new set of targets for 2030 that call on Parties to improve resilience and reduce vulnerability in the areas of water scarcity, food and agricultural production, public health, ecosystems, and cultural heritage, while reducing the adverse effects of climate change, poverty eradication, and livelihoods.

The Paris Agreement acknowledges that addressing "loss and damage" resulting from climate change is a specific aspect of increasing resilience to the adverse effects of climate change. Many vulnerable developing countries, especially low-lying and Small Island Developing States, are struggling with how to prepare for and manage loss and damage associated with extreme weather and the slow onset impacts associated with climate change. Nevertheless, the decisions taken in Paris clarify that the Paris Agreement provisions on loss and damage do not involve or provide a basis for any liability or compensation.

Considering the increasing impacts of extreme weather events, and under pressure from vulnerable countries and international civil society, Parties agreed at COP27 to establish new funding arrangements, including a fund, for assisting developing countries that are particularly vulnerable to the adverse effects of climate change, in responding to loss and damage. It was also recognised that there is a need to identify a wide variety of sources, including innovative sources of finance to support this effort.

The loss and damage fund became operational at COP28 in Dubai in December 2023 and raised over $700 million in pledges for its initial operations, including $100 million from the UAE, and $500 million from the EU and its Member States.

2.3.6 *Fostering Cooperation and Financial Flows*

The Paris Agreement also fosters cooperation among Parties by encouraging the responsible use of international carbon markets and the mobilisation of support to developing countries. Implementing the emissions targets will require very substantial policy action and investments in clean technologies in the coming years in all countries. The Paris Agreement includes the aim of *"making financial flows consistent with a pathway towards low greenhouse gas emissions and climate resilient development"*. Shifting and rapidly scaling up private investment is essential to the transition to a low-emission and climate resilient economy and to avoid "locking-in" high emission infrastructure.

In Paris, the EU, its Member States, and other developed country Parties committed to continuing, in the period from 2020 until 2025, the goal set in Copenhagen to mobilise US$100 billion annually from public and private sources by developing countries. Before 2025, the Parties to the Paris Agreement will set a new collective quantified goal from a floor of US$100 billion per year. This will provide an opportunity to broaden the donor base to include countries previously considered only as recipients of assistance.

Conclusion: The Paris Agreement is applicable to all Parties in a similar fashion: each Party determines its own target or contribution, and all Parties are ultimately subject to a common, transparent governance system. Flexibilities are provided for those developing countries that need it but based on gaps in their capacity.

2.4 Are Global Emissions Peaking?

The Paris Agreement is ambitious in its objectives and calls on Parties to reach global peaking "as soon as possible" and to "undertake rapid reductions thereafter". It assumes that global emissions have not yet reached the maximum level and keep increasing year on year. This is a disappointing reality and illustrates the magnitude of the policy challenge ahead. However, it is encouraging that in many countries, emissions have either been reduced in absolute terms, or the rate of increase is slowing down, and that a gradual decoupling from economic growth is happening.

Developing countries in general, but particularly emerging economies are allowed to increase their emissions temporarily under the Paris Agreement. The fact is that their economic development leads to an increase in emissions. However, they are also aware that they are contributing to climate change that will be experienced in the future also by themselves and are, therefore, willing to invest in low-carbon technology. China announced in its NDC that its emissions would peak no later than in 2030. This means that its historical emissions – although much more recent than those of UNFCCC Annex 1 countries – will continue to rapidly accumulate. Recent analysis seems to indicate that the date of peaking of China's emissions could well be before 2025, given the significant development of renewable energy.[12]

It is most helpful that many Parties submitted their NDCs, but they did so according to a variety of definitions of targets and pathways. Several analyses have been made trying to summarise the overall result of the pledges and policy intentions. If fully implemented, existing policy declarations, including those of NDCs, would bring global warming down from almost a 5°C warming to a range of 2.1°C–2.9°C by the end of the century. Although the "well below 2°C" goal of the Paris Agreement is not yet achieved, it should be underlined that realising every single tenth of a degree Celsius less is significant and worthwhile striving for. Moreover, the exercise of developing an NDC allows each Party to have a good understanding of the sources of its emissions and how to address them most effectively.

For some Parties, as is the case for the EU, the emphasis is on carbon emissions from industry and power, while in some others, such as New Zealand, the bulk of emissions come from agriculture. In the case of Brazil or the Democratic Republic of Congo, most emissions are linked to tropical deforestation. Ideally, preparing an NDC also enables each Party to reflect on its emissions per person, where there are also major differences. In 2021, the global average of greenhouse gas emissions *per capita* amounted to 6.9 tonnes. In the EU it was 7.6 tonnes and steadily declining since 1990. In contrast, the Chinese path was steadily increasing, surpassing the one of the EU. Although falling, the *per capita* emissions of the US are more than twice those of the EU and China. It has been estimated that per person emissions of CO_2 should be limited to approximately 2.3 tonnes by 2050 to be compatible with the 2°C goal of the Paris Agreement.[13]

Finally, the NDCs already include valuable information for policy research and allow tailor-made policy recommendations in view of dealing with the specific needs and potential of countries. The International Energy Agency has been studying recent and forecasted investment for 2030 according to several scenarios, including one leading to net zero emissions.[14] The almost 2 trillion-dollar investment in energy observed for 2023 still needs more than a doubling by 2030. However, the IEA also concludes that since the beginning of the current decade the global investment patterns are developing in a helpful direction: investments in renewables (notably in PV) are promising to reach the 1.5°C target, provided these are accompanied by more efforts to make the electricity system more flexible, to improve energy efficiency and to expand the grid.

Conclusion: The NDC instrument is a useful tool for policy making. NDC policy plans submitted under the Paris Agreement are not yet aligned with delivering the "well below 2°C" goal. Their implementation has been assessed in the global stocktake in 2023 and will be reviewed in 2025.

2.5   The International Dimensions of the European Green Deal

The level of ambition reflected in the European Green Deal, with its commitments to a net zero, circular economy by 2050, is having an impact beyond European borders. The EU aims to strengthen its diplomatic efforts to encourage climate ambition across the globe.

2.5.1 Sharing Lessons on the Climate and Energy Transition

The EU encourages others by sharing its experiences in designing and implementing climate and energy policies, particularly with other major economies. This applies to areas such as carbon pricing, the encouragement of renewable energy technologies, energy efficiency policies or developing clean mobility strategies. Equally, the experience and lessons learned in developing a joint NDC for the continent comprising 27 Member States with quite different emissions profiles and economic conditions can be useful for other countries.

The EU has supported and joined several plurilateral initiatives designed to compare and encourage the development of effective climate policies, included the G7-led Climate Club, which will focus on decarbonising the industrial sector, and the OECD's Inclusive Forum on Climate Mitigation Approaches, which will model the impacts of different countries policies.

Harmonising reporting on efficiency standards among G20 countries is encouraging economies of scale and the lowering of technology costs. Supporting densely forested developing countries to reduce the emissions from deforestation and forest degradation, particularly when it comes to the monitoring through its COPERNICUS earth observation programme from space, will continue to play a role in EU development cooperation.

Finally, to shore up support to the Paris Agreement's goals, the EU is leading a series of international initiatives to set targets to phase down methane emissions, to scale up the deployment of renewable energy and to increase energy efficiency. These are part of a collective effort to achieve a global energy system free of unabated fossil fuels as soon as possible.

2.5.2 Trade-related Climate Measures

The close coordination of trade rules and climate policies, wherever possible, will be increasingly important to ensure that international trade promotes rather than undermines climate ambition. For example, EU policies on renewable energy are designed to ensure that domestic and imported biofuels and biomass are sustainably produced if they are to count towards EU emissions reduction efforts. Equally, to promote sustainable supply chains in products that will be key to the transition to a net zero, circular economy, the EU has put in place regulations that require importers to demonstrate that they have met sustainability standards if they wish to sell certain batteries and forest products in the European market. EU bilateral and regional trade agreements increasingly include commitments from Parties to fully implement the Paris Agreement, and not to lower their climate ambitions as a means of attracting trade or investment.

A recent development in EU climate policy is the Carbon Border Adjustment Mechanism (CBAM) that started in October 2023 with a first phase of data gathering and will be fully applicable as of 2026. Importers of products that are covered by the EU ETS will be required to pay for the carbon embedded in these products at level equivalent to the charge paid by EU producers. Payments will be discounted based on any carbon price that has been effectively paid by the producer in the country of origin. This has increased the interest in carbon pricing policies among the EU's trading partners.

Cooperation in the field of low-carbon technology has received a new boost under the Just Energy Transition Plans (JETPs). The concept is to bring together all relevant players of the public and private sectors, such as technology providers, policy makers, investors, and financial institutions. The EU is an active supporter of this concept and JETPs have been concluded with South Africa, Indonesia, and Vietnam. The Philippines, Senegal, and India are likely to be the next partner candidates. Even if the practical implementation is facing some hurdles, it remains a very useful tool to kick start the climate and energy transition in emerging economies.

2.5.3 Mobilising Sustainable Finance

Sustainable finance has become a key concern in the global policy agenda, particularly following the adoption of the UN 2030 Sustainable Development Agenda and the Paris Agreement. Under Article 2(1) (c), the Agreement calls for *"making financial flows consistent with a pathway towards low greenhouse gas emissions and climate resilient development"*. Mobilising the necessary finance for the transition to low-carbon economies will be a major challenge for all, both developed and developing countries.

Since Paris, the EU and its Member States have contributed the lion's share of global public climate finance. In 2022, the EU's contribution reached €28.5 billion.[15] Moreover, to promote low-carbon investment in third countries, the EU has set targets for climate mainstreaming, during the 2021–2027 period, to ensure that 30% of the Commission's budget, including development assistance, contribute to achieving climate goals. During the same period, the EU institutions and EU Member States plan to put into effect the Global Gateway initiative, a new strategy aimed at mobilising up to €300 billion of global investments for sustainable and high-quality projects aligned with the Paris Agreement, with a view to improving partnerships outside the EU and narrow the global investment gap worldwide.

For the EU to achieve the targets of the Paris Agreement, the 2020 Sustainable Europe Investment Plan estimates that at least €1 trillion in public and private investment will be needed over the next decade.[16] The financial sector has a key role to play in reaching those goals, as large amounts of private capital should be redirected towards sustainable investments. The EU's Capital Markets Union is fostering more sustainable private investments. In 2018, the Commission launched an Action Plan on Financing Sustainable Growth seeking a lead on global work in this area.[17] This resulted in a classification system, or "taxonomy", of sustainable activities, a disclosure framework for non-financial and financial companies, and several investment tools, including benchmarks, standards, and labels. This legislation should allow to significantly raise the amount of private capital into sustainable investments.

> Conclusion: The EU is shifting its international cooperation and financial support, towards implementation of the Paris Agreement. New ways of cooperation are being developed in the field of trade, finance, and low-carbon investment, involving both the public and private sector.

Conclusion

The Paris Agreement is proving to be a durable base for the global effort on climate change for decades to come. It has secured global participation in record time. The Paris Agreement has made the UN Framework Convention on Climate Change operational and more comprehensive. This is a major achievement given the political context, in which multilateral efforts are coming under increasing pressure. The challenge ahead is to get it implemented as designed, in a world of increasing geopolitical tension.

The main achievement of the Paris Agreement is to set a science-based goal of "well below 2°C, while pursuing efforts to 1.5°C" global average temperature rise by around mid-century. Significantly, this is a shared global challenge that leaves behind the UNFCCC's outdated "annexes" and allows for more nuanced distinctions between Parties' national circumstances. The Convention principle of "common but differentiated responsibilities and respective capabilities" has been secured through the Agreement's bottom-up approach to Nationally Determined Contributions (NDCs), which each Party is required to submit, but is free to design. However, each Party's performance will be reviewed by a common and enhanced transparency system, and each NDC must be updated every five years, considering the best available science.

The Paris Agreement also has some weaknesses. While the outcome of the first global stocktake has shown that a science-based approach will generate increasingly specific guidance on what Parties must do collectively, the Paris Agreement does not provide a formal opportunity to discuss or negotiate levels of ambition. While achieving the Paris Agreement goals will require trillions of Euros of investment, the collective finance goals set by the Parties fall far short of this, and the politics of Paris continue to rely heavily on the small subset of "developed country Parties" identified in 1992. Finally, the Agreement's compliance regime does not foresee sanctions but is based on peer pressure.

In addition, the Paris Agreement does not explicitly "organise" the development of common policies or standards, as the Kyoto Protocol did, for example, with respect to individual carbon budgets for developed countries.[18] It is, therefore, key that groups of like-minded countries come together to foster common policy plans, to share their experiences and knowledge of policy making to reinforce implementation of the multilaterally agreed commitments.

Consequently, the success of Paris will continue to rely on political will that is generated within each country, and the assistance, encouragement, diplomatic, and economic pressure Parties bring to bear on each other.

The EU has adopted a common climate target and differentiated efforts among its Member States with due regard to their relative prosperity and the principle of cost-efficiency. The EU developed common policy instruments such as the EU Emissions Trading System and CO_2 standards for cars and appliances along with policies in the field of renewables and energy efficiency. A considerable effort is being undertaken to mainstream climate action into other policies such as research, industry, finance, trade, agriculture, and development cooperation.

The EU is ready to deploy extensive efforts in the field of international cooperation and financial support both with emerging economies and developing countries for the implementation of the Paris Agreement. The involvement of all stakeholders from the private sector, NGOs, and local authorities will be key to a successful outcome. The attack of US President Trump on the Paris Agreement did not shake support for the Agreement within the EU and around the world. However, even with the return of the US to the Paris Agreement, the world's major economies remain divided on which of them is contributing its fair share to reducing emissions. Fortunately, the economics of the low-carbon economy are improving rapidly with clean and sustainable technologies becoming cheaper by the day.

It must be recognised that recently the number of global problems confronting politicians has dramatically increased: wars and political instability causing an upsurge of poverty and refugees; respect for democratic institutions and for expert evidence; and the continued undermining of rules-based multilateral institutions. This leaves climate change as only one of many global challenges to deal with, yet it deserves considerable political attention given the seriousness and the urgency of the problem.

Notes

1 This chapter is the review of the previous one co-authored by Jos Delbeke, Artur Runge-Metzger, Yvon Slingenberg, and Jacob Werksman.
2 The UNFCCC was adopted on 9 May 1992 and opened for signature at the United Nations Conference on Environment and Development that took place from 3 to 14 June 1992.
3 Given their specific circumstances, "economies in transition" were allowed to choose one among a limited number of base-years.
4 These decisions were mostly taken in the Marrakech Accords at the 7th Conference of Parties (COP-7) in 2001.
5 IEA-EDGAR CO2, a component of the EDGAR (Emissions Database for Global Atmospheric Research) Community GHG database version 7.0 (2022) including or based on data from IEA (2021) Greenhouse Gas Emissions from Energy. Available at: www.iea.org/data-and-statistics, as modified by the Joint Research Centre. In Crippa et al. (2022) "CO2 emissions of all world countries". JRC/IEA/PBL 2022 Report, EUR 31182 EN, Publications Office of the European Union, Luxembourg, JRC130363. Available at: https://edgar.jrc.ec.europa.eu/report_2022.
6 "By acclamation" means with no state objecting in the plenary session of the Conference of Parties.
7 Least developed countries and small island developing states continue to be recognised as distinct categories of Parties under the Paris Agreement and are afforded additional flexibilities.
8 Outgoing aviation emissions are included in the EU 2020 targets and in the EU 2030 legislation and countries can decide to include these in their Nationally Determined Contributions (NDCs) under the Paris Agreement.
9 Article 4 of the Paris Agreement.
10 UNFCCC (2023) Decision 1/CMA.5. Outcome of the first global stocktake. Available at: https://unfccc.int/documents/636584.
11 Regulation (EU) 2018/1999 of the European Parliament and of the Council of 11 December 2018 on the Governance of the Energy Union and climate action. OJ L 328, pp. 1–77, published on 21.12.2018.
12 See: "China's 'new normal': Structural change, better growth, and peak emissions", by Fergus Green and Nicholas Stern, Policy brief by the Centre for Climate Change Economics and Policy (CCCEP) and the Grantham Research Institute on Climate Change and the Environment, June 2015. Available at: http://www.lse.ac.uk/GranthamInstitute/publication/chinas-new-normal-structural-change-better-growth-and-peak-emissions/.
13 "Mindful of the inherent uncertainty of such long-term estimates, the information indicates that these Parties' total GHG emission level could be 64.0 (60.0–68.0)% lower in 2050 than in 2019 and their annual per capita emissions would be 2.3 (2.0–2.6) t CO2 eq by 2050. Under scenarios of limiting warming to likely below 2°C (with over 67% likelihood), annual per capita emissions are 2.4 (1.6–3.1) t CO2 eq; hence the estimated long-term per capita emissions of these Parties are at a level consistent with 2°C scenarios. However, for scenarios of limiting warming to 1.5°C (with 50% likelihood by 2100) and achieving net zero CO2 emissions around 2050 and net zero GHG emissions this century, annual per capita emissions by 2050 are required to be two to three times lower, at 1.3 (0.6–2.1) t CO2 eq." Available at: https://unfccc.int/ndc-synthesis-report-2023#Projected-GHG-Emission-levels.
14 International Energy Agency (2023) "World Energy Investment 2023". Available at: https://iea.blob.core.windows.net/assets/8834d3af-af60-4df0-9643-72e2684f7221/WorldEnergyInvestment2023.pdf.

15 Council of the EU and European Council (2022) Available at: Infographic - Europe's contribution to climate finance (€bn) https://www.consilium.europa.eu/en/infographics/climate-finance/

16 European Commission (2020) Available at: https://ec.europa.eu/commission/presscorner/detail/en/ip_20_17.

17 See Chapter 10.

18 However, the rules relating to the implementation of Article 6 of the Paris Agreement will include rules relating to carbon markets.

PART 2

The EU Emissions Trading System

3

THE EU EMISSIONS TRADING SYSTEM

Damien Meadows, Mette Quinn, and Beatriz Yordi[1]

Introduction

This chapter reviews what the EU Emissions Trading System (EU ETS) has achieved so far and how it is intended to function in the coming years, following the major review that was accomplished in 2023 as part of the "European Green Deal".[2] Over the last two decades, the EU ETS has become the main instrument of the EU's climate policy and it is likely to continue that role on the path to climate neutrality by 2050. The 2023 review[3] strengthened the system significantly and established an adjacent system in view of incorporating transport and heating fuels as well as smaller industrial combustion emissions. The ETS also creates significant revenues that are being used to enhance climate action, to address social concerns and to encourage low-carbon innovation. The 2023 review ensures that the use of ETS revenues and the system's ambition go hand in hand.

3.1   How Does the EU Emissions Trading System Work?

The EU ETS is a "cap-and-trade" system that guarantees an environmental outcome by setting a limit on the total amount of carbon emissions from the covered sectors. The number of allowances issued serves as the quantitative cap on emissions, and these allowances are then either auctioned or allocated for free to companies. Companies have an obligation to regularly hand over sufficient allowances to cover their actual emissions. Companies may trade these allowances. Progressively, the total number of allowances in the system is reduced at a steady and predictable rate. This secures an improved environmental outcome over time. This is a "cap" on emissions, and certainly not a "cap on growth", as is sometimes wrongly claimed by critics. Historical data shows that economic activity covered by the system has grown collectively while emissions have been coming down substantially.

DOI: 10.4324/9781003493730-5

The advantage of a market-based system is that it incentivises reductions in emissions across all entities covered in a cost-effective manner. Companies have an economic interest to cut emissions and sell allowances when the market price for allowances is higher than the cost of reducing its own emissions. Conversely, for companies with reduction costs above the market price, it is beneficial to buy allowances. This means that, across the system, there is an incentive for reductions to take place where the costs of abatement are lower, while the environmental outcome remains guaranteed by the overall emissions cap. By covering a variety of economic activities, a broad range of emission reduction options across the economy can be accessed.

By putting a price on carbon, a market failure is corrected, and companies and economic actors are incentivised to take account of this in their operational decision-making and long-term investment planning. Carbon prices also strengthen the business case for making investments in low-carbon technology: the rate of return is improved, and the payback period is reduced compared to more carbon-intensive alternative investments. Putting a price on carbon is, therefore, an important signal for the economy. Moreover, it must be made very clear to all, particularly higher emitting sectors that the supply of allowances will continue to decrease significantly over time.

Emissions trading systems, as well as other market-based measures like carbon taxes, have the potential to generate money that can be used for climate change mitigation and adaptation. Polluters then not only have to pay to pollute, but the revenues generated can then be redeployed to further stimulate innovation and deployment of low-carbon solutions, or to address societal effects of climate constraint such as retraining employees in carbon-intensive industries like coal mining. With increased prices, much more political attention has been paid to the use of the substantially grown revenues. Member States are now committed in law to using all ETS revenues or an equivalent amount to tackle climate change, while dedicated funds are established to address social concerns and to enhance the energy transition through low-carbon innovation and modernisation.

The EU ETS works with the economic cycle: for example, a recession leads to lower emissions, affecting the supply/demand balance in the carbon market and causing a lower carbon price, while an economic recovery could have the reverse effect. A fluctuating carbon price is a normal feature that does not undermine the overall predictability of the EU ETS. Companies can save emission allowances until they need them or sell allowances they do not need. This flexibility, as well as the certainty from the ETS' long-term reduction trajectory, gives an incentive to reduce emissions earlier in time and for individual companies to overachieve.

A well-functioning market requires the trust and confidence that actors will comply with the rules. The EU ETS, therefore, relies on a solid system of monitoring, reporting, verification (MRV) and compliance. This is essential for a market-based measure to work. In case of failure to comply, there is an inflation-corrected penalty of €100 per tonne of excess emissions plus the obligation to make up the shortfall.[4] In most years, operators responsible for over 99% of emissions from stationary installations and aviation have met their obligations on time.

Conclusion: The EU ETS puts a price on carbon. It provides an economic incentive to companies to reduce emissions and ensures that the cap set on their collective emissions is met in a cost-effective manner. Important revenues are created, and these can enhance climate action.

3.2   Price and Emissions Development

The EU ETS operates in phases, as for each phase significant modifications were made to the legislation. Phase-1 from 2005 to 2007 was a pilot phase, as all institutional infrastructure needed to be created, even before the Kyoto Protocol started. Phases-2 and 3 covered, respectively, the years 2008–2012 and 2013–2020 corresponding with the first and second commitment periods under the Kyoto Protocol. Phase-4 covers the period 2021–2030 that corresponds to the European Union's first commitments under the Paris Agreement.

Today, the EU ETS covers slightly less than 40% of the EU's CO_2 emissions. It regulates, in a harmonised way, emissions from some 10,000 sources, mainly installations from electricity and heat generation, manufacturing industry and airlines for their intra-European flights. From 2024, the EU ETS applies to 50% of maritime emissions to and from ports in the EEA and puts in place monitoring and reporting requirements for emissions from municipal waste incineration.

In Figure 3.1, the prices of allowances issued in each phase are shown in different colours. In the Phase-1, the value of EU allowances dropped steeply in 2006 when the first verified emissions figures were reported. This reflects the fact that the EU ETS began in 2005 without a detailed database of actual emissions per installation. This resulted in an excess supply of allowances compared to reported emissions. As these allowances could not be banked into subsequent phases, this excess supply resulted in a price of nearly zero in 2007. At the same time, the market price in 2007 for allowances valid for 2008–2012 was much higher in view of expectations that the system would be more constrained in the future. Prices developed in the €20–30 range.

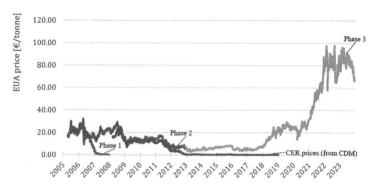

FIGURE 3.1 Price trends for allowances under the EU ETS and EU ETS eligible international credits (CERs) under the Kyoto Protocol (€/tonne)

Source: European Environment Agency, 2022[5]

A second major price drop came at the end of 2008 following the global economic and financial crisis. At the time, international credits began to be used for compliance in the EU ETS at scale. It is important to note that sectors covered by the EU ETS in aggregate were subject to much stronger swings in output than the economy in general. Individual sectors covered by the EU ETS had output drops between 2008 and 2009 of over 30%, and the supply of allowances started to exceed demand.

The period of low prices continued until the Market Stability Reserve was created and policy discussions started about the long-term goal of climate neutrality by 2050. Between 2018 and 2020, prices jumped up to the range of €30 when the pandemic broke out. Since then, prices continue to climb as soon as it became clear that the ambition expressed in the European Green Deal would materialise following strong commitment at the highest political levels. A record of €100 per EU allowance for 1 tonne of CO_2eq was reached on 21 February 2023, and slightly thereafter, prices went down and hovered around €70–80 at the end of 2023.

In parallel with this quite impressive price development, emissions went down steadily. Between 2005 and 2022, the emissions from the power and industry sectors reduced by 37.3%,[6] which is more than the EU average (Figure 3.2). In other words, the EU ETS sectors are doing more than other sectors. Emissions covered by the EU ETS have decreased from over 2 billion tonnes per year in 2008 to less than 1.4 billion tonnes per year in 2022.[7] The EU ETS has continuously ensured reductions in emissions while maintaining a very high level of compliance, also during the COVID-19 pandemic.

Due to the lack of monitoring at installation level and independent verification, no comparable figures exist for the years prior to the introduction

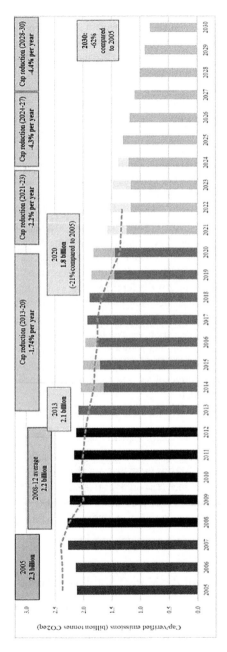

FIGURE 3.2 Emissions cap in the EU ETS compared with verified emissions, 2005–2030[8]

Source: Carbon Market Report 2023, COM(2023)654[9]

of the EU ETS in 2005. However, several studies[10] point to the fact that the carbon price signal has resulted in real emission reductions since the very beginning of the EU ETS. The largest drop in emissions happened, however, between 2008 and 2009, which was to a considerable extent influenced by the onset of the economic crisis in late 2008.

Since 2013, considering extensions of scope, there has been an average yearly reduction in the EU ETS sectors of around 4.7%. The power sector delivered the highest reduction by an average reduction of more than 7% per year since 2013, reflecting fuel switching away from coal and an increased use of renewable energy sources. Emissions from industrial sectors decreased as well, but to a much more limited extent of around 1.2% per year. While additional empirical studies are welcome on the impact of specific policy instruments in driving these emission reductions, existing studies point to a reduction in carbon emissions in the order of 10% between 2005 and 2012, with no significant negative impacts on profits and employment, and an increase in regulated firms' revenues and fixed assets.[11]

Contrary to the significant reduction in stationary sources, the emissions from intra-EU aviation grew by some 5% per year[12] between 2013 and 2020, up to 68 million tonnes in 2019 before the onset of the COVID-19 pandemic.[13] The average annual free allocation in that period was 36.7 million allowances, based on airlines' efficiency in transporting passengers and cargo, while around 5 million allowances on average were auctioned. Airlines are, therefore, buying some 30 million allowances from other sectors every year to offset the growth in their emissions, alongside a small proportion of offset credits from the Kyoto Protocol's Clean Development Mechanism (CDM) that was allowed up to 2020.

Conclusion: The EU ETS covers around 40% of EU's greenhouse gas emissions. By 2022, emissions from the power and industry sectors decreased by 37.3% compared to 2005. The price of EU allowances dropped significantly after the banking crisis of 2008 and recovered only a decade later. On 21 February 2023, the price reached €100.

3.3   The Creation of the Market Stability Reserve

The banking crisis of 2008 and the following economic recession caused a much-reduced demand for EU allowances compared to what was anticipated. On top of that a sizeable inflow of international credits took place as the EU

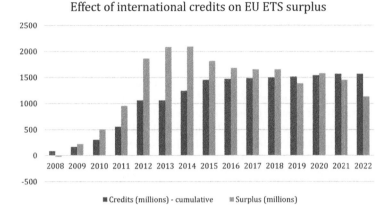

FIGURE 3.3   Surplus of EU ETS allowances with cumulative number of international UNFCCC credits used in EU ETS up to 2022

Source: European Commission

ETS allowed for the use of over 1.6 billion tonnes of international credits created under the Kyoto Protocol (Figure 3.3). By 2012, the market had built up a supply overhang of almost 2 billion allowances. All these factors, including the economic recession, the international credits' influx combined with the effects of energy policies, led to a growing market imbalance weighing heavily on the price that fell to single digits.

While emissions under the EU ETS kept falling, the carbon price of around €5 per tonne prompted a policy debate on how to restore market confidence as well as the effectiveness of the European carbon market. As the political environment at that time did not allow for a tightening of the cap, a short-term legislative response was developed. It was decided to reduce the quantity of allowances for auctioning in 2014–2016 by 900 million[14] that would return to the market at the end of Phase-3, a mechanism referred to as "backloading". This temporary solution made the surplus shrink in the short term by more than 40%.

In the meantime, a longer-term response was put in place by the creation of a "Market Stability Reserve" in 2015.[15] This Market Stability Reserve provides for automatic lowering of the auction volume whenever the cumulative surplus of allowances in the market exceeds 833 million allowances, which leads to allowances being put into the Reserve. Allowances will be released automatically from the Reserve once the cumulative surplus of allowances in the market falls below 400 million allowances. This Market Stability Reserve is intended to act like a sponge that absorbs surplus allowances in times of over-supply, and releases allowances in times of under-supply. The purpose is to maintain levels of liquidity for the carbon market to function properly, estimated to be between 400 and 833 million allowances, to cover both "spot" and "futures" transactions.

The rules of the Market Stability Reserve are automatic and pre-determined. The thresholds and the rate managing the inflows and outflows to and from the Reserve are set in the EU ETS Directive. The principle is that as the supply and demand balance are automatically adjusted, the market is left to determine the price – as is generally intended with market-based instruments. The Market Stability Reserve has been operating since 2019, and the 900 million back-loaded allowances were put directly into the reserve, together with a proportion of the EU ETS surplus allowances withdrawn in accordance with the operating rules of the Reserve. Every year, the Commission informs stakeholders about the functioning of the Market Stability Reserve.

The definition of the surplus is irrespective of how such a surplus originates, whether due to a business cycle downturn, or because of energy policy measures, renewable energy expansion or energy efficiency measures. In this way, the Market Stability Reserve puts an end to questions related to the compatibility of the EU ETS and other policies, especially in the energy sector. The synergy between the EU ETS and other policy measures has been improved considerably through the creation of the Market Stability Reserve, which is of critical importance in view of the important expansion of renewable energy foreseen in the coming decade. Moreover, the recent ETS revision also recognises that Member States can develop additional policies to reduce greenhouse gas emissions from sectors covered by the EU ETS.[16]

The 2023 ETS review analysed the Market Stability Reserve and identified that the intake is prone to a 'threshold effect'. As an illustration, if the total number of allowances in circulation were 834 million allowances, slightly higher than the upper threshold of 833 million, then according to the MSR rules, the 24% of that total number would be put in the MSR. However, if the number were just below the threshold, 832 million allowances, then nothing would be put in the MSR at all. Therefore, the revision created an additional buffer mechanism. In case the total number of allowances in circulation is between 833 and 1096 million tonnes, the reduction of auctioning will instead be equal to the difference between 833 million and the total number of allowances in circulation.[17]

In view of improving the functioning of the EU ETS in the long term, the Market Stability Reserve includes a volume-based adjustment mechanism, whereby allowances held in the reserve above the total number of allowances auctioned during the previous year should no longer be valid as from 2023.[18] This led to the invalidation of 2.515 billion allowances in 2023,[19] more than the total amount of international credits that have been used in the EU ETS. From 2024, the applicable invalidation threshold is fixed at 400 million.

The experience of the carbon market in exceptionally turbulent economic times required corrections to be made to safeguard the proper functioning of the system. This has parallels to what happened in financial markets following the deep financial and economic crisis starting in 2008. It also proved helpful to handle the uncertainty on the carbon market created by the start of the pandemic and the Russian invasion of Ukraine. The Market Stability Reserve has made the EU ETS more environmentally ambitious, more predictable, and shock-resilient than it has ever been.

> Conclusion: The creation of the Market Stability Reserve has made the EU ETS more resilient to external developments, such as economic recession, the import of carbon credits, or developments in energy markets.

3.4 A Strengthening of the Emissions Cap 2024–2030

The 2023 revision of the EU ETS contained an important strengthening of the emissions cap. Based on extensive economic analysis, the part of the 40% target that was attributed to the EU ETS under Phase-4 amounted to a 43% reduction compared to 2005, which translated into an annual Linear Reduction Factor of 2.2%. After a long period of intense negotiations drawing on an in-depth impact assessment, it was agreed that by 2030 an emissions reduction of 62% below 2005 would be an optimal contribution from the EU ETS sectors to the overall target of at least 55%. This significant revision of the cap translated into several operational steps.

Firstly, the Linear Reduction Factor is increased to 4.3% per year from 2024 and becomes 4.4% from 2028 onwards.[20] The latter percentage will continue to apply by default after 2030 as an essential contribution to the EU's long-term goal of climate neutrality by 2050. Without further changes in the legislation, this linear reduction leads to an EU ETS cap of zero in 2045, while issuance of allowances is expected to cease at the latest in 2044.[21] In addition, future ETS revisions will consider how to address net industrial removals of carbon dioxide that could lead to the issue of additional allowances.[22]

Secondly, it was decided to 'rebase' the EU ETS cap, to bring it closer to actual emissions, resulting in a permanent lowering of 90 million tonnes as from 2024 and another of 27 million tonnes as of 2026. In line with this outcome, the revised ETS cap of 1,386 million tonnes for 2024 has been adopted.[23] Combined with the inclusion of maritime emissions, for which the

4.3% linear reduction factor applies from 2021, the 2023 revision of the EU ETS results in an additional cumulative reduction of the cap of approximately 2 billion tonnes between 2024 and 2030, as compared to the cumulative cap under the pre-revision ETS Directive.

Thirdly, the intake of allowances from the Market Stability Reserve has been strengthened. To address the oversupply on the carbon market, it was decided in 2017 to double the rate at which allowances are placed into the Market Stability Reserve from 12 to 24% between 2019 and 2023. As part of the 2023 ETS review, it was decided to continue this 24% rate until 2030.[24] In addition, the invalidation ceiling on allowances in the Market Stability Reserve that is applied annually was updated from the level of allowances auctioned during the preceding year to a fixed level of 400 million allowances.

Finally, Member States have been strongly encouraged to cancel allowances in the event of phasing out the use of coal or lignite in the power sector.[25]

These modifications lead to limiting the supply of allowances and need to be compared to some supply expanding decisions made in the context of RePowerEU, a policy initiative to counter the effects of the Russian invasion of Ukraine on energy markets. It was decided to auction ETS allowances corresponding to a total value of €20 billion in the years 2024–2026.[26] Nearly €8 billion worth of allowances would be brought forward from 2027 to 2029, and €12 billion worth of allowances would be taken out of the portfolio attributed to the Innovation Fund. Even if market participants were to some extent surprised by this policy, the overall outcome did not show a fundamental impact on the price development.

These changes have fundamentally influenced the outlook on the supply and demand of allowances until 2030 (see Figure 3.4). The surplus in the market, built up from the financial crisis of 2008 and the introduction of 1.6 billion international credits into the EU ETS, have been absorbed in the Market Stability Reserve and 2.515 billion allowances have been invalidated at the start of 2023.

Consequently, the combined result of all these cap-related decisions is that normal scarcity for a well-functioning market mechanism has been restored. This has been translated into a fundamental shift in the carbon price, ranging from below €10 in 2017 to around €30 in 2020, and ending up around €80–100 in 2023.

Conclusion: The revision of the EU ETS has led to a much tighter cap. The total amount of allowances will be reduced annually by 4.3% from 2024 and by 4.4% as of 2028, compared to 2.2% before, combined with two lowering's of the cap in 2024 and 2026.

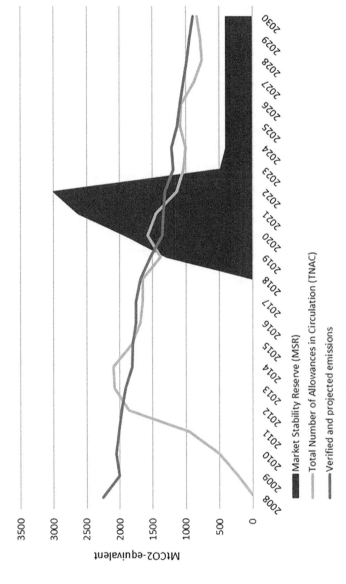

FIGURE 3.4 Outlook on the estimated supply and demand of allowances until 2030

Source: European Commission

3.5 The Creation of ETS2 for Road Transport, Buildings, and Smaller Industry

The 2023 ETS review had another major novelty by introducing a separate market-based instrument for emissions from road transport, buildings and smaller industrial combustion that are covered by the Effort Sharing Regulation (ESR). Current EU policies in these sectors focus on specific regulatory approaches and targets as a framework for policies at national level and provide limited economic incentives to low-carbon alternatives. Analysis shows that emissions from these sectors would not decrease as much as required to achieve the economy-wide 55% emission reduction by 2030.[27]

The new ETS for road transport, buildings and smaller industrial combustion emissions creates an EU-wide carbon price signal for these sectors that will be gradually introduced. It is planned to start as of 2027[28] and is set up as a separate but adjacent emissions trading to the existing EU ETS. This will avoid any disturbance of the well-functioning emissions trading system for stationary installations, maritime and aviation, given the different reduction potentials in those sectors and different factors that influence demand. Any possible merger of the two systems will be assessed after a few years of functioning of the new emissions trading, based on experience.

The new emissions trading system is organised as an upstream system, thus avoiding that regulation falls upon the numerous end-users of fossil fuels. Therefore, the compliance entities are fuel distributors and fuel intermediaries, in total around 10.000 compliance entities. End consumers will not be required to participate in the ETS2. All allowances under the ETS2 will be auctioned and the revenues will be partly pooled in the newly created Social Climate Fund.

ETS2 carbon prices will increase prices for fossil fuels used in buildings that are not already covered by the EU ETS, and for fossil fuel use in road transport.[29] For example, a carbon price of €45 could increase 2030 fuel prices by 11 cents/litre (petrol) to 12 cents/litre (fossil diesel). Possible social and distributional impacts need to be addressed but also need to be put in context as a net reduction of fuel consumption also has positive effects on household income. Moreover, the Social Climate Fund as well as other ETS2 revenues can significantly help to facilitate the financing gap of fuel-saving investments. The 20% poorest households are estimated to be responsible for 9% of emissions related to buildings and vehicles, while the 20% richest emit some 32% of ETS2 emissions. The raising of ETS2 revenue – and its use in favour of the Social Climate Fund – will accordingly receive a more important contribution from the richer households.

The ETS2 will help level the playing field within the sectors, by applying a carbon price more broadly. Moving towards electrified alternatives (e.g. heat pumps, electric vehicles, public transport) is necessary for long-term decarbonisation and will be encouraged as a carbon price creates a disincentive to the direct combustion of fossil fuels. Similarly, the extension of carbon pricing to fuel combustion by smaller industry addresses potential competitive disadvantages of larger producers without adding administrative burden for small industry.

3.5.1   Defining the ETS2 Cap Trajectory

The cap for ETS2 will achieve a 42% CO_2 emission reduction compared to 2005 by 2030.[30] The starting point will be the cap for 2027 defined as the result of a linear trajectory starting at 2024 emission limits calculated in accordance with the Effort Sharing Regulation for the sectors under ETS2, which then decreases by a linear reduction factor of 5.10% a year. The cap for 2028 is rebased on average emissions as reported by regulated entities for 2024 to 2026. After that, it decreases annually by a linear reduction factor of 5.38% of those average emissions.

It is possible that reported emissions in 2024–2026 would be so high that the intended 2030 reductions target would not be met by a linear reduction factor of 5.38% a year. If the difference is meaningful, then the linear reduction factor will be adjusted accordingly.

Emission reductions under the cap will be achieved by a combination of policies. Alongside the carbon price that acts as an economic incentive combined with the use of auction revenues, there is a mix of other EU and national policies, e.g., the targets and measures under the Energy Efficiency Directive and Renewable Energy Directive, CO_2 standards for cars, vans and lorries, energy performance standards for buildings, and national measures to achieve targets under the Effort Sharing Regulation. It has been estimated that ETS2 could contribute around 45% of additionally needed emission reductions compared to effects of current policies in 2030. The more effective complementary policies are, the lower the necessary carbon price incentive will have to be to achieve the emission cap.

3.5.2   The Market Stability Reserve for ETS2

To mitigate the risk of supply and demand imbalances associated with the start of ETS2 and to render it more resistant to market shocks, a rule-based mechanism of the Market Stability Reserve will also be applied to ETS2. The ETS2 Market Stability Reserve will receive an initial endowment of 600 million allowances.

In any given year, if the total number of allowances in circulation is above 440 million allowances, 100 million allowances will be deducted from the volume of allowances to be auctioned, and if the total number of allowances in circulation is fewer than 210 million, 100 million allowances will be released from the reserve and added to the volume of allowances to be auctioned. In case the reserve has fewer than 100 million allowances they will all be released. In addition, safeguards for a smooth ETS2 start can also lead to releases as indicated in the next section. By 1 January 2031, unreleased allowances from the initial endowment will no longer be valid.

3.5.3   Gradual Implementation and Safeguards for a Smooth Start

The new ETS2 will be established as a separate, self-standing system from 2025. The regulated entities will report their emissions for the years 2024, 2025 and 2026. The issuance of allowances and compliance obligations will only start in 2027 to allow the new system to start functioning in an orderly and gradual manner. The agreement on ETS2 was not easily achieved, and four safeguards have been included in view of moderating an excessive price impact on end consumers.

Firstly, the start of the system would be postponed by one year, from 2027 to 2028, in the event of exceptionally high energy prices, by delaying the application of the cap and of the surrendering obligations for the regulated entities. This would happen either if the average gas price in the first six months of 2026 were to exceed the average of gas price in February and March 2022 (€106), or if oil prices in the first six months of 2026 were more than twice the average oil price in the five preceding years.

Secondly, in the first year, the auction volume will be 30% higher than the total quantity of allowances for that year, to provide market liquidity. The additional volume will be deducted from the auction volumes over a three-year period beginning two years later.

Thirdly, the potential risk of excessive price increases is being addressed by a specific mechanism. During the first two years (2027 and 2028), 50 million allowances from the Market Stability Reserve will be automatically released in the event there is a 50% increase in the average allowance price over three months compared to the average price in the six preceding months. As of 2029, the average allowance price would need to double (rather than increase by 50%) compared to the six preceding months. In the event of a tripling of the average allowance price, the release of allowances will be 150 million. If one of the conditions does apply, this measure would not be applied again until at least 12 months after it has been triggered.

Finally, an additional alternative measure aims to increase even further the predictability of the price development in the first three years of the ETS2 operation. Under this measure, where the average carbon price over a period of two consecutive months exceeds a level of €45 (indexed to 2020 consumer prices), 20 million allowances would be automatically released from the ETS2 Market Stability Reserve. If this measure would be triggered first, it should also not apply again until at least 12 months pass. However, should the triggering condition be met again six months after it is triggered, the Commission, assisted by the Climate Change Committee, would assess the effectiveness of the measure, and may decide on a second release of 20 million allowances.

> Conclusion: An adjacent ETS2 has been established covering road transport and buildings as well as smaller industrial combustion emissions. Together with the existing EU ETS, by 2030, at least 70% of EU's emissions will be subject to a binding ETS cap.

3.6 The Growing Importance of EU ETS Revenues

The EU ETS creates a level-playing field for emission reductions between companies and is, in many aspects, comparable to a financial market. The volume of the trading amounts to some €750 billion, and a central registry keeps track of all exchanges. The European Securities and Market Authority (ESMA) oversees the functioning of this market creating trust from traders as well as society in general. One important aspect is the organisation of the auctioning of EU allowances ('EUAs'), the revenue of which is largely redistributed among the Member States.

3.6.1 Raising Revenue through Auctioning of Allowances

Economists start from the assumption that it is best to auction all allowances brought to the market. However, this is not as easy as assumed and, therefore, most emissions trading systems start with low levels of auctioning that are then gradually increased. The EU ETS started in 2005 with almost all allowances given out for free, but eight years later already over half of them were auctioned. A debate over the passing through of the carbon price led to the decision that in principle power generation would no longer benefit from free allocation.[31] From 2021 onwards, it was agreed to auction 57% of all allowances, but this percentage is likely to increase with the creation of Carbon Border Adjustment Mechanism (CBAM) and the gradual phasing out of allowances by 2034. On the other hand, the functioning of the Market Stability Reserve reduces the volumes to be auctioned if surplus conditions prevail. The total amount of allowances to be auctioned between 2021 and 2030 is estimated to range between 5.2 billion and 6.2 billion allowances, depending on the emissions profile taken into account for the operation of the Market Stability Reserve.[32]

The Auctioning Regulation fixes the rules for auctioning in detail.[33] It is based on the principles that operators have full, fair and equitable market access and that the same information is available to everybody at the same time. An evolution took place from limited auctions by individual Member States to an EU-wide auctioning process using a common auction platform. The European Energy Exchange (EEX) based in Leipzig has been carrying out the role of the EU ETS common auction platform on behalf of 25 Member States as well as for Norway and Iceland. Germany and Poland have opted out of the common platform but also use the EEX auction platform (Figure 3.5).

The common auction platform at EEX is the most significant auction process for environmental assets ever designed and implemented. So far, over 2,500 auctions have been undertaken, raising over €180 billion. The robust price development over the last few years helped expand the auctioning revenue that amounted to €39 billion in 2022, out of which €30 billion was directly transferred to the Member States.

Member States are committed to use these revenues for climate-related policies and measures. Before 2023 however, Member States were only encouraged to spend this revenue to climate purposes, and they did use approximately

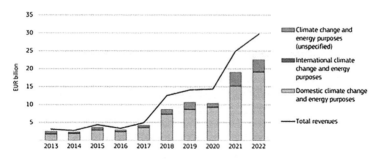

FIGURE 3.5 Revenues from EU ETS and their reported use in 2013–2022

Source: European Commission, 2023[34]

75% of these for specified climate- and energy-related purposes.[35] Germany, for example, used its EU ETS revenues for international and national climate funds, Spain for paying renewable energy incentives, while France earmarked these revenues for improving the insulation of social housing.

As the EU ETS has become more established as a cornerstone of the EU's climate action, it has also attracted greater attention in terms of the revenues that are generated from applying the 'polluter pays' principle that is in the EU Treaty. In 2021, the Commission proposed[36] that one-quarter of Member States' auction revenue from the EU ETS be directed to the EU budget, later increased to 30%,[37] in parallel with the EU budget being used effectively to tackle climate change. The decision on this 'Own Resources' issue is pending at the time of writing. In addition, €20 billion from the sale of EU ETS allowances are being used, from 2023, to accelerate the reduction in the use of fossil fuels following Russia's invasion of Ukraine pursuant to Repower EU.[38]

3.6.2 EU Solidarity and the Use of Auctioning Revenue

The EU ETS is a harmonised system with one single price and the same rules for all market participants, which results in a cost-effective and efficient policy instrument. However, it had to be designed against the background of a wide *per capita* income disparity of more than a ratio of 1:10 between the EU's Member States. Striking the right balance between efficiency on the one hand and solidarity on the other has been of capital importance.

The EU ETS has a general principle that auction revenues accrue to the Member States where the corresponding emissions are generated. However, a re-distributive element has also been created. More precisely, 88% of allowances to be auctioned have been distributed amongst Member States based on their historical share of verified emissions, while 10% has been distributed amongst certain Member States for the purpose of solidarity and growth. Up to 2020, a further 2% was distributed amongst Member States whose emissions were at least 20% below their Kyoto Protocol base-year emissions in 2005.[39] This provision was specifically designed to benefit those Member States that had undergone substantial economic restructuring after the collapse of Communism in Central and Eastern Europe. It was instrumental in mobilising political support for the EU ETS from all Member States.

Distributional elements have also been inserted in the revision of the EU ETS for the period 2021–2030. The 10% distribution was kept, and an EU ETS-funded Modernisation Fund has been established.

The Modernisation Fund initially benefitted ten EU Member States with lower GDP.[40] It initially consisted of approximately 310 million allowances.

The financial resources in the Modernisation Fund have been distributed among lower-income Member States,[41] and at least 70% of the Fund's resources have been earmarked for priority projects in renewable electricity generation, improving energy efficiency (including in transport), buildings, agriculture and waste, energy storage and modernising energy networks. No support was given for energy generation facilities using solid fossil fuels, apart from a limited exception regarding district heating systems in Romania and Bulgaria. Priority projects also include support for a "just transition" in "carbon-dependent" regions including redeployment, reskilling, education or job-seeking initiatives.

In the 2023 review of the EU ETS, the resources of the Modernisation Fund have been topped-up with 110 million allowances, to be shared among 13 EU Member States with lower GDP – the original ten plus Greece, Portugal, and Slovenia. At least 80% of the Fund's resources are directed to priority projects, while the list of priorities is broadened. The list of exclusions is also strengthened to harmonise the approach across the EU, avoid carbon lock-in and stranded assets.

The EU ETS used to allow for national derogations from the general rule of auctioning, specifically to support the modernising of the electricity sector in certain EU Member States. Eight Member States have made use of the derogation[42] during 2013–2020, and the total value of reported investment support during the years 2009–2016 is estimated to have been some €11 billion. About 80% of this was dedicated to upgrading and retrofitting infrastructure, while the rest of the investments were in clean technologies or diversification of supply. Under Phase-4, only three Member States still used this possibility and as of 2025 this provision will be discontinued.[43] The corresponding allowances are added to the Modernisation Fund.

An Innovation Fund with at least 450 million allowances was launched in 2020. It replaced the so-called NER300 fund (referring to the New Entrant Reserve from which the 300 million allowances came).[44] Funded entirely by the EU ETS, it is one of the world's largest funding programmes for promoting innovation in renewable energy, industrial low-carbon processes and technologies, energy storage, hydrogen and Carbon Capture and Storage (CCS).

In the 2023 review, the Innovation Fund has been expanded and aligned with the changing market needs. While it remains focused on breakthrough innovation, it is expanded to scaling up innovative technologies. The Fund's resources have been increased to some 530 million allowances and could increase by a further 50 million allowances by the mid-2020s if these are not used for free allocation to industry. Free allowances becoming available through the introduction of Carbon Adjustment Mechanism (CBAM) will also accrue to the Innovation Fund. Overall, around €40 billion is expected to be available for the Innovation Fund.[45]

3.6.3 *The Social Climate Fund*

A major new element of the 2023 ETS review is the creation of the Social Climate Fund (SCF). It aims to address the social impacts of the new ETS2 on the most vulnerable households, transport users and micro-enterprises. The SCF can be seen as the solidarity element between Member States for the new ETS2, as all Member States contribute and receive, but lower income Member States get more support. The Fund will start in 2026 and has an envelope of €65 billion until 2032, mainly financed from ETS2 auction revenues. The envelope is increased to €86.7 billion volume by a mandatory 25% co-financing by Member States. In 2025, Member States must submit their spending plans for the Social Climate Fund to the Commission.

Similar to ETS, Member States have to use the revenues from auctioning ETS2 allowances on climate purposes and will report about this every year. They can spend the revenues on measures contributing to the decarbonisation of heating and cooling of buildings, the reduction of the energy needs of buildings, as well as financial support for low-income households in worst-performing buildings. Similarly, for transport, the purposes concern the uptake of zero-emission vehicles, the deployment of infrastructure for zero-emitting vehicles, supporting the shift to public forms of transport, improving multimodality and addressing social aspects for low- and middle-income transport users in other ways. They can also spend ETS2 revenues on any of the purposes listed for the existing ETS, but – in view of the impacts of ETS2 – should prioritise activities that can contribute to address social aspects. They can use their ETS2 auctioning revenues to co-finance 25% of the total costs of the plans approved under the Social Climate Fund, and in some cases they can also provide direct financial compensation to the final consumers of the fuels.

Conclusion: More than half of the ETS allowances issued are auctioned. These are partly redistributed reflecting income disparities between Member States. Member States are committed to use these revenues for climate action. At EU level, an Innovation Fund and a Modernisation Fund are substantially endowed and, as of 2026, a new Social Climate Fund has been set up.

Conclusion

Emissions from the power and industry installations covered by EU ETS decreased by 37.3% by 2022 compared to 2005, and this was achieved cost-effectively. It promoted new jobs and expanded sectors involved in the energy transition while preparing the EU economy for greater carbon reductions in line with reaching economy-wide net zero emissions by 2050. The gradual but consistent reduction of greenhouse gas emissions led to the decision to expand the system significantly by adding the fossil fuels being used in buildings, road transport and small industry.

The EU ETS has been innovative, but is also constantly evolving, partly through "learning-by-doing" and partly through changing economic conditions. In this respect, two key elements were of major importance: the nature and strictness of the overall emissions cap and the extent of auctioning of allowances.

The EU ETS has an absolute cap that determines its overall environmental ambition. The political climate surrounding cap decisions has been characterised by a general fear from industry that the cap would be set in too strict a manner. The EU experience illustrated how initially the cap-setting tended to be overly generous. Once familiarity with the trading system and trust in the robustness of emission monitoring were established, the conditions were in place for a gradual tightening of the allocation conditions. The EU opted for defining an absolute limit to emissions and did not choose an output-based cap based on production levels, as such a system would be much more complicated and offer no guaranteed environmental outcome. At the same time, much attention was given to address the risk of carbon leakage.

Another interesting evolution is the extent to which the EU ETS started as a system where allocations were almost all made for free, to one where over half of allocation is by auctioning. This transition, coupled with other reforms of the EU ETS, resulted in the raising of significant amounts of revenue. This has not only been an implementation of the "polluter pays" principle but has also created a "double-dividend" whereby revenues generated are deployed to help innovation and deployment of new technologies, for example, or to modernise energy systems and infrastructure, as well as to address social concerns. Not only is pollution discouraged by the price of carbon, but the revenues generated by the EU ETS are being used by Member States and the EU to further enhance climate action. Other than environmental taxes, few other policy tools have this "double-dividend" potential by virtue of the successful application of the instrument.

Over almost two decades, the EU ETS had to withstand several crises, which required the system to adapt in several ways: through adding the Market Stability Reserve, the strengthening of the Linear Reduction Factor, and the development of new financial funds. Subtle distributive elements have ensured the support of less wealthy stakeholders and governments. These adjustments have ensured that the EU ETS withstood very recent crises – the economic downturn due to the global pandemic and energy market disruptions due to Russia's invasion of Ukraine.

Over time, the EU ETS succeeded in winning robust and wide policy support. Adjustments have enhanced the impact of the "double-dividend" in such a way as to strengthen fairness elements and the safeguards to maintain the competitiveness of European businesses, while maintaining the effectiveness of the environmental instrument itself.

Notes

1 The authors are grateful for the contributions to this chapter received from Jan Nill, Madalina Radulescu, Julia Ziemann and Javier Esparrago.
2 The development of the EU Emissions Trading System (EU ETS) up to 2018 is comprehensively elaborated in *Towards a Climate-Neutral Europe: Curbing the Trend*, edited by Jos Delbeke and Peter Vis (published by Routledge, 2019) which built on the earlier books *EU Climate Policy Explained*, edited by Jos Delbeke and Peter Vis (published by Routledge, 2015) and *EU Energy Law: The EU Emissions Trading Scheme*, edited by Jos Delbeke (published by Claeys & Casteels, 2006), which deals with the origin of the EU ETS and its early years of operation. This chapter is a review of the chapter originally drafted by Damien Meadows, Peter Vis and Peter Zapfel.
3 Directive (EU) 2023/958 of the European Parliament and of the Council of 10 May 2023 amending Directive 2003/87/EC as regards aviation's contribution to the Union's economy-wide emission reduction target and the appropriate implementation of a global market-based measure, and Directive 2023/959 amending the EU ETS Directive (Directive 2003/87/EC) amending Directive 2003/87/EC establishing a system for greenhouse gas emission allowance trading within the Union and Decision (EU) 2015/1814 concerning the establishment and operation of a market stability reserve for the Union greenhouse gas emission trading system. The consolidated EU ETS Directive is published at https://eur-lex.europa.eu/legal-content/EN/TXT/?uri=CELEX%3A02003L0087-20230605.
4 Between 2005 and 2007, the penalty rate was €40 per tonne of excess emissions.
5 European Environment Agency (2022) "Trends and projections in Europe in 2022". EEA Report No 10/2022, p. 21. Available at: https://www.eea.europa.eu/publications/trends-and-projections-in-europe-2022.
6 See *The 2023 Carbon Market Report*, p. 3 for further information, COM(2023)654.
7 See for more information *Trends and Projections in the EU ETS in 2018*. EEA Report No. 14/2018.
8 Emissions cap in the EU ETS compared with verified emissions (considering the 2023 revision of the ETS Directive, i.e., rebasing in 2024 and 2026, including the maritime transport sector in 2024 and the linear reduction factor of 4.3% in 2024–2027 and 4.4% from 2028). Aviation is not included. Due to changes in scope, the 2005–2007 figures are not directly comparable with the latest ones. From 2021, the EU ETS no longer covers installations in the UK, only electricity generators in Northern Ireland. Legend: bars (cap), light shaded bars in 2014–2016 (allowances backloaded from auctions), light shaded bars from 2019 (feeds of allowances to the Market Stability Reserve), dashed line (verified emissions).
9 REPORT FROM THE COMMISSION TO THE EUROPEAN PARLIAMENT AND THE COUNCIL on the functioning of the European carbon market in 2022

pursuant to Articles 10(5) and 21(2) of Directive 2003/87/EC, COM(2023)654 (2023). Available at: https://eur-lex.europa.eu/legal-content/EN/TXT/?uri=COM: 2023:654:FIN.

10 Ellerman, A.D., Buchner, B.K. Over-Allocation or Abatement? A Preliminary Analysis of the EU ETS Based on the 2005–06 Emissions Data. *Environ Resource Econ* **41**, 267–287 (2008). https://doi.org/10.1007/s10640-008-9191-2 and Ellerman, A. D., Convery, F. J., & De Perthuis, C. (2010). *Pricing carbon: the European Union emissions trading scheme.* Cambridge University Press.

11 The joint impact of the European Union emissions trading system on carbon emissions and economic performance, Antoine Dechezleprêtre, Daniel Nachtigall, Frank Venmans, Journal of Environmental Economics and Management Volume 118, March 2023.

12 Increase of CO_2 emissions in years 2014, 2015, 2016 and 2017 compared to 2013. See e.g. Table 1-6 in the EEA report "Trends and projections in the EU ETS in 2023".

13 European Commission (2020) Emission trading: greenhouse gas emissions reduced by 8.7% in 2019. Available at: https://climate.ec.europa.eu/news-your-voice/news/emissions-trading-greenhouse-gas-emissions-reduced-87-2019-2020-05-04_en

14 Commission Regulation (EU) No 176/2014 of 25 February 2014 amending Regulation (EU) No 1031/2010 in particular to determine the volumes of greenhouse gas emission allowances to be auctioned in 2013–2020. OJ L 56, 26.2.2014, pp. 11–13. Available at: http://eur-lex.europa.eu/legal-content/EN/TXT/PDF/?uri=CELEX:32 014R0176&from=EN.

15 Decision (EU) 2015/1814 of the European Parliament and of the Council concerning the establishment and operation of a market stability reserve for the Union greenhouse gas emission trading scheme and amending Directive 2003/87/EC. Available at: https://eur-lex.europa.eu/legal-content/EN/TXT/?uri=CELEX%3A0 2015D1814-20230515.

16 Recital 12 of Directive (EU) 2023/959.

17 Article 1(5) of Decision (EU) 2015/1814.

18 Article 2 of Directive (EU) 2018/410, amending Decision (EU) 2015/1814.

19 Commission Communication C/2023/2929, publishing the total number of allowances in circulation in 2022 for the purposes of the Market Stability Reserve under the EU ETS (*OJ* C172/1, 15 May 2023)

20 The Linear Reduction Factor applies to the average annual total quantity of allowances issued by Member States over for the period from 2008 to 2012. This fixed starting point has been maintained.

21 In the event of additional allowances being issued in respect of EU ETS extension, e.g., in respect of municipal waste incineration and aviation, then the application of the same linear reduction factor would lead to zero issuance in a later year.

22 See Article 24a of the ETS Directive, and the Parliamentary answer given on this issue (https://www.europarl.europa.eu/doceo/document/E-6-2009-1622-ASW_EN. html?redirect) referred to in the Commission Communication on Sustainable Carbon Cycles (COM(2021)800).

23 Commission Decision on the Union-wide quantity of allowances to be issued under the EU Emissions Trading System for 2024, Decision C (2023) 4950 of 27 July 2023.

24 Decision (EU) 2023/852 of the European Parliament and Council of 19 April 2023 (OJ L 110/21, 25 April 2023), subsequently reaffirmed and replaced by Article 2 of Directive (EU)2023/959.

25 Amendment to Article 12(4) of the ETS Directive, from Directive (EU) 2023/959.

26 Regulation (EU) 2023/435 852 of the European Parliament and Council of 27 February 2023, Article 5 of which amends the EU ETS Directive as regards REPowerEU.

27 Impact assessment accompanying the 2030 Climate Target Plan, SWD/2020/176 final, Section 6.7

28 In the event of exceptionally high energy prices, the start would be postponed by one year.

29 Since 2005, the existing ETS has covered around half of building-related emissions, notably from electricity use in buildings and most emissions from district heating, as well as transport-related emissions from the majority of trains, trams and from electric vehicles.

30 The scope of application of the ETS2 follows the 2006 IPCC Guidelines for National Greenhouse Gas Inventories and are outlined in Annex III of the ETS Directive. The sectors of buildings and road transport include the following categories: Combined Heat and Power Generation (CHP) and Heat Plants, insofar as they produce heat for commercial/institutional or residential buildings, either directly or through district heating networks; Road Transportation, excluding the use of agricultural vehicles on paved roads; Commercial/Institutional buildings and Residential buildings. Non-ETS industry correspond to the following sources of emissions: Energy industries, excluding those covered by the ETS1 and Manufacturing Industries and Construction. Emissions in the sectors agriculture, fisheries and forestry remain outside the scope of the ETS2.

31 S.M. de Bruyn, R. Vergeer, E. Schep, M. Hoen, M. Kurteland, J. Cludius, K. Schumacher, C. Zell-Ziegler, S. Healy Ex-Post Investigation of Cost Pass-through in the EU ETS: An Analysis for Six Sectors Publications Office, Luxembourg (2015): Sijm, J. P. M., Hers, J. S., & Lise, W. (2008). *The implications of free allocation versus auctioning of EU ETS allowances for the power sector in the Netherlands* (No. ECN-E—08-056). ECN. ; Alexeeva-Talebi, V. (2010). Cost pass-through in strategic oligopoly: Sectoral evidence for the EU ETS. *ZEW-Centre for European Economic Research Discussion Paper*, (10-056). ; Lise, W., Sijm, J., & Hobbs, B. F. (2010). The impact of the EU ETS on prices, profits and emissions in the power sector: simulation results with the COMPETES EU20 model. *Environmental and Resource Economics, 47*, 23–44. ; Jouvet, P. A., & Solier, B. (2013). An overview of CO2 cost pass-through to electricity prices in Europe. *Energy Policy, 61*, 1370–1376.

32 These estimates include the auctioning of allowances for Member States, the EU ETS's Innovation Fund, Modernisation Fund and its contribution to the Social Climate Fund, as well as to REPowerEU. Auctioning of allowances for maritime and aviation is included.

33 Commission Regulation (EU) No 1031/2010 of 12 November 2010 on the timing, administration and other aspects of auctioning of greenhouse gas emission allowances pursuant to Directive 2003/87/EC (OJ L 302, 18.11.2010).

34 European Commission (2023) Report from the Commission to the European Parliament and Council: EU Climate Action Progress Report 2023. Available at: https://eur-lex.europa.eu/legal-content/EN/TXT/HTML/?uri=COM:2023:653:FIN

35 See page 15 of the 2023 Carbon Market Report, COM(2023)654, and the EEA indicators published at https://www.eea.europa.eu/en/analysis/indicators/use-of-auctioning-revenues-generated?activeAccordion=546a7c35-9188-4d23-94ee-005d97c26f2b.

36 Proposal to amend the Decision on the system of own resources of the European Union, COM (2021) 570.

37 Proposal to amend the Regulation on the methods and procedure for making available the own resources based on the Emissions Trading System, the Carbon Border Adjustment Mechanism, reallocated profits and the statistical own resource, COM (2023) 333.

38 Regulation (EU) 2023/435 of the European Parliament and of the Council of 27 February 2023 (published in the OJ L 63/1, 28.3.2023).

39 Article 1(12) (inserting new Article 10(2) and new Annexes IIa & IIb) of Directive 2009/29/EC of the European Parliament and of the Council of 23 April 2009 amending Directive 2003/87/EC so as to improve and extend the greenhouse gas emission allowance trading scheme of the community. OJ L 140, 05.06.2009, pp. 63–87. Available at: http://eur-lex.europa.eu/legal-content/EN/TXT/PDF/?uri=CELEX:32009L0029&from=EN.

40 Member States with less than 60% of EU average per capita GDP in 2013, at market prices: Bulgaria, Czech Republic, Estonia, Croatia, Latvia, Lithuania, Hungary, Poland, Romania, and Slovakia. In the 2023 ETS revision, Member States with a GDP per capita at market prices below 75% of the Union average during the period from 2016 to 2018 have been added (in practice, Slovenia, Portugal and Greece).

41 According to a key defined in Annex IIa to the ETS Directive. The distribution of funds is based on both verified emissions and GDP of beneficiary Member States, as set out in the 2014 European Council Conclusions.

42 Article 10c of the Directive, made use of by Cyprus, Czech Republic, Estonia, Lithuania, and Poland up to 2020, and by Bulgaria, Romania, and Hungary up to 2024.

43 Article 10ca.

44 More details of about this Fund, and the investments it has contributed to, are on the website of the European Commission. Available at: http://ec.europa.eu/clima/policies/lowcarbon/ner300/index_en.htm.

45 At an estimated carbon price of EUR 75/tonne of CO_2, 2023 Carbon Market Report. COM(2023)654.

4

ADDRESSING CARBON LEAKAGE UNDER THE EU ETS

Damien Meadows, Beatriz Yordi and Peter Vis[1]

Introduction

This chapter reviews how the EU Emissions Trading System (EU ETS) has been dealing with carbon leakage, an issue that has been sensitive since the start in 2005. A system of free allocation was gradually developed and harmonised throughout the EU, to make sure the principle of the single market was respected. The 2023 EU ETS revision rationalised the system further and strengthened incentives for the deployment of low- and zero-carbon technologies. In addition, a Carbon Border Adjustment Mechanism (CBAM) has been created for some key industrial products as an alternative measure to free allocation.[2]

4.1 The Problem of Carbon Leakage

Economists usually advocate that all allowances should be auctioned in accordance with the polluter-pays principle, a principle explicitly mentioned in the EU Treaty. However, this could lead to negative impacts on the competitiveness of European companies if done while other major economies are not putting a similar price on the external costs of emissions or taking other comparably stringent actions to reduce greenhouse gas emissions.

Emission trading is very transparent in terms of its price signal and, while recognising that there are many factors involved in investment and operational decisions, an important political issue is not to risk that industrial production moves abroad and leads to an increase in global emissions if the technology used in these economic activities would not be as carbon efficient as in Europe (referred to as "carbon leakage").

The competitive effect on companies and carbon leakage can fundamentally be addressed in two ways. One way is by making internal corrections in the regulations to make sure that the above-mentioned adverse effects are being avoided. That is the path the EU has been following until now, by giving

DOI: 10.4324/9781003493730-6

out allowances for free to companies in view of dampening negative effects from carbon pricing. The alternative is to have an external correction and put a comparable carbon price on imports from countries not applying similarly stringent carbon pricing. The EU Green Deal has created such an external correction in the form of a Carbon Border Adjustment Mechanism for a limited number of carbon-intensive products.

4.2   The EU Approach to Free Allocation

Up until now, the risk of carbon leakage related to the EU ETS has been addressed through a system of free allocation. Since 2013, the rules have been harmonised to ensure that companies are treated the same way irrespective of the Member State they are established in. Free allocation to the power sector has been phased out. Major attention is given to make sure free allowances are targeted to sectors and economic activities where the risk of carbon leakage is real and to encourage low-carbon transformation. To that end, a complex cluster of technical issues needed to be elaborated.

The 2023 EU ETS review significantly tightened the cap over the period 2021–2030, which now amounts to 12.3 billion allowances. Over that period, a total of around 5.3 billion allowances remains available for free allocation, after setting aside the allowances for the Innovation Fund and the future Social Climate Fund and adding the 3% free allocation buffer. This corresponds to approximately 43% of allowances for the period between 2021 and 2030 that would be allocated for free.

The 2023 ETS review introduced several technical conditions to maximise the effect of the available free allowances and to direct these to where they are most justified. Furthermore, the introduction of CBAM (see Section 4.3) will gradually replace the free allocation for selected sectors. The updated rules for free allocation are being finalised, and one could expect the overall amount of free allocation for the period 2026–2030 to be around 2.3 billion allowances, which reflects an estimated 200 million reduction due to the gradual phasing-in of the CBAM.

So far, the predominant part of the free allocation has gone to a limited number of sectors such as steel, cement, and chemicals as shown in Figure 4.1. Roughly half of the free allocation went to sectors that are covered by the CBAM Regulation, and accordingly, these free allocations will be gradually phased out by 2034.

The system of free allocation is harmonised and rule-based consisting of 54 benchmarks and a list of sectors and subsectors deemed to be vulnerable to carbon leakage. The benchmarks have been subject to periodic updates in view of the evolving technology and market conditions. Based on this information, Member States calculate, in advance of a five-year trading

Share of Free Allocation in 2021-2023

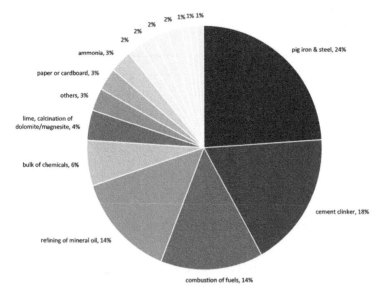

FIGURE 4.1 Share of free allocation (%) in 2021–2023

Source: European Enviromental Agency, 2023[3]

period (2021–2025 and 2026–2030) and in accordance with common rules, the number of free allowances they propose for each installation. These plans are then examined and subject to approval by the European Commission. In principle, free allocation is decided well before the period in question, with any subsequent adjustments being on the basis of real emissions.

4.2.1   Benchmarks

In total, 54 technological benchmarks exist. Given the diversity in the manufacturing sector, it is not possible for every product to have a specific benchmark, but 52 key product benchmarks have been established covering a major part of industrial emissions. The remainder are covered either by the application of a heat-based energy benchmark, or to a minor extent by a fuel-based energy benchmark. Finally, a very small percentage of allowances are allocated in relation to a specific process emissions rule based on past emissions levels.[4] There was a separate benchmark for aviation activities, described in Chapter 5, that applied until 2023. Table 4.1 gives (a) the benchmark values

TABLE 4.1 Initial benchmark values for 2013–2020 (tonne CO_2 per 1000 tonnes of output produced), and the benchmark values that apply for 2021–2025[5]

BM number	Product	BM 2021–2025	BM 2013–2020
1	Refinery products	0.0228	0.0295
2	Coke	0.217	0.286
3	Sintered ore	0.157	0.171
4	Hot metal	1.288	1.328
5	EAF carbon steel	0.215	0.283
6	EAF high alloy steel	0.268	0.352
7	Iron casting	0.282	0.325
8	Pre-bake anode	0.312	0.324
9	[Primary] aluminium	1.464	1.514
10	Grey cement clinker	0.693	0.766
11	White cement clinker	0.957	0.987
12	Lime	0.725	0.954
13	Dolime	0.815	1.072
14	Sintered dolime	1.406	1.449
15	Float glass	0.399	0.453
16	Bottles and jars of colourless glass	0.29	0.382
17	Bottles and jars of coloured glass	0.237	0.306
18	Continuous filament glass fibre products	0.309	0.406
19	Facing bricks	0.106	0.139
20	Pavers	0.146	0.192
21	Roof tiles	0.12	0.144
22	Spray dried powder	0.058	0.076
23	Mineral wool	0.536	0.682
24	Plaster	0.047	0.048
25	Dried secondary gypsum	0.013	0.017
26	Plasterboard	0.11	0.131
27	Short fibre kraft pulp	0.091	0.12
28	Long fibre kraft pulp	0.046	0.06
29	Sulphite pulp, thermo-mechanical and mechanical pulp	0.015	0.02
30	Recovered paper pulp	0.03	0.039
31	Newsprint	0.226	0.298
32	Uncoated fine paper	0.242	0.318
33	Coated fine paper	0.242	0.318
34	Tissue	0.254	0.334
35	Testliner and fluting	0.188	0.248
36	Uncoated carton board	0.18	0.237
37	Coated carton board	0.207	0.273
38	Carbon black	1.485	1.954
39	Nitric acid	0.23	0.302
40	Adipic acid	2.12	2.79

(*Continued*)

TABLE 4.1 (Continued)

BM number	Product	BM 2021–2025	BM 2013–2020
41	Ammonia	1.57	1.619
42	Steam cracking	0.681	0.702
43	Aromatics	0.0228	0.0295
44	Styrene	0.401	0.527
45	Phenol/acetone	0.23	0.266
46	Ethylene oxide/ethylene glycols	0.389	0.512
47	Vinyl chloride monomer	0.155	0.204
48	S-PVC	0.066	0.085
49	E-PVC	0.181	0.238
50	Hydrogen	6.84	8.85
51	Synthesis gas	0.187	0.242
52	Soda ash	0.753	0.843
53	Heat benchmark	47.3	62.3
54	Fuel benchmark	42.6	56.1

Source: European Commission (2021).[6]

that formed the initial reference point for free allocation for 2013–2020, and which were the starting points for calculating the trajectories for benchmark value improvements for 2021–2025 and (b) the benchmark values that apply for 2021–2025.

Note that the benchmark values applicable for the period 2026–2030 will be calculated in 2025, based on verified information collected from operators, and adopted in a Commission Implementing Act.[7] In principle, these benchmark values will be in the range between 6 and 50% below the initial values.

These benchmark values take account of the most efficient techniques, substitutes, and alternative production processes. Most product benchmark values are derived from the average performance of the 10% most efficient installations in a sector in the EU in 2007–2008, based on data from all EU Member States. Free allocation is then calculated based on past production quantities, rather than inputs to the production process,[8] in view of maximising incentives for emissions reductions and energy efficiency savings.

Free allocation has been a sensitive policy issue from the outset. The initial setting of the benchmark values was a complicated process, partly because of different industrial strategies followed by different companies in the same sector. Given the economic value of free allocations, it is not surprising that the benchmarking decision and the free allocation process led to several legal challenges, where the judgements upheld the validity of the benchmark values in all cases.[9]

In the 2023 ETS revision, further improvements were made to free allocation. Firstly, the principle of equal treatment was applied to encourage cleaner and less emitting technologies. For example, the same free allocation will be made for a tonne of hydrogen, whether produced from using fossil fuels or from electrolysis using renewable energy. As electrolysis using renewable energy does not produce greenhouse gases, the production of clean hydrogen has an economic incentive from the EU ETS that was hitherto absent. Moreover, installations can stay in the EU ETS for several years if they reduce their emissions, rather than falling outside the system (and thereby losing incentives that free allocation gave to them).[10] The EU ETS will also cover smaller clean installations, for example, the production of hydrogen from renewables at a level of 5 tonnes per day (rather than 20 tonnes, which was the previous level).

Secondly, free allocation has been made conditional on companies investing in decarbonisation. If a company is obliged by the Energy Efficiency Directive[11] to undertake energy audits, then 20% of its free allocation will be withheld if it does not implement the recommendations from these, except where the pay-back time for investments exceeds three years or the costs of investments are disproportionate.[12] In addition, installations which are in the least efficient 20% for product benchmarks will have a 20% reduction of free allocation unless they develop and apply climate-neutrality plans. Allowances which are freed up due to these conditionalities will be used, in the first place, to avoid the application of a cross-sectoral correction factor to overall free allocations.

4.2.2   Carbon Leakage List

A wide range of industries are included in a list of sectors *"deemed to be exposed to carbon leakage"* and they receive allocation at the level of 100% of the relevant harmonised benchmark. Industrial facilities not covered by this status were allocated 80% of the relevant benchmark in 2013, declining annually in a linear manner to a level of 30% between 2020 and 2026 and then reducing to zero between 2027 and 2030. In the 2018 ETS revision, one exception was introduced, to keep free allocation for district heating at 30% of the benchmark level until 2030. The 2023 ETS revision introduced another rule for district heating in certain Member States to receive up to 30% additional free allocation over 2026–2030, provided an investment volume equivalent to the value of the additional free allocation is invested to significantly reduce emissions in accordance with a climate-neutrality plan.[13]

The list of industries *"deemed to be exposed to a significant risk of carbon leakage"* was first adopted in 2009[14] for five years, and a second list adopted for 2015–2020.[15] A sector was *"deemed to be exposed to a significant risk of carbon leakage"* if the sum of additional costs related to both the direct emissions and the indirect impacts from the use of electricity would lead to an increase of production costs of 5% or more and the sector's intensity of trade with third countries was above 10%. Sectors were also included if either EU ETS direct and indirect additional costs would lead to an increase of production costs of at least 30%, or the sector's intensity of trade with third countries exceeds 30%. Most of the sectors and sub-sectors were included on the 2009 list because their intensity of trade with third countries exceeded 30%.[16] Other sectors were included on the list based on a qualitative assessment, considering the extent to which it is possible for installations to reduce emission levels or electricity consumption, current and projected market characteristics, and profit margins.

4.2.3 Seizing the Benefit of Technological Progress

For 2021–2030, differentiation is maintained between industry sectors that are exposed to a significant risk of carbon leakage, on the one hand, and other industry sectors on the other hand. Whether a sector is included on the carbon leakage list is determined in general based on a single criterion[17] that reflects both the mathematical outcomes of carbon intensity and trade intensity of the sector.[18] This limitation led to a list of 50 sectors and 12 sub-sectors.

For the period 2021–2025, a combined data collection from thousands of industrial installations provided the basis to update the benchmark values and the determination of production levels needed for free allocation purposes. As from 2021, the existing benchmark values have been updated to reflect technological progress within a range of 0.2% and 1.6% per year, applicable between 2008 and the middle of the five-year period from 2021 to 2025. This ensures that financial incentives for those sectors experiencing more rapid technological progress and emission reductions are maintained. By way of exception, the benchmark value for hot steel was only updated by the lower rate of 0.2% for allocations in 2021–2025. The reductions for each benchmark value, therefore, ranged between 3 and 24% of the initial benchmark value for allocations during 2008–2023. In the 2023 ETS revision, the minimum adjustment of benchmark values was raised to 0.3% per year, and the maximum adjustment increased to 2.5% per year. Consequently, benchmark values will be reduced by between 6 and 50% of the initial benchmark values for the free allocations in respect of 2026–2030. A specific rule applies again to the calculation of the benchmark value for hot metal: less emitting installations newly covered by this benchmark because of the review will not be taken into account for the adjustment of the benchmark value for 2026–2030.

The Free Allocation Regulation[19] determines detailed implementation rules including on definitions, modifications to the monitoring rules regarding the data collected by Member States, the production-level data, and the determination of historical activity levels. Following the 2023 ETS revision, the Free Allocation Regulation has been amended to provide for the equal treatment of products irrespective of the route of production[20] – this will concern hydrogen, ammonia, cement clinker, primary steel ('hot metal'), and sintered iron ore. The benchmark values for refineries and for hydrogen will be decoupled to reflect the increasing importance of production of green hydrogen outside of refineries.

Allocations will also be adjusted if installations' operations increase or decrease by more than 15%, to align free allocations more closely with actual production levels.[21] An implementing act on allocation adjustments was adopted in 2019.[22]

4.2.4   The Correction Factor

Since 2013, a safeguard clause ensures that the number of allowances given out for free based on benchmarks does not exceed the available amount agreed within the overall cap.[23] In respect of 2013–2020, this maximum share of free allocation was defined as the historic share[24] of emissions of those installations in the overall EU ETS cap.[25] A cross-sectoral correction factor was, therefore, foreseen between 2013 and 2020 to limit free allocations to all operators to the same extent to ensure that the pre-determined limit of free allocation was not exceeded.

The original ETS legislation foresaw that the benchmark values were to be multiplied by production values. Operators were given a choice of base year for production values, which resulted in a significant inflation of allocation and triggered the application of a significant cross-sectoral correction factor for the period 2013–2020. In 2013, the cross-sectoral correction factor was around 6% increasing to around 18% by 2020. This reduction applied equally to the free allocations of all operators, regardless of the differing extent of exposure to global competition.

The application of the correction factor generated support for a more targeted carbon leakage system for the post-2020 period. As a result, the updates of the carbon leakage list and of the benchmark values have reduced the need, if not completely avoiding, the application of the cross-sectoral correction factor up to 2030, and no cross-sectoral correction factor has been applied in the period 2021–2025. In case the correction factor would be applied, up to 3% of the total quantity of allowances by 2030 would be used to give additional free allocation rather than be auctioned by

Member States, and allowances freed up by the 2023 revision's conditionality provisions would also be used to avoid it.[26]

4.2.5   The State Aid Provisions and the New Entrants Reserve

The ETS Directive's general rule that no free allocation is given to electricity generation is based on the premise that generators are expected to pass through the costs of carbon in electricity prices. As a result, energy-intensive industry sectors have an increased "indirect" cost of electricity prices. In view of this, the Directive states that Member States should grant State aid, i.e., national subsidies, for the benefit of sectors exposed to a significant risk of carbon leakage due to higher electricity prices. As of 2023, 14 Member States grant such State aid,[27] which must nevertheless comply with the EU's State aid guidelines, basically requiring that it does not lead to distortions of competition within the EU's internal market. Member States spending on this aid should not exceed 25% of their ETS auction revenue in any year. This system will continue until 2030 but with much improved transparency.

A New Entrants Reserve has been created, setting aside allowances[28] for new investments, either in terms of entirely new installations or significant production increases of existing installations. Harmonised benchmarking rules have been set out for allocations to new entrants, and allocations are reduced by the Linear Reduction Factor. The New Entrants Reserve for the period 2021–2030 is drawn from some 325 million unallocated allowances from the period 2013–2020, including 200 million allowances that would otherwise have been placed in the Market Stability Reserve. Furthermore, allowances from downwards allocation adjustments due to reduced activity levels are fed into the reserve.

Regarding installations that close, no free allocation is given any longer to an installation that has ceased its operations unless the operator shows that production will be resumed within a reasonable time. The same rule applies for the partial closure of installations.

> Conclusion: The EU ETS contains a rules-based system of free allocation to address the risk of carbon leakage. Over the period 2021–2030, an amount of approximately 5.3 billion allowances is available for free. Technological benchmarks are regularly updated, and incentives are provided for investments in low-carbon technologies.

4.3 The Creation of a Carbon Border Adjustment Mechanism (CBAM)

As the EU's climate ambition levels increase over time, the free allocation of EU allowances also reduces over time. A Carbon Border Adjustment Mechanism was first envisaged in the ETS Directive in 2009[29] and has now been created. This was a major policy decision that was taken as part of the EU Green Deal. Its purpose is to be non-discriminatory and to maintain the incentive effect of pricing carbon while reducing the incentive to emit elsewhere and export into the EU without this being taken into account.[30]

4.3.1 The CBAM Design

CBAM is a charge on imported goods. This charge will be levied on an annual basis, from 1 January 2026. CBAM liability is based upon the embedded emissions of imported goods covered by the scope of the measure. The embedded emissions will have to be reported annually by importers or their representatives, and independently verified by accredited verifiers.

CBAM is designed to replicate the carbon pricing instrument of the EU ETS, but only with respect to goods imported into the EU. The EU ETS is a regulatory system designed around fixed installations rather than goods, and goods produced in covered installations in the European Economic Area incur the cost of the carbon price (and its incentive effect to reduce emissions) regardless of their destination.

Given that a charge on embedded carbon is complex to measure, the decision was made to keep things as simple as is feasible. In its initial form, CBAM will cover a few energy-intensive products, namely, iron and steel, cement, aluminium, fertilisers, hydrogen, and electricity. The scope also includes some selected precursor products such as clinker and ammonia. The exact product categories are identified by Customs Nomenclature codes, listed in Annex I to the CBAM Regulation. The greenhouse gases covered are carbon dioxide, nitrous oxide, and perfluorocarbons. These sectors and gases are already covered by the EU ETS.

Goods that are within the scope of CBAM imported from all countries are covered, except for countries that are part of the European Economic Area that apply the EU ETS, and Switzerland, that has a linking agreement with the EU ETS.[31] The carbon price in these jurisdictions is aligned, and there are no other exemptions.

4.3.2 Defining the CBAM Liability

Liability is triggered by importation into the EU. Import formalities are already a requirement for traded goods, and the administration of CBAM is streamlined with the national authorities who already oversee the levying of customs duties (if applicable) and VAT. However, unlike customs duties and VAT, the liability is not related to the monetary value of the imported goods but is based on the embedded carbon in the products and any carbon price already paid in respect of those products.

Detailed reporting rules for the CBAM's transitional phase were adopted to calculate the embedded carbon related to production of the imported goods in the country of production.[32] Direct and indirect emissions are covered and must be reported, although initially indirect emissions will incur a CBAM liability only for cement and fertilisers, due to State aid, i.e., national subsidies given to EU producers of the other goods covered by CBAM in some Member States to compensate for higher electricity costs resulting from the EU ETS. The rules for calculating embedded carbon covering different goods and production processes are explained in detail in the EU's official documents.[33] The goal, once again, is parallelism with the EU ETS MRV rules.

Data has to be declared by the importer on embedded carbon and that depends on the involvement of third country suppliers, in the absence of which default factors will be used.[34] Contracts for the procurement of goods will have to provide for the provision and quality of this data, and confidentiality will be required before commercially sensitive information is divulged. Declarations made annually by the importer or the importer's representative are required based on the data provided, and the reliability of this data must be attested by independent verifiers.[35] Verifiers will have to be EU-accredited, whether based in the EU or in third countries. To an extent, this independent verification is a safety check for importers or their representatives and gives solidity and transparency to the system. The importer, or indirect customs representative, who has the status of an "authorised CBAM declarant", is liable for the declaration of embedded carbon and they may sue their third country suppliers and/ or verifiers if gross negligence can be established, as applies in the world of financial auditing.

Once the quantity of embedded emissions is established, a polluter-pays charge applies based on the EU ETS's carbon price – as determined weekly by the regular auctions of EU allowances for the EU ETS. National authorities will sell to importers or their representatives "CBAM certificates", denominated in tonnes of CO_2-equivalent. At the end of every quarter, the importer, or "authorised CBAM declarant", must ensure that it holds in its CBAM registry account CBAM certificates covering 80% of the embedded carbon emissions in all goods imported since the beginning of the calendar year. Once a year, for the first time by 31 May 2027, these certificates will need to be surrendered in a quantity sufficient to match the embedded emissions of the goods imported during the previous calendar year. Goods will not be delayed at importation, but the liability and holdings of CBAM certificates will accumulate until the end of the relevant calendar year. Once surrendered, the CBAM certificates will be cancelled.

The CBAM liability will be reduced to the extent that transitional free allocation in the EU ETS continues for the covered products. The introduction of CBAM liability will be progressive, starting in 2026 and will be complete by 2034 (see Table 4.2). Until then an adjustment will be made to reflect that in 2026 only 2.5% of the calculated CBAM liability will be applicable, while this amount increases the following years. This does not preclude faster reductions to transitional free allocation in some sectors between 2031 and 2034, as the ETS Directive has yet to provide the precise amount in those years, for example, because substitute processes can be used more generally.[36] The free allowances that become available due to the implementation of CBAM will be auctioned and the revenues flow to the EU ETS Innovation Fund.

The number of CBAM certificates issued will not have a cap. Neither will these certificates be tradable. Unused CBAM certificates can be partially sold back to the national authorities. If importers want to hedge against fluctuations of the price of certificates, they can do this by taking a position linked to the EU ETS allowance price. Importers or their representatives are also able to open EU ETS registry accounts and can engage in future contracts to mitigate the risk of a fluctuating or a significantly rising EU carbon price.

Given these are new measures for importers, it has been decided to have a transitional period running from 1 October 2023 to 31 December 2025 during which no payments are due but reporting obligations will apply. This is sometimes referred to as a "data collection phase". Its purpose is to enable EU national administrations, importers and their third country suppliers to establish the data gathering systems. Reporting will cover quantities of imported goods, the country of production, and the embedded carbon in the goods.

Given the novelty of the reporting requirements, until the end of 2025 reporting is quarterly and, in the first few quarters, simplified monitoring and

TABLE 4.2 Reductions of transitional ETS free allocations over 2026–2034

Year	% Reduction of EU ETS transitional free allocation
2026	2.5%
2027	5%
2028	10%
2029	22.5%
2030	48.5%
2031	61%
2032	73.5%
2033	86%
2034	100%

Source: Directive (EU) 2023/959,[37] Article 10a(1a).

reporting rules apply. From the start of reporting, both direct and indirect emissions must be calculated and declared on all goods covered by the scope of CBAM. The declarant may claim a reduction related to carbon prices already paid in the country of production of the goods.[38] From 1 January 2026, from when payments are due, the monitoring, reporting, and verification methodologies for the definitive phase will be adopted, informed by the experience gained during the transitional phase. Reports will then be due on an annual basis, with annual surrendering of CBAM certificates.

4.3.3   Reduction for a Carbon Price Paid[39]

Article 9 of the CBAM Regulation allows a reduction of CBAM liability corresponding to a carbon price effectively paid in the country of production, that will reduce the need for CBAM certificates. The logic of this is that the price of carbon paid on embedded emissions should not be paid twice, and that the carbon price on imports should be equivalent to the carbon price applied to EU production of similar goods.

The CBAM Regulation defines what constitutes a carbon price paid in the country of production.[40] It includes carbon taxes and emissions trading systems ensuring reductions of greenhouse gases. Such carbon price systems would need to be regulatory carbon pricing systems, at either national or subnational levels, as reductions will only be allowed where there is a "legal act providing for the carbon price",[41] which excludes a carbon price paid in the context of voluntary offsetting.

However, emissions trading systems established by legal acts may themselves be linked with the cooperation mechanisms of Article 6 of the Paris Agreement or allow for the use of offsets. Greater clarity on what the characteristics and preconditions are for a reduction of CBAM liability may be established, including as regards determining how third-country carbon pricing systems qualify for a reduction. Fuel taxes or excises have similar characteristics as carbon taxes, and some – such as the OECD[42] even count them as 'effective carbon rates' – but the CBAM Regulation is clear that a 'carbon price' must be calculated on the basis of greenhouse gas emissions. Of course, the reduction will only be for the amount paid, so if the carbon price paid in the originating country amounts to €8 per tonne and the EU ETS price is €80 a tonne, then the balance of €72 per tonne will be paid on the imported goods. This mechanism will already automatically adapt to the differing stringencies of carbon pricing systems.

It makes sense for third countries to price carbon, and the Commission and EU Member States have been sharing experience and assisting third countries with doing this for more than a decade. The introduction of CBAM does seem to be prompting accelerated developments in this direction in several jurisdictions, such as Turkey,[43] Brazil, and Indonesia. The Chinese ETS, which is already bigger than the EU ETS, is in the process of being extended to other sectors of the economy. Albania, Bosnia and Herzegovina, Kosovo, North Macedonia, Georgia, Moldova, Montenegro, Serbia, and Ukraine have undertaken legal commitments to apply EU ETS-level MRV by 2026 and have specific provisions in the CBAM Regulation relating to carbon pricing.[44] Such developments are also motivated by third countries wanting to have revenues nationally that would otherwise go to the EU. Many third countries might introduce a carbon price, whether via a carbon tax or emissions trading systems, and the Commission and EU Member States should increase their activities to help third countries apply effective carbon pricing.

4.3.4   Monitoring the Introduction of CBAM

CBAM is a new policy instrument that has not yet been tried before. It is, therefore, important to closely monitor the results and to modify elements where appropriate. By 2028, and every two years thereafter, the Commission will report on the impact on the CBAM on *"international trade, including resource shuffling"*, as well on other aspects, such as *"carbon leakage, including in relation to exports"*.[45]

The EU is wary of any unwanted displacement effects known as "resource shuffling", whereby low-carbon products are sent to Europe and the dirtier high-carbon products sent to the rest of the world. However, exporters to the EU start to realise that the way for goods to minimise liability to incur the costs of CBAM is to minimise the amount of embedded carbon. Third countries and their companies already comply with numerous product standards for sales within the EU, including CO_2 performance standards, such as exist for new cars. The EU market is of such a size that there is an incentive to comply with the new regulatory requirements. Companies from third countries may find opportunities for producing competitively priced low-carbon products and export them to the EU.

It is expected that the CBAM will continue to effectively address the risk of carbon leakage of EU production of CBAM goods as transitional free allocation in the EU ETS is removed. CBAM can also be expected to increase the cost of imported goods. There is also the incentive for EU purchasers of goods not to have to report on the embedded carbon of goods sourced from within the EU, as they already report on emissions from the production of those goods and are held accountable for this. The EU's motivation for the CBAM is entirely environmental – enabling the EU to be more ambitious on climate change – and to the climate benefit of the world.

The CBAM is not a protectionist measure, and the best environmental and economic outcome is that third countries also price greenhouse gas emissions. The CBAM rules, as adopted by the EU, provide for no specific rules for exported goods.[46] Relief from domestic regulatory charges or export subsidies could be contrary to WTO rules. This means that EU exports will have a higher cost of production, linked to the price of carbon in Europe, and – as is the case today – EU exporters will compete on global markets with products that will not necessarily have paid a carbon price at their point of production. By continuing to apply EU carbon costs on manufactured goods exported from the EU, lower-embedded carbon goods will continue to be disseminated across the world.

Reviews are foreseen for extension of the scope of CBAM, and consideration whether to cover manufactured products further along the value chain. There is a concern that manufacturing could relocate outside the EU to serve the EU market with more complex manufactured goods that are not covered by CBAM. If, for example, washing machines or cars are manufactured in the EU using imported steel that is subject to CBAM, manufacturers of these more complex goods might be tempted to relocate manufacturing outside the EU, and import the finished goods into the EU market escaping a CBAM charge on the steel. By the end of 2024, the Commission will, therefore, identify products further down the value chain of the goods covered by CBAM that it recommends being considered for inclusion within the scope of CBAM. Recital 67 of the Regulation indicates that CBAM should have the aim of including by 2030 all the goods covered by the EU ETS. Though non-binding, this is an indication that the scope of CBAM is expected to be extended, though much depends on the results of the Commission's assessments of the impacts of CBAM.

4.3.5   CBAM as an Impetus for More Intensive Policy Cooperation

The EU has put into law a workable model of a CBAM. Will all producers of imported goods comply with the disclosure requirements? Some countries have expressed the view that CBAM is discriminatory.[47] Least Developed Countries expect to be allowed to develop before constraining their emissions to the same extent as developed countries. The application of carbon pricing to the products of developing countries that are imported to the EU on an equal basis to the level of carbon pricing in the EU is claimed by some to not be consistent with Common But Differentiated Responsibilities (CBDR), a core principle of the UN Climate Change Convention and the Paris Agreement.[48] The scope of the EU ETS covering international aviation and maritime is consistent with CBDR,[49] and the EU is confident that CBAM does comply with WTO requirements.

Recital 72 of the CBAM Regulation advocates that a forum of countries with carbon pricing instruments or other comparable instruments ("Climate Club") should be set up. Article 2 provides more clarification on how countries may be added to the list of countries exempted from CBAM, and closes with a provision stating that *"The Union may conclude agreements with third countries or territories with a view to taking into account carbon pricing mechanisms in such countries or territories for the purposes of the application of Article 9"*, Article 9 being the one that allows for a reduction of CBAM liability with respect to a carbon price paid in a third country.

Such bilateral or plurilateral agreements may, in the medium- or longer-term influence flexibility or simplifications with respect to the geographic scope of CBAM's application to imported goods. When other countries apply explicit carbon pricing and introduce similar carbon border adjustments on imports, a way to bilaterally exempt each other's goods could potentially be covered by these provisions to provide for reciprocity of CBAM charges, such as envisaged in academic literature on carbon clubs.[50]

In this context, an opportunity may also arise to use the revenues generated by the sale of CBAM certificates even if the amount will initially be low. It is proposed that 25% of the revenues go to cover administration costs and 75% into the EU budget. This creates the perception that CBAM is a revenue-raising instrument whereas its declared primary objective is to reduce carbon leakage. Of course, some international climate finance is paid from the EU budget, though this is just a small part of what the EU budget is used for. If all the revenues after covering administrative costs were used to provide additional international climate finance purposes, either to support Least Developed Countries and vulnerable communities to fund adaptation or to facilitate their climate policies, it would probably be appreciated by those countries.

Conclusion: A Carbon Border Adjustment Mechanism has been established covering imports of iron and steel, cement, aluminium, fertiliser, hydrogen, and electricity. Free allocation for those products will be phased out by 2034. Explicit carbon prices paid in the country of origin can reduce the CBAM liability and increase the incentive for establishing more carbon pricing systems.

Conclusion

The EU Emissions Trading System is a key instrument for the EU to reduce its greenhouse gas emissions cost-effectively. From the outset, account has been taken of the risk of carbon leakage and the potential impact on the competitiveness of EU industry compared to countries and regions without a similar carbon price. The EU ETS has been evolving over time, and so has the way the EU deals with those issues.

The EU ETS started as a system where allocations were almost all made for free. At the time the EU ETS was established, the allocations were only possible to made in a rather *ad hoc* manner managed by each Member State separately, with a supervisory role exercised by the European Commission. In the 2008 EU ETS revision, it was possible to agree to have the similar treatment of companies all over the EU. The handling of carbon leakage by free allocation continued from 2005 up to now, with increasing levels of focus and conditionality. However, the increasing climate ambition brings down the total amount of allocation, including the part to be freely allocated. As part of the 2023 revision, a Carbon Border Adjustment Mechanism has been created. It will be gradually introduced and progressively replace free allocation to the sectors covered. So far, however, the EU ETS has succeeded to maintain the competitiveness of European businesses, while maintaining the effectiveness of the environmental instrument, as shown by the 37.3% reduction in emissions from power and industry installations that was achieved between 2005 and 2022.[51]

The CBAM is a new instrument of climate policy and has inevitable uncertainties associated with any new policy approach. Exporters and governments all over the world have started to prepare for the new reality it creates. The basis for establishing the CBAM liability is the carbon embedded, and this will undoubtedly encourage the imports of cleaner products as well as address the problem of carbon leakage. It will generate revenues that could be used for many climate-related purposes, such as funding additional international climate finance. The CBAM may also become the start of a pragmatic new form of international cooperation in which carbon pricing plays a key role, as advocated by some economists in the form of carbon or climate clubs.

It has taken a long time for the EU to put in place a carbon border adjustment mechanism, although the idea has been long debated. With Europe undertaking ever higher climate ambition, it is difficult to see what else can done in the absence of equivalent ambition and regulatory approaches by other countries. In an ideal world, all countries would apply carbon pricing to correct the mispricing of the climate externalities, but unfortunately the world is not ideal. What is a globally useful contribution by the EU is continuing to integrate carbon pricing into its economy and thereby demonstrate the multiple advantages of such an instrument in the common endeavour of reducing man-made greenhouse gas emissions. If it does that while retaining the vibrancy of its industries, Europe will serve to demonstrate the viability of such policy tools as carbon pricing and carbon border adjustments.

Notes

1 The authors are grateful for the contributions received by Heiko Kunst, Anna Hedderich, Madalina Radulescu and Ruben Vermeeren.
2 Regulation (EU) 2023/956 of the European Parliament and of the Council of 10 May 2023 establishing a carbon border adjustment mechanism (OJ L 130, 16.5.2023).
   ADD "Commission adopts detailed reporting rules for the carbon border adjustment mechanism's transitional phase", DG Taxation and Customs Union, 17 August 2023. Available at: https://taxation-customs.ec.europa.eu/news/commission-adopts-detailed-reporting-rules-carbon-border-adjustment-mechanisms-transitional-phase-2023-08-17_en#:~:text=On%2017%20August%202023%2C%20the,until%20the%20end%20of%202025.
3 European Environment Agency (2023) "EU Emissions Trading System (ETS) data viewer". Available at: https://www.eea.europa.eu/data-and-maps/dashboards/emissions-trading-viewer-1.
4 First established by Commission Decision of 27 April 2011 determining transitional Union-wide rules for harmonised free allocation of emission allowances pursuant to Article 10a of Directive 2003/87/EC of the European Parliament and of the Council, 2011/278/EU; OJ L 130, 17.5.2011, pp. 1–45. Available at: http://eur-lex.europa.eu/legal-content/EN/TXT/PDF/?uri=CELEX:32011D0278&from=EN.
5 For benchmarks defined without consideration of exchangeability of fuel and electricity.
6 European Commission (2021) "Update of benchmark values for the years 2021–2025 of phase 4 of the EU ETS", Available at: https://climate.ec.europa.eu/system/files/2021-10/policy_ets_allowances_bm_curve_factsheets_en.pdf.
7 Article 10a(8), 8th paragraph, of Directive 2003/87/EC.
8 Although the two fallback benchmarks are based on inputs.
9 Case C-460/15 Schaefer Kalk GmbH & Co KG; Case C-456/15 Borealis Polyolefine GmbH (with other Joined Cases); Case C-180/15 Borealis AB and others; Case C-506/14 Yara Suomi Oy and others. For more details see "Report on the functioning of the European carbon market" COM(2017)693 and "Report on the functioning of the European carbon market" COM(2018)842 final at https://ec.europa.eu/commission/sites/beta-political/files/report-functioning-carbon-market_en.pdf & https://ec.europa.eu/clima/sites/clima/files/ets/docs/com_2018_842_final_en.pdf). Court cases are listed in each document in Appendix 5.
10 According to Article 2(1), the operator of an installation may decide that it remain within the scope of the EU ETS until the end of the current five-year period or also for the next five-year period.
11 Directive (EU) 2023/1791 of 13 September 2023. Article 8 of Directive 2012/27/EU requires energy audits or the implementation of certified energy management systems.
12 Article 10a(1), third sub-paragraph.
13 Article 10b(4). The Member States where this derogation applies are Poland, Bulgaria, Latvia, and the Czech Republic. Further details are set out in Commission

Implementing Regulation (EU) 2023/2441 of 31 October 2023 laying down rules for the application of Directive 2003/87/EC of the European Parliament and of the Council as regards the content and format of climate-neutrality plans needed for granting free allocation of emission allowances.

14 Commission Decision of 24 December 2009 determining, pursuant to Directive 2003/87/EC of the European Parliament and of the Council, a list of sectors and subsectors which are deemed to be exposed to a significant risk of carbon leakage, 2010/2/EU. OJ L 1, 5.1.2010, pp. 10–18. Available at: http://eur-lex.europa.eu/legal-content/EN/TXT/PDF/?uri=CELEX:32010D0002&from=EN This decision was subsequently amended in 2011, 2012 and 2013; for more details see: http://ec.europa.eu/clima/policies/ets/cap/leakage/documentation_en.htm

15 2014/746/EU: Commission Decision of 27 October 2014 determining, pursuant to Directive 2003/87/EC of the European Parliament and of the Council, a list of sectors and subsectors which are deemed to be exposed to a significant risk of carbon leakage, for the period 2015 to 2019 (notified under document C(2014) 7809). OJ L 308, 29.10.2014, pp. 114–124. Available at: http://eur-lex.europa.eu/legal-content/EN/TXT/PDF/?uri=CELEX:32014D0746&from=EN. The second list has been extended to apply for the year 2020 by Article 4 of Directive (EU) 2018/410.

16 The level of disaggregation for sectors and sub-sectors was undertaken at a detailed level, so-called "NACE-4", with more disaggregated analysis for specific sub-sectors where this was considered justified.

17 The generally applicable criterion is the mathematical produce of emissions and trade intensity higher than 0.2.

18 Article 10b of Directive 2003/87/EC, as amended by Directive (EU) 2018/410, includes supplemental routes for inclusion.

19 Commission Delegated Regulation (EU) 2019/331 of 19 December 2018, determining transitional Union-wide rules for harmonised free allocation of emission allowances pursuant to Article 10a of Directive 2003/87/EC of the European Parliament and of the Council. Available at: https://eur-lex.europa.eu/legal-content/EN/TXT/PDF/?uri=OJ:L:2019:059:FULL&from=EN.

20 Commission Delegated Regulation (EU) .../... of ... . 2024 amending Delegated Regulation (EU) 2019/331 as regards transitional Union-wide rules for harmonised free allocation of emission allowances (not yet adopted at time of writing, but most recently published for public feedback at https://ec.europa.eu/info/law/better-regulation/have-your-say/initiatives/13861-EU-emissions-trading-system-ETS-update-of-the-free-allocation-rules_en).

21 Article 10a(2)) and (21), and recital (12).

22 Commission Implementing Regulation (EU) 2019/1842 laying down rules for the application of Directive 2003/87/EC of the European Parliament and of the Council as regards further arrangements for the adjustments to free allocation of emission allowances due to activity level changes.

23 Article 10a(5) of Directive 2003/87/EC.

24 The "historic share" is established by emissions levels in the years 2005–2007.

25 From 2021 the primary legislation defines the maximum share of free allocation in a more upfront and transparent manner.

26 If this 3% is not needed to avoid a correction factor applying, some of the allowances will be used to increase the size of the Innovation Fund and the Modernisation Fund.

27 See Section 4.1.3 of the 2018 Carbon Market Report COM(2018) 842 final. Available at: https://ec.europa.eu/clima/sites/clima/files/ets/docs/com_2018_842_final_en.pdf.

28 300 million allowances were taken from this New Entrants Reserve to fund the "NER300" fund for innovative renewable energy technologies and carbon capture and storage projects (though none of the latter were actually funded due to a lack of projects).

29 See recital 25 of Directive 2009/29/EC, introducing Article 10b(1)(b) into Directive 2003/87/EC.

30 Regulation (EU) 2023/956 of the European Parliament and of the Council of 10 May 2023 establishing a carbon border adjustment mechanism (OJ L 130, 16.5.2023)

31 See Annex III to CBAM Regulation of (EU) 2023/956 of 10 May 2023 establishing a carbon border adjustment mechanism.

32 Commission Implementing Regulation (EU) 2023/1773 of 17 August 2023 laying down the rules for the application of Regulation (EU) 2023/956 of the European Parliament and of the Council as regards reporting obligations for the purposes of the carbon border adjustment mechanism during the transitional period (OJ L 228, 15.8.2023).

33 https://taxation-customs.ec.europa.eu/carbon-border-adjustment-mechanism_en. The Commission published default values for determining embedded emissions during the CBAM transitional period on 22 December 2023 (https://taxation-customs.ec.europa.eu/system/files/2023-12/Default%20values%20transitional%20period.pdf).

34 Published on 22 December 2023 by the European Commission. Available at: https://taxation-customs.ec.europa.eu/news/commission-publishes-default-values-determining-embedded-emissions-during-cbam-transitional-period-2023-12-22_en.

35 For commentary on CBAM implementation and verification requirements see *Report Navigating Europe's Carbon Tariff* by the Conference Board (2023). Available at: https://www.conference-board.org/publications/navigating-europe-carbon-tariff.

36 Article 10a(2) and Article 10b both relate to the period up to 2030.

37 Directive (EU) 2023/959 of the European Parliament and of the Council of 10 May 2023 amending Directive 2003/87/EC establishing a system for greenhouse gas emission allowance trading within the Union and Decision (EU) 2015/1814 concerning the establishment and operation of a market stability reserve for the Union greenhouse gas emission trading system (Text with EEA relevance), EP, CONSIL, 130 OJ L (2023). Article 10a(1a) http://data.europa.eu/eli/dir/2023/959/oj/eng.

38 Article 9(1) of Regulation (EU) 2023/956.

39 Delbeke, J., Vis, P., (2023) "How CBAM can become a steppingstone towards carbon pricing globally", EUI, STG, Policy Brief, 2023/06. Available at: https://hdl.handle.net/1814/75472.

40 Article 3(29) of the CBAM Regulation (EU) 2023/956.

41 Article 7(1)(f) of Commission Implementing Regulation (EU) 2023/1773 of 17 August 2023.

42 OECD (2021) *Effective carbon rates*. Available at: https://www.oecd.org/tax/tax-policy/effective-carbon-rates-2021-brochure.pdf.

43 Parry, I., Minnett, D. and Zhunussova, K. (March 2023) "Climate mitigation policy in Türkiye". *IMF Working Papers, 2023/*108, and "Potential impact of the carbon border adjustment mechanism on the Turkish economy" by EBRD, Turkish Ministry of Environment, Urbanization and Climate Change & Climate Focus.

44 See Article 2, paragraphs (7) to (11), and Annex III, Part II of Regulation (EU) 2023/956.

45 Article 30(6)(a) of Regulation (EU) 2023/956.

46 Article 30(5) of Regulation (EU) 2023/956 provides for the Commission to regularly assess the effectiveness of the CBAM in addressing the carbon leakage risk of EU-produced goods for export to third countries which do not apply the EU ETS or a similar carbon pricing mechanism.

47 New Delhi Statement on Environment 7th Meeting of BRICS Environment Ministers (27 August 2021), paragraph 5. Available at: https://static.pib.gov.in/WriteReadData/specificdocs/documents/2021/aug/doc202182731.pdf and China's

remarks at COP28. Available at: https://www.reuters.com/sustainability/china-urges-eu-ensure-new-carbon-tax-complies-with-wto-rules-2023-09-14/ and https://www.spglobal.com/commodityinsights/en/market-insights/latest-news/energy-transition/120423-cop28-china-eu-face-uphill-battle-to-coordinate-carbon-policies.

48 Blog post of the European Journal of International Law by Jakub Bednarek. Available at: https://www.ejiltalk.org/is-the-eu-realizing-an-externally-just-green-transition-a-short-analysis-of-the-carbon-border-adjustment-mechanism-from-the-perspective-of-the-cbdr-principle-and-the-right-to-development-of-ldcs/.

49 See recital 20 of Directive (EU) 2023/959 that elaborates on this in detail, as well as the revised Nationally Determined Commitment of the EU and its Member States of 17 October 2023.

50 Nordhaus, W. (2015) "Climate clubs: Overcoming free riding in international climate policy". *American Economic Review*, 105(4), pp. 1339–1370.

51 EU Climate Action Progress Report 2023, COM(2023)653, p. 14.

5

THE INTERNATIONAL DIMENSION OF THE EU ETS

Damien Meadows and Beatriz Yordi[1]

Introduction

The EU created its emissions trading system (EU ETS) as a key instrument to implement the Kyoto Protocol and to incentivise cost-effective emission reductions. Over time, the instrument has been continued and reinforced to deliver the ambitious targets the EU has taken under the Paris Agreement. Even if most of the operations of the EU ETS are contained to the EU, its international dimension is growing. Cooperation with constituencies having similar emission trading systems is intensifying, and since 2020, the EU ETS is linked with the Swiss emissions trading system.

Following the announcement and establishment of the Carbon Border Adjustment Mechanism (CBAM), more countries have been investigating how to set up carbon pricing and this issue has become an important part of global climate diplomacy. The EU ETS offers valuable experience that counties can draw from; it used to integrate carbon credits created under the Kyoto Protocol, which is also relevant in view of finalising the negotiations on Article 6 of the Paris Agreement. Of growing importance too are the climate impacts from the aviation and shipping industries that are largely between countries, and the emissions of these are partially covered by the EU ETS.

5.1 International Cooperation on Carbon Markets

At the time of the 1997 Kyoto Protocol, the international carbon market was conceived as something that would happen between the Parties in a "top-down" fashion. In the intervening 20 years, it became clear that international carbon pricing was rather the result of choices by national and regional governments to put obligations on certain economic actors in their jurisdictions, rather than being driven by developments at the UN level. While the UNFCCC process remains important in a general climate policy context, there has never been a serious attempt to establish a company-based

DOI: 10.4324/9781003493730-7

emission trading system through UN institutions. The Paris Agreement does not even mention carbon pricing explicitly,[2] despite its importance for tackling climate change.

The EU has led the way in developing actual carbon pricing through its emissions trading system. The EU ETS started in 2005, prior to the first commitment period of the Kyoto Protocol. It grew over time, with more countries joining the EU and the EU ETS since – Romania, Bulgaria, and Croatia. The first formal linking of the EU ETS with States that were not part of the EU was the extension to the neighbouring countries of the European Economic Area – Norway, Iceland, and Liechtenstein – in 2008. Furthermore, the EU and Switzerland established a two-way link between their emissions trading systems that took effect on 1 January 2020.

The expansion of carbon pricing is essential to collectively deliver on the Paris Agreement. There is a growing recognition that the magnitude of the climate change challenge requires that a price be put on carbon, to create incentives for companies to invest in low-carbon activities. Many developed and developing countries are looking into establishing their own emissions trading systems, at national or sub-national level. China has a nation-wide system since 2020, and countries such as Brazil, Indonesia, Thailand, or Vietnam are investigating carbon pricing systems. Singapore and South Africa created a carbon tax, and a part of that fiscal liability can be fulfilled with carbon credits. In Africa, the interest in carbon pricing is also picking up.

This trend has been reinforced since the EU announced and adopted CBAM to address the risk of carbon leakage from key sectors under the EU ETS. Within these sectors, imports from third countries may benefit from a reduced CBAM-charge if it can be proven that a carbon price was effectively paid in the country of production. In such case, the corresponding amount can be deducted from their final CBAM-charge based on the EU ETS. This latter element has triggered interest in carbon pricing in many of the EU's trading partners. They are interested in understanding how their own carbon pricing could generate revenue nationally and help tackle climate change while, at the same time, exports from their countries would avoid paying part of the CBAM-charge.

This is not to underestimate the political challenges to develop legislation to put a price on emissions whether in the form of trading systems or taxes. This has been amply experienced, for example, through the United States' inability to pass federal legislation to put a price on emissions over the last 20 years, despite several near successes.[3] Australia established a national emissions trading system that would have become linked with the EU ETS, but a change in government halted the national system. In the United Kingdom, the political commitment to carbon pricing was tested by its decision to leave the EU, but it established a national emissions trading system that

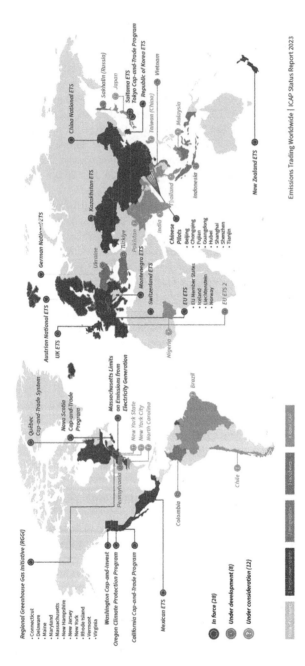

FIGURE 5.1 Carbon pricing initiatives in place or in development

Source: ICAP (2023)[4]

applies largely the same design choices that are embodied in the EU ETS. The experience also showed that the EU ETS was able to adapt to such a new situation, including through a safeguard provision that protected its environmental integrity[5] during the process.

Some of the most promising policy developments outside Europe today are happening in Asia. South Korea has a national greenhouse gas emission trading system that has been up and running since January 2015. Drawing on seven pilot emissions trading systems, China has a nation-wide system from 2020 that covers the power sector,[6] which should be extended to six other sectors. Experience of the Kyoto Protocol's Clean Development Mechanism played an important role in enhancing understanding of market-based approaches. These systems experience implementation issues like the ones the EU ETS went through.

New Zealand has an emissions trading system that has been in operation since 2008. In the United States, despite the failures at federal level, the north-eastern states have been operating the Regional Greenhouse Gas Initiative (RGGI) since 2009[7] and California has an emissions trading system operating since January 2013. Canada has developed a national carbon pricing system, building on the actions by Quebec (linked with California), Nova Scotia, and other provinces and complementing it with carbon taxes elsewhere.

These national and sub-national experiences offer prospects for developing an international carbon market. In the future, allowances could be traded across jurisdictions and a common carbon price could emerge within a wider geographical area. Just as the EU ETS has provisions for integration of international credits, it also explicitly allows for the linking of carbon markets by means of "mutual recognition" of carbon allowances,[8] through bilateral agreements between the EU and third countries or regions. The possibility of linking also extends to sub-national systems if it is considered desirable and robust from environmental integrity standpoint.

The "bottom-up" development of an international carbon market via national legislation, as well as the linking agreements between them, need rules for monitoring, reporting, and verification of emissions. They are a key infrastructure requirement for any carbon market to function properly. Like contemporary financial systems, carbon markets need a solid underpinning by a robust emissions accounting system as well as a central registry. The EU ETS installed a system of self-reporting by companies that is verified by independent third-party verifiers and this approach is being widely followed. One of the main lessons learnt from the EU ETS's pilot phase was the need for reliable industry-wide and plant-specific emissions data. To facilitate such a process, bilateral cooperation as well as initiatives such as the Florence Process at the European University Institute[9] and the International Carbon Action Partnership have proven to be valuable.[10, 11]

Conclusion: The EU and other countries such as Canada, China, Korea, and New Zealand have a carbon pricing system in place. Increasing climate challenges, access to finance as well as carbon leakage measures such as CBAM raise international interest in carbon pricing. The EU ETS can be linked with other comparable systems.

5.2 Experience with International Credits

In addition to establishing a price for greenhouse gas emissions in Europe, the EU ETS has also been the main driver for emission reduction projects[12] around the world. It was indeed the main market for, or importer of, credits from the Kyoto Protocol's project-based mechanisms, the Clean Development Mechanism (CDM) and Joint Implementation (JI) and is estimated to have been responsible for the use of approximately 1.6 billion international credits up to 2020.[13] The EU ETS significantly facilitated the financing of offset projects around the world including, for example, in renewable energy investments. However, on balance the experience was not positive as the generation of many credits was flawed, and it impacted the EU ETS's price signal while Europe received little recognition for the scale of its support.

The EU initially relied solely upon the UNFCCC to generate and validate the offset credits. Exclusions were made, however, for credits based on projects where the emission reductions were not permanent, as is the case for forestry-based credits or for projects that were considered politically unacceptable, such as for new nuclear power stations. Gradually, however, the EU realised that it needed to improve its qualitative and quantitative conditions[14] for the use of international credits.

Firstly, the experience showed that the UNFCCC structure was unable to enforce high environmental standards and the EU always had qualitative conditions for credits to be used under the EU ETS.[15] Additional quality standards were put in place in 2011 for projects involving HFC-23 destruction and adipic acid production.[16] In the end, it was found necessary to prevent JI credits that lacked credibility from being used for compliance purposes in the EU ETS.[17]

Secondly, the influx of international credits also had a downside from a quantitative perspective. Exactly when the 2008 economic crisis was creating a surplus of allowances, many international credits entered the EU ETS. As is explained in Chapter 3, this influx of international credits further inflated the recession-induced surplus and led to the lower-than-expected carbon price in Europe for several years. It was thus vital that there was a quantitative limit on the overall quantity of credits that could enter the EU ETS.

In 2014, the EU decided to define its 2030 climate target only in terms of a domestic reduction commitment, in other words without relying on the use of international credits. The approach of the Kyoto Protocol of allowing carbon credits of foreign origin was discontinued. Any new market for international credits will have to come from Article 6 of the Paris Agreement that still needs finalisation. The EU ETS is no longer a source of demand for credits and will remain so for as long as the current legislation is not modified.

Conclusion: The EU ETS absorbed some 1.6 billion tonnes of international credits (CDM and JI). The EU was the main source of global demand for such offset credits, which stimulated interest in market-based approaches in some countries. Given the doubtful quality and additionality of many credits, the EU decided on a reductions target for 2030 to be achieved domestically.

5.3 Aviation Emissions

5.3.1 The International Governance for Aviation Emissions

Aviation and shipping's combined climate impacts already make up around 10% of Europe's contribution to climate change, and they will grow to more than one-third by 2050 unless significant measures are put in place. Annual global CO_2 emissions from aviation increased from 435 million tonnes in 1990 to over 900 million tonnes by 2019. ICAO suggested that international civil aviation's CO_2 emissions could multiply five-fold by 2050 compared to their level in 2005 in the absence of additional measures. Moreover, aviation also has impacts on the climate through releases of nitrogen oxides, water vapour and particles. The IPCC has estimated that the total climate impact of aviation is currently two to four times higher than the effect of its carbon dioxide emissions,[18] and these overall climate impacts have so far not received sufficient attention.

To date, most aviation activity has been between developed countries. In the coming decades, the predominant part of emissions growth is expected to come from flight routes to, from, and between developing countries. The global differences in aviation emissions are one reason why the UNFCCC's issue of Common but Differentiated Responsibilities (CBDR) has been central to international discussions. This is illustrated by Figure 5.2, showing the distribution of aviation emissions between four key regions *per*

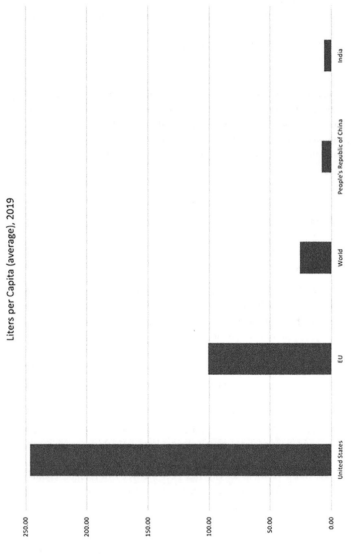

FIGURE 5.2 Average annual per capita jet fuel use in litres, 2019

source: ICCT[19]

capita. The US is responsible for more than nine times the jet fuel use of the average global citizen, while China and India *per capita* used only 3% and 2.4%, respectively, as much jet fuel as the US. Nevertheless, China was the second largest emitter from aviation overall, behind the US and far ahead of India. Addressing greenhouse gas emissions from aviation requires coherent policy action for international and domestic flights. The mandate of the Convention on International Civil Aviation covers only international flights while domestic flights amount to around 400 million tonnes per year, representing approximately 40% of global aviation emissions. It is, therefore, important that the NDCs submitted under the Paris Agreement cover aviation's emissions.[20]

The EU includes emissions from all flights within the European Economic Area (domestic and international), as well as departing flights to the UK and to Switzerland in its 2023 Nationally Determined Commitment (NDC).[21] This is in line with the bottom-up approach of the Paris Agreement, albeit less than the coverage of aviation in the EU's 2015 NDC and its 2020 update.[22] Article 4(4) of the Paris Agreement states that developed countries should continue to take the lead by undertaking economy-wide emission reduction targets, while developing countries are encouraged to move over time towards economy-wide emission reduction or limitation targets.[23]

The Secretariat of the ICAO claims that "*CO_2 emissions from international aviation are ... not covered by Nationally Determined Contributions (NDCs) under the Paris Agreement*".[24] On the other hand, the UN Environment Programme (UNEP) has welcomed the EU taking responsibility for international aviation and maritime emissions in its Nationally Determined Commitment (NDC).[25] The UN Secretary-General, António Guterres, has been a committed proponent for climate action.[26]

Greater coherence within the "UN family" as well as in the positions taken by governments at the international level could clearly be useful.[27] Issues of "regulatory capture" have been looked at in other sectors of the economy,[28] and this could partly explain the disappointing contributions by ICAO to date. The EU Parliament and Council have pressed for over 20 years for greater action,[29] including "*for undertaking specific actions to reduce greenhouse gas emissions from aviation if no such action is agreed within the International Civil Aviation Organisation by 2002*". While the Kyoto Protocol foresaw that Annex I Parties[30] should pursue limitation or reduction of international aviation and shipping emissions, working through ICAO and the IMO, the Paris Agreement states that all sources of emissions are covered but did not give a new mandate to those UN agencies.

More than 50% of aviation emissions relating to the EU come from just 6% of flights,[31] and these long-haul flights do not pay any carbon price or tax for their emissions. Therefore, the EU ETS was applied originally to international aviation, covering both incoming and departing flights. The airlines' association IATA, as well as US airlines and the US administration, heavily attacked the EU for regulating non-EU-based airlines, and the system was temporarily constrained to intra-European flights only. Following litigation brought by the US to the European Court of Justice (ECJ), it was confirmed that the EU ETS law is compatible with international law, and with the EU/US Open Skies Agreement and the Chicago Convention. The ECJ reaffirmed that States have the sovereign right to determine the conditions for admission to or departure from their territory and require all airlines to comply. The ECJ also confirmed that the EU ETS has no extra-territorial effect because no obligations are imposed in the territory of any other state.

5.3.2 The EU ETS Includes Aviation within Europe

The EU has developed market-based measures as an essential part of a comprehensive approach alongside improvements in technology of aircraft and fuels, or in navigation operations. As from 2012, all flights between European airports have been covered under its EU ETS and today this includes emissions from some 500 airlines. Equal treatment on routes is a key principle of the EU ETS and has been maintained throughout, although this initially required substantial enforcement action. More than 100 commercial airlines based outside the EU conduct flights within the European Economic Area and they all comply with the EU ETS.

The intra-EU coverage has been extended three times, namely concerning departing flights to Switzerland (from 2020), departing flights to the United Kingdom (in 2021), and most flights to and from the EU's outermost regions (from 2024). The 2024 extension increases the emissions coverage of the EU ETS by around 7%. In parallel, the Swiss ETS is undertaking a similar extension for departing flights to the EU's outermost regions from January 2024.

The inclusion of intra-European aviation in the EU ETS has already resulted in a cumulative surrendering of over 200 million allowances from within the absolute cap on emissions, and around 15 million international credits issued under the Kyoto Protocol. This is an environmental outcome well in excess of ICAO's CORSIA scheme[32] (Table 5.1).

It should also be noted that aviation's inclusion in the EU ETS has augmented the functioning of the Market Stability Reserve. Following the 2023 ETS revision, net demand from aviation will be included in the total number of allowances in circulation (TNAC) from 2024 onwards.[33] The precise net demand from aviation will be calculated prior to 2024, which then can be considered in future reviews of the Market Stability Reserve.

TABLE 5.1 Aircraft operators – verified emissions, free allocation and allowances auctioned

Year	2013	2014	2015	2016	2017	2018	2019	2020	2021	2022
Verified emissions (mn tonnes CO_2eq)	53.5	54.8	57.1	61.5	64.4	67.5	68.2	25.2	27.9	49.1
Change year-on-year	–	2.5%	4.1%	7.7%	4.8%	4.8%	1%	–63%	30%	75%
Free allocation	32.4	32.4	32.1	32.0	33.1	31.3	31.3	32.5	24.0	23.1
Allowances from special reserve for new entrants/fast-growing operators	–	–	–	–	1.1	1.1	1.0	0.8	0.3	0.25
Allowances auctioned	0	9.3	16.4	6.0	4.7	5.6	5.5	9.2	3.8	3.7

Source: COM(2022) 516; COM(2023) 654 final.[34]

States can also rely on national measures as a practical complement to emissions trading. Passenger charges are in place in several countries including the US, India, Germany, and the United Kingdom. The German air passenger duty is lowered by the level of EU ETS auction revenue that the government receives.[35] Passenger duties apply directly to passengers and not to airlines. Fuel taxes are also an option, although this will only happen if States ensure that common lines are taken across government: while the 2023 African climate summit called for levies on fossil fuel use in aviation,[36] this has been opposed earlier by government representatives in ICAO.[37] Airlines have generally been exempted from taxes such as VAT as well as from the fuel taxes that, for example, apply to road transport. It is an enduring myth that the 1944 Chicago Convention prevents the taxation of fuel supplied to aircraft, and there has thus far been insufficient political will to address this tax exemption. A rare step forward in this area was made in the EU-UK Trade and Cooperation Agreement, where the EU27 Member States and the UK agreed they should be able to tax aviation fuel, even if neither Party has yet proposed to do so.[38]

While fossil fuel use in road transport is generally subject to taxation, this has not been the case for aviation. The barriers have been bilateral air service agreements, and the EU Energy Taxation Directive.[39] In 2021, the Commission emphasised that "*the mandatory tax exemption concerning international aviation and waterborne navigation is in particular problematic because is not coherent with the present climate challenges and policies*".[40] The normalisation of fossil fuel taxation for aviation is awaiting the finalisation of the Energy Taxation Directive, which is a critical part of the European Green Deal. In the absence of such fossil fuel taxation, there is obviously less of an economic case for the large-scale use of alternative fuels.

5.3.3   The 2023 EU ETS Review

The 2023 ETS review decided on a fourth extension of scope to include flights involving States not implementing ICAO's CORSIA scheme as of January 2027 in order to support multilateral action. An important assessment will take place in July 2026[41] as to whether and how major third countries are implementing the ICAO scheme. For there to be fair contributions across the economy, additional action may be applied for departing flights and the economic costs from airlines applying the CORSIA scheme should be deducted from EU ETS costs. Finally, in the event of an almost universal application of a strengthened ICAO CORSIA scheme, it was agreed that the EU ETS should continue applying only to flights within the EEA, to Switzerland, to the United Kingdom and to flights to States not implementing the CORSIA scheme.

This is quite different from the situation 15 years ago, where the EU ETS covered both directions of flight with no such double-counting reductions. It is also noteworthy that Member States have agreed a positive reference to addressing extra-European flights, in view of matching the maritime sector's contribution of a *"fair share to the increased climate objectives of the Union as well as to the objectives of the Paris Agreement"*,[42] which begins to take effect in 2024. The earliest date at which this could occur for long-haul flights under the legislation is 1 January 2027, which is the same year that carbon pricing is foreseen to start to apply to emissions from buildings and road transport. By that time, ICAO should have delivered evidence that its instrument can deliver its promised results. There is no general application of the EU ETS to departing flights for at least three years. The decision by the Council and European Parliament on ETS application from January 2027 is an important one, as it would increase the ETS cap by over 100 million tonnes per year if departing flights are covered. The legislative process beginning in July 2026 must be concluded by September 2028, to exempt incoming flights to Europe with effect from January 2027.[43]

Three other important changes were made to the EU ETS. Firstly, free allocation will be phased out from 2026 onwards, given that airlines generally pass through costs to customers when there is equal competition on routes. In 2024 and 2025, free allocation levels will be reduced by 25% and 50%, respectively. In place of free allocation, 5 million allowances will be put into the EU ETS Innovation Fund, and 20 million allowances will be used to support large-scale deployment of eligible alternative fuels by aviation (see below). The remaining allowances will be auctioned by Member States, with a requirement that revenues be used for climate policies.

Secondly, following a decade when the *de facto* aviation ETS cap has been derived on a bottom-up basis, it has now been determined top-down and will be reduced by the 4.3% linear reduction factor that is applicable across the wider ETS. Bankruptcies and the closure of airlines will no longer reduce the aviation ETS cap and will instead supplement the EU ETS Innovation Fund. There is a modest expansion of ETS scope, to cover most flights between EU Member States and outermost territories, including flights from the outermost territories to Switzerland and to the UK. This increases the scope of the aviation ETS by around 7%. Domestic flights, between an outermost region and the Member State of which it is part, remain exempted from the EU ETS until 2030. The aviation ETS cap has been increased in relation to airlines' activity on these routes,[44] and the overall residual free allocation to airlines will be updated, based on their emissions in the year 2023.

Thirdly, the EU ETS Innovation Fund can specifically support actions to reduce the overall climate impacts of aviation,[45] thereby increasing the incentive for reductions by up to a factor of four. The Innovation Fund has committed over €4 billion to support the development of renewables, hydrogen, and alternative fuels. Further policy action is to be considered by December 2027 and promising options are already identified such as reducing the content of aromatics in jet fuel and avoiding supersaturated areas where condensation trails are most likely to occur.[46]

Finally, increasing transparency regarding the total impact of aviation beyond CO_2 emissions has been addressed as an important issue. The Commission has committed to publish more data from 2023 onwards[47] and binding monitoring, reporting, and verification rules should apply to airlines in respect of their non-CO_2 climate effects from 1 January 2025.[48]

5.3.4   Sustainable Aviation Fuels

The EU ETS already gives *de facto* an economic incentive of around €300 per tonne for the use of alternative fuels instead of fossil kerosene. This is because sustainable alternative fuels are zero-rated under the EU ETS, while emissions from kerosene bear a carbon cost in line with the "polluter pays" principle. However, kerosene is significantly cheaper to produce from fossil fuel than from other approaches and, in the absence of economic justification to use such fuels, actual levels of use have thus far been far below the targets proposed.[49] This is not surprising when alternative fuels cost between two and four times more to produce. The actual use of alternative fuels reported in the EU ETS was around 300 tonnes in 2022. The adoption of the European Green Deal's proposal on aviation fossil fuel taxation will improve the relative commercial attractiveness of alternative fuels but, at the time of writing, this pillar of the Green Deal has not been finalised.

Therefore, in an innovative development led by the European Parliament and the Council, 20 million ETS allowances (worth around €1.8 billion in 2023) will be given out on a first-come, first-served basis to airlines to cover the remaining cost difference for this use of eligible fuels compared to fossil kerosene.[50] This should galvanise the actual use of these fuels from January 2024 onwards and can be favourably compared with incentives in the US Inflation Reduction Act. Airlines that use alternative fuels can, when they report their independently verified emissions in the subsequent year, ask for the allocation of allowances to cover the cost difference. The airlines' ETS verifiers will confirm the levels of use, thereby limiting the potential for fraud.

This novel ETS support is only available for flights which are covered by the EU ETS. The system is based on the supply of fuel at airports and, when eligible aviation fuel cannot be physically attributed in an airport to a specific flight, the allowances are to be given out proportionately to emissions from flights of the aircraft operator from that airport that are covered by the EU ETS. Therefore, airlines cannot claim that alternative fuels were used for intra-European flights unless they can show that this is truly the case.[51] For airlines whose emissions take place on predominantly long-haul flights, the level of support will be lower unless the EU ETS applies in the future to those routes.

The ETS support differentiates between eligible fuels based on their desirability: synthetic fuels have a support level of 95%, while biofuels have ETS support ranging between 50 and 70%. To support smaller airports, as well as airports on islands and in outermost regions, there is support for 100% of the cost difference. This is expected to be the case for over 300 airports in Europe.

An advantage of carbon pricing is that there is information asymmetry, as business usually knows operating costs better than governments. To give support to alternative fuels, a support level must be determined, and the Commission will publish these support levels for eligible fuels. These levels will be updated annually and should bring important transparency and visibility to the actual costs of alternative fuels. Airlines are also required to give visibility to the funding that they receive from the ETS for alternative fuels.

Finally, if the 20 million allowances are used up because of a large increase in the use of alternative fuels, a review clause is included to consider increasing the availability of EU ETS support, in particular for the use of synthetic fuels.[52] Such an increase would require agreement of the European Parliament and Council. If the ETS cap were to be increased because of, for example, broader scope, then additional allowances from the cap increase might be used for this purpose.

In addition to this, and to the incentives for alternative fuels from carbon pricing and fossil fuel energy taxation, a single-market measure was agreed to require specific levels of alternative fuels to be blended into kerosene at the largest airports in the EU. This measure, "ReFuelEU aviation",[53] splits off requirements that were previously under the Renewable Energy Directive and applies to flights to third countries from those airports, and flights within Europe between such airports. It sets targets for both fuel suppliers and airlines to use a certain share of alternative fuels starting from the year 2025 and increasing in the year 2030 and thereafter. The measure also obliges aircraft operators to uplift at least 90% of the quantity of aviation fuel from the covered EU airport, that is used on flights departing from those airports, to prevent evasion of extra costs from the use of more expensive fuels than fossil kerosene.

5.3.5 Development of CORSIA within ICAO

ICAO adopted an aspirational and collective goal of "*carbon-neutral growth from 2020*",[54] depending on the efforts of all states and airlines. This is in stark contrast to the reality that growing emissions from international civil aviation are far from being consistent with the goals of the Paris Agreement.

At ICAO's 2022 Assembly, the goal was weakened to 85% of 2019 CO_2 emissions, as the baseline above which offsetting should take place was raised by over 80 million tonnes.[55] The COVID pandemic reduced global airline activity temporarily and by 2023 the business volume had resumed its 2019 levels. Moreover, developing countries have consistently argued that richer nations are responsible for the bulk of climate change and, therefore, should contribute greater reductions. There is a long list of reservations to the 2016 ICAO Assembly Resolution suggesting that this matter is far from closed.[56]

Since 2013, ICAO has developed "CORSIA", an intended global market-based measure that stands for "Carbon Offsetting and Reduction Scheme for International (Civil) Aviation". As of 2021, CO_2 emissions exceeding 85% of 2019 levels between two States that have volunteered to be covered would have been offset. With effect from 2027, CORSIA is meant to be mandatory for 34 countries that constitute most non-domestic aviation emissions (in particular, China, EU, India, Russia, Brazil, and the United States). CORSIA is set out in "Standards and Recommended Practices" (SARPs) that add Annexes to the Chicago Convention, along with implementing provisions and guidelines. Offsetting is only for international civil aviation's CO_2 emissions above the level of 85% of 2019,[57] unlike the EU ETS, which covers all CO_2 emissions from flights covered by the intra-European scope. CORSIA should last until 2035 and may be extended. A review of its operation will take place in ICAO in 2025.

It is important to note that, while the EU ETS covers most emissions from business aviation within Europe, CORSIA does not generally cover business aviation. Therefore, there is a "gap" relating to business flights between Europe and other regions of the world, in particular the United States, where no climate measure applies to such flights. In the 2023 ETS review, the issue of business aviation had political significance, and the ETS support for alternative fuels was specifically limited to commercial airlines. In reviews of CORSIA and the EU ETS, it will be important to see if this exception is addressed.

The following issues are of particular importance to the operation of CORSIA:

5.3.5.1   Participation

While the EU has been through the legislative process of implementing CORSIA, this is not the case in other major countries. China has notified a difference to ICAO that has not been published, and its public reservation states, *inter alia*, that

This is not conducive to maintaining the credibility of ICAO and the unity among member States, nor to ensuring the effective fulfilment of the mandate of the ICAO Assembly and the Council on matters of international aviation and climate change.[58]

It remains to be seen whether China will apply CORSIA from 1 January 2027. Meanwhile, in the United States, no legislation has been adopted to require airlines to surrender any offset credits. It is also not clear that the US will seek to apply CORSIA if major developing countries also do not implement it.

Non-discriminatory application on flight routes is fundamental for a market-based measure to work and ICAO has recognised that any scheme must *"apply to all aircraft operators on the same routes between States with a view to minimising market distortion"*.[59] The ICAO SARPS and implementing rules, however, provide that States should not be able to enforce the scheme on any airline based in another country except if "mutual agreement" is given.[60] "Mutual agreement" is, by definition, bilateral and should not be a feature of a system that claims to be global and multilateral and is unlikely to lead to equal treatment on flight routes. In this situation, if States do not apply high standards to airlines based in their State, then the EU legislation allows disapplication of the ICAO scheme to maintain a level-playing field on routes.[61]

5.3.5.2 Meaningful Offsets

Experience with the EU ETS has shown that credits should represent real emission reductions. Under the 1944 Chicago Convention, the eligibility criteria for environmental quality standards for carbon credits are not legally binding.[62] CORSIA also accepts several offsetting and crediting programmes with variable levels of environmental integrity and without guaranteed permanence or adjustments in States' greenhouse gas inventories. Credits are currently being issued in quantities that are much higher than expected demand, which will not lead to a meaningful carbon price that is essential for the economics of reducing fossil fuel emissions.

The 2023 EU ETS revision delivers certainty on what credits can be used by EU-based airlines for offsetting on extra-European flights,[63] including for credits issued under Article 6(4) of the Paris Agreement. Credits can only come from countries that are part of the Paris Agreement and which, from 2027, participate in CORSIA. Timely adjustments must be made to national greenhouse gas inventories and no double-counting is allowed. Given the importance of a level-playing field on routes, the EU ETS has "override" provisions that could enable the EU to lower its standards.[64]

5.3.5.3 Governance Arrangements and Avoidance of "Double Counting"

At the heart of equivalence are robust and comparable Monitoring, Reporting and Verification (MRV) provisions, adopted by the ICAO Council in 2018. The MRV obligations are meant to apply to the operators based in States that undertake international flights. Reporting should apply in respect of emissions from 2019.

This MRV exercise alone is valuable as a comprehensive data-gathering exercise for the baseline that serves as the starting point to measure emissions growth of international aviation from 85% of 2019 levels. This continuing monitoring obligation will serve as the basis for calculating the growth in subsequent years to determine the liability that should be distributed among participating operators. In view of meaningful policy updates in the future, the MRV provisions of CORSIA are most welcome.

The EU, as a supporter of multilateralism, has implemented the ICAO scheme through an amendment to the EU ETS. More clarity is needed about when and how other countries put in place their national provisions, not least in China,[65] India, and the United States. As of January 2023, the position of the US Federal Aviation Authority is that "*continued U.S. support for CORSIA assumes a high level of participation by other countries*", noting that

> The United States supported the decision to adopt the CORSIA SARPs based on the understanding that CORSIA is the exclusive market-based measure applying to international aviation, … avoiding a patchwork of country- or regionally-based regulatory measures….[66]

While the EU is in favour of avoiding a "patchwork" of policies, there should be fair contributions across the economy, both for carbon pricing and for taxation of fossil fuels, as well as a significant contribution to the goals of the Paris Agreement.

Conclusion: The EU ETS includes aviation between European airports on a non-discriminatory basis and is part of a system to reduce emissions by 62% by 2030 below 2005 level. ICAO has developed a global market-based instrument "CORSIA", which should offset CO_2 emissions from international aviation that exceed 85% of their level in 2019. The scheme started in 2021 and is supposed to become mandatory from 2027.

5.4 Maritime Emissions

5.4.1 *The International Governance of Shipping Emissions*

Annual global greenhouse gas emissions from shipping are around 1 billion tonnes. By 2050, the International Maritime Organisation (IMO) estimates that these could grow by between 50 and 250%, depending on economic and energy developments. Alongside CO_2, there are emissions of methane and nitrous oxide, as well as black carbon. The latter has significant climate impacts, not least in the Arctic, where it dulls the reflective properties of ice, thereby increasing heat absorption by ice, accelerating its melting. International journeys account for most of these emissions, with only 10–15% attributed to national "domestic" shipping.

The EU's CO_2 emissions from domestic shipping emissions have, by 2021, been reduced by 26.7% below 1990 levels,[67] but international shipping emissions related to the EU, i.e., from ships calling to EEA ports from third countries and ships sailing between two or more EU Member States, have continued to increase and were, in 2021, around 26.4% above 1990 levels. Around 90% of traded goods are carried by ships.[68]

Many technologies exist to retrofit and to build more efficient ships. Operational measures can reduce emissions and fuel costs, especially slow steaming. However, there are continuing market barriers that have limited the uptake of these emission reduction possibilities.[69]

In recognition of the need for economy-wide action, the European Commission adopted in 2013 a Strategy for progressively integrating maritime emissions into the EU's climate policy.[70] This Strategy led to a 2015 Monitoring, Reporting and Verification (MRV) Regulation for maritime transport[71] so that today the emissions of large ships using European ports are being accurately and transparently reported.[72] It has become a robust system that provides a platform for further action. Already it helps reduce costs by increasing information and transparency on fuel use. In the context of the Green Deal, the maritime sector was proposed to be included in the EU ETS to incentivise more cost-effective emission reductions.

The EU's MRV Regulation for maritime transport also facilitated the adoption of high-quality MRV standards within IMO. In 2016, the IMO's Marine Environment Protection Committee (MEPC) adopted amendments to the MARPOL Convention for a global data collection system for fuel consumption of ships.[73] The collection of fuel consumption data began in 2019. It has a similar technical scope as the EU's MRV for shipping (with the same 5,000 gross tonnage threshold) requires reporting annually and introduces a document to demonstrate compliance.

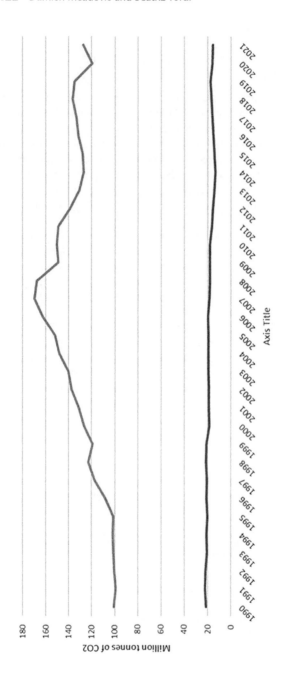

FIGURE 5.3   Domestic and international shipping emissions [1990–2021] (MtCO$_2$-eq)

Source: European Environment Agency (2023)[74]

5.4.2 *Extension of EU ETS to Maritime Emissions*

As of 2024, maritime emissions will be gradually included in the EU ETS for 50% of the emissions caused by a voyage. This has been made possible thanks to the factual evidence gathered under the 2015 MRV Regulation for maritime transport. Notwithstanding, climate action in the shipping sector is also being promoted through a basket of other measures.

The following issues are of particular importance for the EU ETS extension to maritime emissions:

5.4.2.1 Scope

The first key issue to highlight is the EU's approach to geographical scope. As for aviation, it is essential to preserve a level-playing field for maritime activities. For the maritime industry, it was obvious that regulation by nationality would be a recipe for inaction as ships can change flag between national registries with ease.

The EU ETS is flag neutral and applies to all routes that leave or come to European ports. This follows the approach of the 2015 MRV Regulation, basing itself on emissions on journeys to and from European ports but will only apply to half of those emissions. This approach is consistent with the Paris Agreement and is a practical way to solve the issue of common but differentiated responsibilities and capabilities, which has been a long-standing challenge in the UNFCCC context.[75] The ETS Directive does not put any compulsion on developing countries to apply carbon pricing to the 50% of emissions beginning and ending at their ports. It is encouraging that, for example, the Shanghai ETS applies to shipping.[76] It would have made little sense environmentally to cover only intra-European voyages and, unlike the situation with aviation, it was always accepted that ships would be given equal treatment irrespective of where they were flagged.

There are several exceptions to this coverage.[77] Firstly, there are time-limited derogations possible up to December 2030 in respect of voyages by passenger ships between islands with populations below 200,000.[78] This is essentially a social measure, recognising that it may take time for ferries to be upgraded, electrified, or to begin to use alternative fuels. Secondly, in recognition that ice-class ships have been less fuel efficient than other shipping, there is an exception according to which such ships can surrender 5% less allowances up to December 2030. Thirdly, there is a derogation for voyages by passenger ships operating in the context of a transnational public service contract between two Member States. This only applies to a newly established ferry service between Cyprus and Greece.[79] And finally, there is an exemption for voyages between a port in an outermost region and a port located in the same Member State, which includes voyages between ports within an outermost region and voyages between ports in the outermost regions of the same Member State, up to 2030.

Secondly, in terms of greenhouse gases covered, carbon dioxide must be priced because it is the main source of emissions from the shipping sector. Non-CO_2 emissions constitute a significant share of emissions from ships and, according to the Fourth IMO Greenhouse Gas Study 2020,[80] methane emissions increased significantly over the period from 2012 to 2018. Methane and nitrous oxide emissions are expected to grow over time, with the development of vessels powered by liquefied natural gases or other energy sources. Therefore, the shipping MRV rules apply to methane and nitrous oxide emissions from 2024,[81] and these emissions will be included in the EU ETS from 2026. Black carbon is harder to accurately monitor, and so has not been included in the EU ETS for the time being. However, it makes up around three-quarters of shipping's non-CO_2 climate impacts, and, therefore, it has a special mention as an area where the EU ETS Innovation Fund can fund emission reductions.

Thirdly, in terms of the ships that come under the EU ETS, the coverage is broadly the same as those regulated by the 2015 MRV Regulation. This means that large ships are regulated, above 5,000 gross tonnage. These ships are responsible for more than 85% of maritime-related emissions, while constituting around half of the number of ships calling into EU ports, taking into account the ship types covered. There is one exception, which is that it was decided that offshore ships will be covered by the EU ETS from January 2027, above a level of 400 gross tonnes. A review will take place no later than December 2026 that will examine the potential inclusion in the ETS of other ships below 5,000 gross tonnes but above 400 gross tonnes.

5.4.2.2 Phase-in of Coverage, and Use of Revenues

Shipping companies are required to surrender allowances for their fossil fuel emissions under the above scope at a level of 40% of verified emissions reported for 2024. The surrender date for 2024 emissions is 30 September 2025 and, if shipping companies maintain the level of fossil fuels that took place in 2022, this could mean that they contribute around €3 billion in terms of carbon costs. In 2025, the surrender percentage increases to 70% of verified emissions and thereafter, from 2026 onwards, shipping companies will be responsible for surrendering allowances for 100% of their verified emissions every year.[82]

This is the first time that a phase-in approach has been used in the EU ETS. It is justified partly because shipping companies will not be receiving transitional free allocation in the same way as some other sectors have done.

It is also important to highlight that this phase-in approach does not undermine the environmental integrity of the EU ETS. When fewer allowances are surrendered compared to the verified emissions from maritime transport in 2024 and 2025, once the difference between verified emissions and allowances surrendered has been established, Member States will cancel allowances corresponding to that difference.

As the EU ETS is covering a broader range of economic activities, it is appropriate that the ETS cap is increased correspondingly. The European Green Deal was announced in 2019, and the Council and Parliament endorsed the Commission's proposal that the maritime cap increase apply the linear reduction factor of 4.3% from the year 2021 to the cap addition for maritime, resulting in an increase of the ETS cap of 78.4 million allowances for 2024 (reduced by the 4.3% LRF for 2024 itself).[83] However, as the ETS cap is re-based downwards by 90 million tonnes in 2024, the cap reduction is more modest while the ETS is covering more economic activities.

There will then be a second increase of the total quantity of allowances in 2026 and 2027, because of the scope extension for maritime transport activities that take place in those years, for methane and nitrous oxide emissions, and for the coverage of emissions of offshore ships, respectively. The cumulative increase in the number of allowances is expected to be around 20 million allowances up to 2030, and the linear reduction factor will apply from those years to the level of allowances that are issued in the first year of inclusion.

Inclusion of emissions from maritime transport in the EU ETS will bring in additional revenue, and Member States have agreed that they shall use all resulting ETS revenues to tackle climate change.[84] In the context of this scope extension, Member States are also encouraged to support the decarbonisation of maritime transport and marine biodiversity protection. In fact, the Commission made a public statement that 20 million allowances, equivalent to around €1.8 billion, should be deployed through the EU ETS Innovation Fund to accelerate the decarbonisation of ships and ports. Maritime activities are already benefitting from the Innovation Fund, and the Innovation Fund is explicitly required to look at reducing shipping's overall climate effects, including from black carbon. Member States can also use the EU ETS Modernisation Fund to support improvements in the maritime area.

Until December 2030, Member States with a particularly high ratio of shipping companies under their responsibility compared to their population will receive an additional quantity of allowances, corresponding to 3.5% of the additional quantity of allowances due to the maritime cap increase. Greece, Cyprus, and Malta are the three Member States benefitting from this provision[85] and they will use the revenues from the auctioning of these allowances for climate policies.

5.4.2.3 Monitoring, Reporting, and Verification

The ETS provisions on monitoring, reporting, and verification for maritime transport are based on the foundation provided by the 2015 MRV Regulation but with an amendment making the reporting at company level rather than in relation to individual ships.[86] In addition, the 2015 MRV Regulation is extended from January 2024 to the other ships and emission types which will be covered by the EU ETS from 2026 and 2027. This relates to offshore vessels below 5,000 gross tonnes, and emissions of methane and nitrous oxide. More stringent penalties for non-compliance are also introduced, in terms of expulsion orders for non-compliant ships, or detention orders where a ship is flagged in a Member State and enters one of its ports.

5.4.2.4 Responsibility for Emissions between the Shipowner and Charterer

The emissions from a ship depend partly on the ship's energy efficiency and measures taken by the shipowner. They are also strongly affected by the fuel used, the cargo carried, and the route and the speed of the ship, which are often under the control of a different entity from the shipowner[87] The shipping company[88] often passes responsibilities for purchasing fuel or taking operational decisions affecting the greenhouse gas emissions through a contractual arrangement and, at the time the contract is negotiated, the ultimate emissions from the ship are uncertain. Unless carbon costs are passed on to the ship's operator, the incentives to implement operational measures for fuel efficiency would be limited. Therefore, in line with the "polluter pays" principle and to encourage the adoption of efficiency measures and the uptake of cleaner fuels, the 2023 ETS revision specifically provides that the shipping company should be entitled, under national law, to claim reimbursement for the costs of surrendering allowances from the entity that is directly responsible for decisions affecting the greenhouse gas emissions of the ship.

5.4.2.5 Building Wider Action

The EU remains strongly in favour of multilateral action and, therefore, a detailed review clause was agreed,[89] according to which progress in the IMO will be assessed, and changes proposed to the ETS Directive as appropriate.

In addition, in the same way as the 2015 MRV Regulation does not consider any stop in a port outside Europe as ending a ship's voyage for the purpose of the law,[90] the 2023 ETS revision discourages evasion by limiting the definition of "port of call" to ports which do not present a heightened risk of evasion. This relates only to neighbouring container transhipment ports where the share of transhipment exceeds 65% of its total container traffic, where that port is located less than 300 nautical miles from the EU.[91] This definition does not apply to a port where a third country effectively applies measures equivalent to the EU ETS, because this effectively addresses the risk of evasion.

Secondly, the EU ETS Innovation Fund should be useable outside the EU for maritime projects with clear added value for the Union.[92] This is the only place where the co-legislators provided for the use of the Innovation Fund outside European territory, and it can help third countries establish and advance their levels of climate action.

Thirdly, the review clause directs the Commission to monitor implementation and to detect evasive behaviour to prevent it at an early stage. If appropriate, the Commission should propose measures to ensure the effective implementation of the ETS in relation to maritime transport, including to address trends regarding shipping companies seeking to evade its requirements. This relates to geographical application, but also to the potential use of ships below the threshold of 5,000 gross tonne.

In parallel to the 2023 ETS revision, a single market measure specifically to require ships to use renewable and low-carbon fuels was agreed. This measure, known as "FuelEU maritime",[93] applies to the same geographical scope as the ETS extension, and requires the greenhouse gas intensity of fuels used by shipping to decrease by 2% in the year 2025, and by 6% in 2030. Thereafter, the reduction in greenhouse gas intensity should reach 31% in 2040 and 80% in 2050. These reductions are to be calculated based on lifecycle emissions. The use of shore-side electricity by ships is also required, subject to exceptions.[94]

5.4.3   Developments in the IMO

Since 2018, the IMO has been more active in trying to support reducing shipping emissions, and it agreed, for the first time, a strategy for the reduction of greenhouse gases from ships.[95] This had a long-term target to peak greenhouse gas emissions from international shipping as soon as possible and to reduce the total annual greenhouse emissions *"by at least 50% by 2050 compared to 2008 whilst pursuing efforts towards phasing them out…"*. There was also a commitment to improve the energy intensity of international shipping and a long list of "candidate measures" that will be further considered within the IMO. The reality is that agreement on any of these potential measures will be difficult as reconciling the diverging principles of non-discrimination and common but differentiated responsibilities remains difficult.

In July 2023, the IMO went much further by adopting a revised strategy to reduce greenhouse gas emissions from international shipping.[96] The revised strategy affirms the common ambition to reach net-zero greenhouse gas emissions from international shipping by close to 2050. It also confirms an indicative checkpoint for 2030, by when total greenhouse gas emissions from international shipping should have been reduced by at least 20%, striving for 30%, below 2008 levels. A second indicative checkpoint has been adopted for 2040, by when total greenhouse gas emissions from international shipping should have been reduced by at least 70%, striving for 80%, below 2008 levels.

The IMO is also aiming to reduce in-sector maritime emissions. Like international aviation, international shipping generally benefits from tax exemption on its fuel and no VAT applies to passenger traffic. The fact that ships have a capacity to stock a great quantity of fuel significantly limits any potential action to limit greenhouse gas emissions based on fuel sales. The introduction of the Energy Efficiency Design Index (EEDI) in 2013 is having a positive effect. More than 2,700 new ocean-going ships have been certified and the standards are becoming more stringent every five years. This does not trigger any absolute reduction of the total emissions from international shipping but improves the technology that ships use.

Another area of work of the IMO relates to fuel and its sulphur content, under Annex VI of the MARPOL Convention.[97] While these measures are taken to improve air quality, the consequential increase in fuel prices does create an increased incentive to use less fuel and consequently emit less CO_2.

The EU supports the IMO regarding technology transfer and capacity building and makes a substantial contribution through its funding of the Global MTTC Network (GMN).[98] The aim of this Network of Maritime Technologies Cooperation Centres (MTCCs) is to help beneficiary countries limit and reduce greenhouse gas emissions from their shipping sectors through technical assistance and capacity building. The pricing of maritime emissions through the EU ETS will help reduce emissions, and therefore, help reach the targets of the IMO's strategy to reduce greenhouse gas emissions from international shipping.

Conclusion: The EU system of Monitoring, Reporting, and Verification of CO_2 emissions for large ships paved the way for the application of market-based measures. From 2024, the EU ETS starts to apply for maritime emissions covering 50% of emissions from voyages.

Conclusion

Carbon markets like the EU ETS have been developed in several other places in the world. The EU ETS, however, is still the largest market in operation in terms of traded volume and ambition. Globally, carbon markets have largely similar but sometimes also different features, which leads to interesting exchanges of experiences. Economists have made good theoretical arguments about linking these systems with one another, but *de facto* only a few experiences exist to date. The EU linked up with Switzerland, Norway, Iceland, and Liechtenstein,[99] and California linked with Quebec. A *de facto* link that existed for some time was the recognition of credits under the CDM created by the Kyoto Protocol. Weak governance and compliance structures, however, led several important players to become increasingly prudent and the EU decided to deliver its 2030 target only through domestic action. The implementation of the CBAM could help bring a new dynamic to other countries pricing carbon, as it recognises carbon prices effectively paid in the production of goods exported to the EU.

A most tangible part of the EU ETS is its gradual expansion to cope with emissions related to aviation and shipping. It is a huge challenge to stabilise and then reduce the emissions of these transport modes and so far, the results have been disappointing. The EU, therefore, has been steadfast in deploying its carbon market also to these activities, albeit on an incremental basis.

Intra-European aviation is now firmly anchored into the EU ETS with an ambitious target and a phasing out of free allowances. Emissions from other international flights are, up to December 2026, only contributing to climate action through ICAO's offset system known as CORSIA. However, ICAO failed to set meaningful emissions reduction targets, nor is it able to require high integrity offset credits with adjustments of State inventories. Emissions from aviation keep growing very fast globally, and the stark decline in activity and emissions due to the COVID pandemic turned out by 2023 to be only temporary. Aviation emissions continue to undermine the delivery of the goals of the Paris Agreement and more national and regional action is likely to be required, in parallel to the ICAO scheme which will continue only if major third countries also implement it by 2027.

For shipping, the EU established a detailed and transparent MRV system in 2015 and, as of 2024, the EU's fair share of shipping emissions will be gradually brought under the EU ETS. The IMO agreed on the long-term goal for shipping to be net zero by close to 2050, as well as on essential 2030 and 2040 milestones without which a far-off target lacks credibility.

Technology will undoubtedly play an important role in bringing down emissions. One of the recurring themes is that electricity has the potential to be a significant game-changer in all modes, for cars, rail, shipping, and aviation. That is good news, as power generation is on its path to full decarbonisation over the next decade. Equally, hydrogen (and derivatives, such as ammonia and green methanol) may find its way to ships and planes and these energy carriers can also be produced in a green and sustainable way. Through carbon pricing, the EU ETS Innovation Fund will play an important role for deploying these technologies. Together with a pronounced modal shift, these uses can deliver a critical contribution to the very urgently needed decarbonisation of transportation.

Notes

1 The authors are grateful for the valuable contributions by Julia Ziemann (European Commission) and Javier Esparrago (EEA).
2 Paragraph 137 of the accompanying COP Decision "also recognises the important role of providing incentives for emissions reduction activities, including tools such a domestic policies and carbon pricing".
3 The McCain-Lieberman bill for a comprehensive cap and trade system was first proposed in 2003. In 2009, the United States came close to having a similar system to the EU ETS, by the House of Representatives' passage of the Waxman-Markey bill. However, the companion bill in the Senate, the Kerry-Boxer bill (S. 1733), was not passed and near-term prospects for passage of Federal legislation that puts a price on greenhouse gas emissions now appear low. The Inflation Reduction Act adopted at federal level in 2022 is landmark climate legislation for the United States, but only puts a price on a limited set of methane emissions.
4 ICAP (2023) *Emissions Trading Worldwide: Status Report 2023.* Berlin: International Carbon Action Partnership. Available at: https://icapcarbonaction.com/system/files/document/ICAP%20Emissions%20Trading%20Worldwide%20 2023%20Status%20Report_0.pdf. More information on the state of play can be found at: https://icapcarbonaction.com/en/publications/emissions-trading-worldwide-2023-icap-status-reportAn updated interactive map (copyright ICAP) is available at: www.icapcarbonaction.com/ets-map.
5 Article 12(3-a), introduced to the EU ETS Directive by Regulation (EU) 2017/2392.
6 Han, G., Olsson, M., Hallding, K. and Lunsford, D. (2012) "China's carbon emission trading: An overview of current development". FORES, Bellmansgatan 10, SE-118 20 Stockholm. Available at: http://www.sei-international.org/mediamanager/documents/Publications/china-cluster/SEI-FORES-2012-China-Carbon-Emissions.pdf.
7 ICAP (2015) *Emissions Trading Worldwide: ICAP Status Report 2015.* Available at: https://icapcarbonaction.com/images/StatusReport2015/ICAP_Report_2015_02_ 10_online_version.pdf.
8 Article 25.
9 See https://www.eui.eu/events?id=545488.
10 See, for example: Bruyninckx, H., Qi, Y., Nguyen, Q.T., and Belis, D. (Eds.) (2014) *The Governance of Climate Relations between Europe and Asia: Evidence from China and Vietnam as Key Emerging Economies.* New York: Claeys & Casteels.
11 See, for example, Wettestad, J. and Jevnaker, T. "Rescuing EU emissions trading: The climate policy flagship". Available at: https://webgate.ec.europa.eu/ilp/pages/saml-request.jsf.
12 Although it is important to keep in mind that the EU's funding of these emissions reductions outside Europe led to a corresponding increase in emissions within the EU, this feature has been frequently misunderstood. The invalidation of 2.55

billion allowances in 2023 exceeds the entire amount of 1.6 billion international credits that came into the EU ETS.

13 See Section 4.1.3 of the 2018 Carbon Market Report COM(2018) 842 final. Available at: https://ec.europa.eu/clima/sites/clima/files/ets/docs/com_2018_842_final_en.pdf.

14 The study on additionality is available at: https://ec.europa.eu/clima/sites/clima/files/ets/docs/clean_dev_mechanism_en.pdf.

15 The initial conditions excluded forestry credits, see Directive 2004/101/EC for more details. In 2008, it was decided that the only new CDM projects for which the EU ETS should provide demand post-2013 should be those established in Least Developed Countries, see Directive 2009/29/EC.

16 Commission Regulation (EU) No 550/2011 of 7 June 2011 on determining, pursuant to Directive 2003/87/EC of the European Parliament and of the Council, certain restrictions applicable to the use of international credits from projects involving industrial gases; OJ L 149, 8.6.2011, pp. 1–3. Available at: http://eur-lex.europa.eu/legal-content/EN/TXT/PDF/?uri=CELEX:32011R0550&from=EN.

17 See Article 58(2) of Commission Regulation (EU) No 389/2013 of 2 May 2013 establishing a Union Registry pursuant to Directive 2003/87/EC of the European Parliament and of the Council, Decisions No 280/2004/EC and No 406/2009/EC of the European Parliament and of the Council. Available at: https://eur-lex.europa.eu/legal-content/EN/TXT/?uri=CELEX:32013R0389.

18 IPCC (2022) *Climate Change 2022 Mitigation of Climate Change*. Ch. 14, p. 1506. Available at: https://www.ipcc.ch/report/ar6/wg3/downloads/report/IPCC_AR6_WGIII_FullReport.pdf.

19 The average amounts *per capita* are: US 246 litres, EU 101 litres, China 8 litres, India 6 litres, World average 26 litres. Figure based on fuel sales per country data from US Energy Information Administration and Population based on World Development Indicators, November 2018.

20 UNEP has welcomed the EU taking responsibility for aviation emissions in its NDC, in its Emissions Gap Report 2022 'The Closing Window'. See Table 3.4, Details on net-zero targets of G20 members, in the UNEP Emissions Gap Report 2022 'The Closing Window'.

21 Council of the EU (2023) Paris Agreement: Council submits updated NDC on behalf of EU and member states https://www.consilium.europa.eu/en/press/press-releases/2023/10/16/paris-agreement-council-submits-updated-ndc-on-behalf-of-eu-and-member-states/

22 The economy-wide reduction in the earlier NDCs include "*emissions from outgoing flights that start in the EU*".

23 Cited in the 2023 ETS revision, in recital 20 of Directive (EU) 2023/959.

24 Statement by the ICAO at the Glasgow UNFCCC COP. Available at: https://www.icao.int/environmental-protection/Documents/SBSTA2021_ICAO%20statement_Final.pdf.

25 See table 3.4, Details on net-zero targets of G20 members, in the UNEP Emissions Gap Report 2022 'The closing window'.

26 See, for example "UN chief warns against 'sleepwalking to climate catastrophe'". *UN News*. Available at: https://news.un.org/en/story/2022/03/1114322.

27 The most detailed analysis in this area dates from 2012, which notes 'that airlines "believe they can control the political agenda through their ministries of transport" – as one observer who formerly worked for the industry described it"'. Available at: http://web.archive.org/web/20210714082512/https://www.innovations.harvard.edu/sites/default/files/2345329.pdf.

28 See, for example, the IMF Report on Regulatory Capture in Banking. Available at: https://www.imf.org/en/Publications/WP/Issues/2016/12/31/Regulatory-Capture-in-Banking-18798.

29 Decision No 1600/2002/EC of the European Parliament and of the Council of 22 July 2002 laying down the Sixth Community Environment Action Programme (OJ L 242, 10.9.2002).

30 Annex 1 to the UNFCCC.

31 https://www.aviation24.be/airlines/eurocontrol-data-snapshot-half-of-co2-emissions-come-from-just-6-of-flights-the-long-haul-ones/.

32 See Decision (EU) 2023/136 of the European Parliament and of the Council of 18 January 2023 amending Directive 2003/87/EC as regards the notification of offsetting in respect of a global market-based measure for aircraft operators based in the Union.

33 See recital 104 of Directive (EU) 2023/959, together with Article 1(4a) of Decision (EU) 2015/1814.

34 REPORT FROM THE COMMISSION TO THE EUROPEAN PARLIAMENT AND THE COUNCIL on the Functioning of the European carbon market in 2021 pursuant to Articles 10(5) and 21(2) of Directive 2003/87/EC (as amended by Directive 2009/29/EC and Directive (EU) 2018/410), (2022), Table 6. Available at: https://eur-lex.europa.eu/legal-content/EN/TXT/?uri=CELEX:52022DC0516&qid=1704967050609; REPORT FROM THE COMMISSION TO THE EUROPEAN PARLIAMENT AND THE COUNCIL on the functioning of the European carbon market in 2022 pursuant to Articles 10(5) and 21(2) of Directive 2003/87/EC, COM(2023)654 final (2023), Table 7. Available at: https://eur-lex.europa.eu/legal-content/EN/TXT/?uri=COM:2023:654:FIN.

35 See, for example, the 2021 reduction set out at LuftVStAbsenkV 2021 Luftverkehrsteuer-Absenkungsverordnung 2021 (buzer.de).

36 https://africaclimatesummit.org/.

37 "*The imposition of taxes on such fuels …would be a matter of great concern*" (Resolution A41-27). ICAO Resolutions are for sale at: https://store.icao.int/en/assembly-resolutions-in-force-as-of-7-october-2022-doc-10184.

38 See Article 430 of the EU-UK Trade and Cooperation Agreement, EUR-Lex – 22021A0430(01) – EN – EUR-Lex (europa.eu).

39 Directive 2003/96/EC of 27 October 2003.

40 Proposal for a Council Directive restructuring the Union framework for the taxation of energy products and electricity (recast), COM/2021/563.

41 See Article 28b(3) of Directive 2003/87/EC.

42 Recital 20 of Directive (EU) 2023/959 amending the EU ETS Directive.

43 The underlying ETS Directive applies to both departing flights and incoming flights from January 2027. However, there are delegated powers to exempt incoming flights which have been exercised twice (in respect of Switzerland and the United Kingdom).

44 Commission Decision C (2023)7164 of 27 October 2023, which consolidates the aviation-related addition to the overall EEA-wide ETS cap at the level of 28 866 578 allowances for 2024.

45 Article 10a(8) of Directive 2003/87/EC. Commission Delegated Regulation C(2023)6043 of 15 September 2023 broadened the scope of the ETS Innovation Fund accordingly, see recital 8 and Article 11.

46 See, for example. https://www.nytimes.com/2023/08/08/climate/curbing-contrails-a-climate-solution-in-the-skies.html.

47 Statement by the Commission, eur-lex.europa.eu/legal-content/EN/TXT/PDF/?uri=CONSIL:ST_8344_2023_ADD_1.

48 Article 14 of Directive 2003/87/EC, introduced by Directive (EU) 2023/958.

49 See, for example, the U.S's first ICAO Action Plan with its aspirational alternative fuel use target for 2020, where actual use was less than one-hundredth of this amount.

50 Article 3c(5) of Directive 2003/87/EC, introduced by Directive (EU) 2023/958.

51 See Commission Implementing Regulation (EU) 2023/2122 of 17 October 2023 amending Implementing Regulation (EU) 2018/2066 as regards updating the monitoring and reporting of greenhouse gas emissions pursuant to Directive 2003/87/EC of the European Parliament and of the Council, which implements this accounting approach for attributing zero-rated emissions under the EU ETS, as well as for the novel ETS support mechanism.

52 See Article 3c(6) of Directive 2003/87/EC, penultimate paragraph.

53 Regulation (EU) 2023/2405 of the European Parliament and of the Council of 18 October 2023 on ensuring a level playing field for sustainable air transport.

54 In the context of the Airport Carbon Accreditation initiative and of the UNFCCC, carbon neutrality means zero emissions. In the ICAO context, it meant the offsetting of emissions above a baseline of the level that international aviation emissions will be in the average of the years 2019 and 2020, although this baseline was subsequently weakened to 85% of 2019 emission levels.

55 See recital 32 of Directive (EU) 2023/958. A proposal to make it even weaker was not accepted, see Assembly Working Paper A41-WP/467, web archived at https://web.archive.org/web/20230809140123/https://www.icao.int/Meetings/a41/Documents/WP/wp_467_en.pdf (accessed 9 August 2023).

56 www.icao.int/Meetings/a39/Pages/resolutions.aspx.

57 In 2022, ICAO changed the baseline of the Corsia scheme to 85% of 2019 CO_2 emissions for the years from 2024 to 2035. This raises the baseline to 516 million tonnes from the previous baseline of 435 million tonnes (if all countries participated). Therefore, 80 million tonnes less offsetting per year would take place with full participation. See recital 32 of Directive (EU) 2023/958.

58 See https://www.icao.int/Meetings/a41/Pages/resolutions.aspx.

59 See paragraph 10 of ICAO Assembly Resolution 39-3. Available at: https://www.icao.int/environmental-protection/Documents/Resolution_A39_3.pdf.

60 See sections 1.3.2 and 1.3.3.

61 Article 25a(7) and (8) of Directive 2003/87/EC.

62 https://ec.europa.eu/clima/sites/clima/files/transport/aviation/docs/gmbm_legal_study_en.pdf.

63 Article 11a of the EU ETS Directive.

64 See Article 25a, paragraphs 8 and 9, of the EU ETS Directive.

65 China's public reservation to Corsia states, *inter alia*, that "This is not conducive to maintaining the credibility of ICAO and the unity among member States, nor to ensuring the effective fulfilment of the mandate of the ICAO Assembly and the Council on matters of international aviation and climate change". See https://www.icao.int/Meetings/a41/Pages/resolutions.aspx.

66 See https://www.federalregister.gov/documents/2023/01/25/2023-01405/agency-information-collection-activities-requests-for-comments-clearance-of-renewed-approval-of?utm_source=CP+Daily&utm_campaign=cb602425be-CPdaily250120 23&utm_medium=email&utm_term=0_a9d8834f72-cb602425be-110244593.

67 See http://www.eea.europa.eu/data-and-maps/data/data-viewers/greenhouse-gases-viewer. It should be noted that 'domestic' emissions are considered for the purposes of UNFCCC reporting to be emissions internal to each Member State, as no decision on the allocation of other emissions has yet taken place.

68 https://www.oecd.org/ocean/topics/ocean-shipping/.

69 See, for example, the analysis of market barriers to cost effective maritime emission reductions at https://ec.europa.eu/clima/sites/clima/files/transport/shipping/docs/market_barriers_2012_en.pdf.

70 2013 Commission Communication on Integrating maritime transport emissions in the EU's greenhouse gas reduction policies (COM (2013)479).

71 Regulation (EU) 2015/757 of the European Parliament and of the Council of 29 April 2015 on the monitoring, reporting and verification of carbon dioxide emissions from maritime transport (OJ L 123, 19.5.2015).

72 Applicable since 1 January 2018 for vessels larger than 5,000 gross tonnage calling at any EU and Norwegian and Icelandic port.

73 Resolution MEPC 278(70).

74 European Environmental Agency (2023) "EEA greenhouse gas projections – data viewer". Available at: https://www.eea.europa.eu/data-and-maps/data/data-viewers/eea-greenhouse-gas-projections-data-viewer.

75 See recital 20 of Directive (EU) 2023/959 for a fuller explanation.

76 https://icapcarbonaction.com/en/news/shanghai-ets-expands-cover-shipping.

77 Article 12(3(-e to -a) of Directive 2003/87/EC as amended by Directive (EU) 2023/959.

78 See Commission Implementing Decision (EU) 2023/2895 of 19 December 2023 laying down the list of islands and ports referred to in Article 12(3-d) of Directive 2003/87/EC of the European Parliament and of the Council and the list of transnational public service contracts or transnational public service obligations referred to in Article 12(3-c) of that Directive.

79 See Commission Implementing Decision (EU) 2023/2895 of 19 December 2023.

80 See recital 20 of Directive (EU) 2023/959, last paragraph, for a fuller explanation.

81 Commission Delegated Regulation (EU) 2023/2776 of 12 October 2023 amending Regulation (EU) 2015/757 of the European Parliament and of the Council as regards the rules for monitoring greenhouse gas emissions and other relevant information from maritime transport.

82 Article 3gb of Directive 2003/87/EC.

83 Commission Decision C (2023)4950 on the Union-wide quantity of allowances to be issued under the EU Emissions Trading System for 2024, adopted on 27 July 2023.

84 Article 10(3) of Directive 2003/87/EC.

85 Article 3 ga(3), second paragraph, of Directive 2003/87/EC.

86 Regulation (EU) 2023/957 of the European Parliament and of the Council of 10 May 2023 amending Regulation (EU) 2015/757 to provide for the inclusion of maritime transport activities in the EU Emissions Trading System and for the monitoring, reporting and verification of emissions of additional greenhouse gases and emissions from additional ship types (OLJ L 130, 16.5.2023).

87 See recital 32, and Article 3gc.

88 See Commission Implementing Regulation (EU) 2023/2599 of 22 November 2023 laying down rules for the application of Directive 2003/87/EC of the European Parliament and of the Council as regards the administration of shipping companies by administering authorities in respect of a shipping company.

89 Article 3gg of Directive 2003/87/EC.

90 Article 3(b) of Regulation (EU) 2015/757.

91 Commission Implementing Regulation (EU) 2023/2297 of 26.10.2023 identifying neighbouring container transhipment ports pursuant to Directive 2003/87/EC of the European Parliament and of the Council.

92 Article 10 a (8), thirteenth sub-paragraph of Directive 2003/87/EC.

93 Regulation (EU) 2023/1805 of the European Parliament and of the Council of 13 September 2023 on the use of renewable and low-carbon fuels in maritime transport, and amending Directive 2009/16/EC.

94 See Article 5 of Regulation (EU) 2023/1805.

95 http://www.imo.org/en/KnowledgeCentre/IndexofIMOResolutions/Marine-Environment-Protection-Committee-%28MEPC%29/Documents/MEPC.304%2872%29.pdf.

96 https://www.imo.org/en/MediaCentre/PressBriefings/pages/Revised-GHG-reduction-strategy-for-global-shipping-adopted-.aspx.
97 International Convention for the Prevention of Pollution from Ships (MARPOL) of 1973.
98 Project funded by the European Union (2016–2019) entitled "Capacity Building for Climate Mitigation in the Maritime Shipping Industry" amounting to €10 million of funding over four-year period.
99 See Decisions of EEA Joint Committee No 334/2023 and No 335/2023 of 8 December 2023, amending Annex XX (Environment) to the EEA Agreement in respect of the 2023 ETS revisions.

PART 3

Climate Action by Member States and Economic Sectors

6

THE EFFORT SHARING REGULATION

Cecile Hanoune[1]

Introduction

Reaching the climate objectives at the lowest cost possible has been important for European businesses as well as for consumers. In addition to cost-effectiveness comes fairness, which has many dimensions. The EU accepts its global responsibility to reduce greenhouse gas emissions at a faster pace than other countries. Furthermore, there is the issue of a fair distribution of effort between the EU's Member States. Political decisions on the EU's climate ambition have always been agreed unanimously and consensus is sought for the individual greenhouse gas emission reduction targets of each Member State, which are adopted under the ordinary legislative procedure with qualified majority. This requires great attention to the political, economic, and industrial differences between Member States and the distributive impacts of the EU's overall climate policy.

This chapter looks more closely at the details of the differentiation of effort between Member States, more specifically in the sectors of the economy initially not covered by the EU ETS. It is of utmost importance that Member States put in place policies to deliver on their part of the overall 55% target. An integrated energy and climate governance system monitors such progress based on plans they are submitting to the EU. Through an equitable sharing of effort and a pro-active follow-up of the policies undertaken by its Member States, the EU has been able to demonstrate leadership on how to tackle global climate change.

6.1 Emissions from the Effort Sharing Sectors

While the EU ETS regulates the greenhouse gas emissions from fixed installations and European aviation, the Effort-Sharing Decision[2] and its successor, the Effort Sharing Regulation[3] regulate emissions of the sectors outside the scope of the EU ETS. These emissions currently cover more than 60% of the EU's greenhouse gas emissions. They typically come from a set of

DOI: 10.4324/9781003493730-9

diffuse sources such as from road vehicles, the heating of private households and business premises, small- and medium-sized industry, agriculture, waste management facilities, and products containing fluorinated gases (which are often powerful greenhouse gases). Their diffuse nature makes them less suitable to be readily incorporated into the EU ETS as it was initially designed (Figure 6.1).

Road transport is the largest source of these, representing more than a third of the emissions in the Effort Sharing sectors, followed by the heating of buildings and agriculture. The Effort Sharing sectors reduced their emissions more slowly than the EU ETS sectors. After the fall in 2020 emissions due to the COVID-19 pandemic, emissions in the Effort Sharing sectors rebounded in 2021. The increase was most pronounced for transport. The agriculture sector saw a slight decrease in emissions in 2021 compared to 2020 but overall, the decrease has been less than 3% compared to 2005.

Most of the policies applicable to the Effort Sharing sectors, such as on road vehicles, buildings, and agriculture are determined by the Member States, such as national taxation policies, urban planning, transport, and mobility

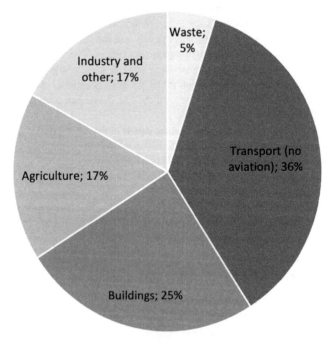

FIGURE 6.1   Main greenhouse gas emitting Effort Sharing sectors in 2021

Source: EEA (2023)[4]

policies, as well as the granting of environmental permits. Crucial for success in reducing greenhouse gas emissions is ensuring the coherence of policies at the respective levels of public intervention, from the European to the national or local level. If all pull together in the same direction, impressive results can be achieved. If there are inconsistencies, on the other hand, such as where company taxation provisions favour cars and create disincentives to use public transport, the combination of policies will be much less efficient. Mobilising policy levers at the right level of governance in a way consistent between different levels of governance are key to effectively reduce emissions.

In addition to the EU-level commitment, all EU Member States individually are members of the UN Framework Convention on Climate Change, the Kyoto Protocol, and the Paris Agreement. It is for the Member States to act themselves and to ensure the consistency of actions at different levels of governance. The European Union, for its part, endeavours to concentrate its efforts and regulate on those areas where there is a clear added value. An important example in Effort Sharing sectors in this respect is vehicle efficiency legislation: not all Member States manufacture cars, yet cars are widely sold and used across the EU. Therefore, there is strong logic for the EU to regulate the emissions performance of cars, whereas the promotion of public transport or of cycling in urban areas, for example, is more coherently managed at local level.

A major novelty of the 2023 revision of the EU ETS is the creation of a separate adjacent emission trading system at EU level covering road transport and heating fuels. The new system covers a little more than 50% of Effort Sharing emissions and is expected to contribute around 50% of the additional emission reductions required in the coming decade in the Effort Sharing sectors. The combination of a trading system applicable to economic operators and binding targets for Member States is likely to reduce the impact of carbon pricing on individual consumers. In the sectors covered by the new trading system, the emission reductions delivered by the private sector may not necessarily meet the Effort Sharing targets, which are differentiated based on fairness considerations. Member States would then have to take further action in these sectors or will have to acquire annual emission allocations (AEAs).

> Conclusion: Climate policies in the field of transport, buildings, and agriculture are primarily undertaken at the level of each Member State. Reductions in emissions are being pro-actively monitored through an energy and climate governance system. The new ETS for transport and heating fuels will support further reductions in these sectors.

6.2   Effort Sharing 2013–2020

In view of a coherent policy framework at European level, Member States adopted in 2002 a so-called "Burden Sharing Agreement"[5] for the period 2008–2012. It shared out their joint commitment taken under the Kyoto Protocol, covering all emissions of the economy. Furthermore, these "Burden Sharing" targets for Member States could also be met through offset credits from the Clean Development Mechanism.[6] However, in view of the creation of the EU ETS and its uniform carbon price applicable across a large share of the emissions of each Member State, it was not straightforward to continue this method of sharing national targets for all emissions, including those of the EU ETS, beyond the first commitment period of the Kyoto Protocol.

6.2.1   Setting Differentiated Targets

That is why in 2008 the Commission proposed the EU's "Effort Sharing Decision",[7] which "extracted" the EU ETS from targets set for Member States, leaving the differentiated national targets only covering the Effort Sharing sectors for the period 2013–2020. The 2020 targets were expressed as a percentage change compared to 2005.[8]

The concern to ensure fairness was at the heart of the 2020 target-setting exercise. Member States with high income levels, expressed through their relative ranking above the EU average in GDP *per capita* terms in 2005,[9] were required to reduce emissions compared to 2005 by a maximum of 20%. Conversely, Member States with lower *per capita* GDP were allowed to reduce emissions by less than the EU average, i.e., almost 10% below 2005 levels. Thirteen Member States were allowed to increase their emissions by 2020 compared to 2005, up to a maximum of 20%. That maximum applied for Bulgaria, which had, and still has, the lowest *per capita* income of any EU Member State. Figure 6.2 offers an overview of the distribution of the 2020 non-ETS Member States' targets.

6.2.2   Developing More Elements of Redistribution

Differentiation allowed the comparatively lower income Member States to increase emissions in sectors where consumption levels and associated emission levels were typically still well below EU average, such as in transport. Overall, the 2020 climate and energy package had several of these re-distributional elements included. Not only were the Effort Sharing greenhouse gas reduction targets differentiated by considering different income levels, but so were the 2020 renewable energy targets for each Member State.

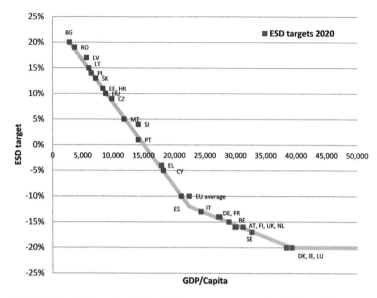

FIGURE 6.2   2020 national effort sharing targets compared to 2005 resulting from the methodology in relation to 2005 GDP *per capita*

Source: European Commission (2016)[10]

The lower income Member States, which typically had a more carbon inefficient industrial structure, were covered by the EU ETS that effectively harmonised effort for all participants irrespective of where they were located. For example, a steel plant in a lower income Member State was subject to the same free allocation rules and stringency, as well as the same carbon price, as its counterparts in higher income Member States. Although the EU ETS created a level-playing field for all industries, there was a provision made for the re-distribution of auctioning revenues towards lower income Member States, allowing them to compensate for the costs of modernising of their economies.

These re-distributional elements were a strong requirement for several Member States to be able to accept the overall architecture of 2020 climate and energy targets. The Impact Assessment accompanying the 2020 climate and energy proposals[11] indicated clearly that a target setting exercise within the EU based on cost-efficiency only would have, in relative terms, higher cost impacts on lower income Member States than higher income ones. By applying the re-distributional elements of target differentiation and auctioning revenue re-distribution, cost impacts were projected to be distributed much more equally between Member States as a share of GDP *per capita*, as is shown in Figure 6.3.

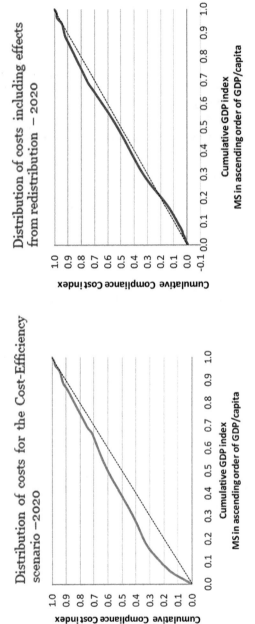

FIGURE 6.3   Distribution of costs of the 2020 climate and energy package, comparing impacts of cost efficient distribution of non-ETS and renewable energy target with re-distributed targets and auctioning revenue based on relative income levels

Source: Capros et al. (2008)[12]

6.2.3 Experience to Date

Since 2013, EU-wide emissions in the Effort Sharing sectors have been below the annual limit and in 2020, they were more than 16% below 2005 levels, thereby overachieving their 2020 target of −10% compared to 2005 levels. However, emissions went as low as −14% in 2014 due to the economic recession but rebounded afterwards and saw a profound fall in 2020 due to the pandemic.

This underlines that solid implementation of existing policies remains of the greatest importance. Transport is a good example. Legislation at the EU level, notably those related to CO_2 standards for passenger cars, improves the efficiency of the car fleet over time. However, Member States have a critical task to complement these efforts with other policies, such as fuel and road pricing policies to manage transport demand. Similarly restructuring of the Common Agricultural Policy, such as tackling the over-production of certain agriculture produce and productivity gains, have led to reductions in greenhouse gas emissions. Nevertheless, further focused mitigation actions will be needed in the context of Member States' strategic plans under the Common Agriculture Policy. Finally, EU measures in the context of the Energy Performance for Buildings Directive[13] and Eco-design measures[14] have significantly improved the insulation of new buildings and the efficiency of newly installed boilers. With the relatively low replacement rates of the building stock, however, Member States still have a strong role to play in incentivising energy efficiency improvements and reductions in greenhouse gas emissions for existing buildings.

Ex post evaluation of climate policies indicates that the strongest drivers for emission reductions have been innovation in low-carbon technologies, such as renewable energy, as well as raising productivity and efficiency in the economy. Structural change between economic sectors, such as away from manufacturing towards services, has so far had only a marginal effect on reductions of greenhouse gas emissions across the EU.[15]

6.2.4 Flexible Provisions

While the EU is in overall compliance with its 2020 targets, all individual Member States complied with their obligations under the Effort Sharing Decision. However, several Member States with relatively deep reduction targets had shortfalls for achieving their targets domestically by 2020 (Figure 6.4).

The Effort Sharing Decision recognises that it may be difficult for all Member States to achieve their targets domestically every single year, due to the inherent variability of emissions, for instance related to weather conditions. Therefore, some flexibilities are allowed. There is flexibility within

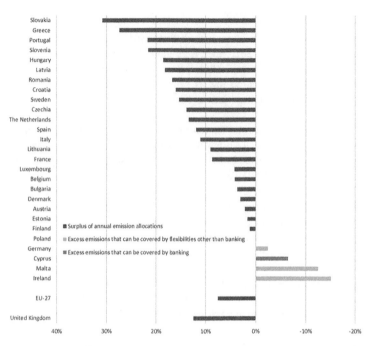

FIGURE 6.4   Difference between Member States' 2020 target under the Effort Sharing Decision and emissions in the Effort Sharing sectors in 2020 (in % of 2005 base year emissions). Positive and negative values, respectively, indicate over-delivery and shortfall

Source: European Commission (2022)[16]

the period, notably the possibility of "banking" over-compliance in one year to the next and limited "borrowing" from the emission allocations of future years, both within the period until 2020.

In case these "banking" and "borrowing" flexibilities are not sufficient, "trade" is also allowed, whereby a Member State in shortage can buy part of the over-delivery of another one. This trade is also potentially an incentive to invest in over-achieving targets in Member States where reductions can be achieved at lower costs.

For the period 2013–2020, however, this incentive has not been significant as the EU overall delivered its target. In 2020, four Member States had emissions above their target. Cyprus used a saved surplus from previous years (banking); Malta and Germany covered their excess emissions by buying emission allocations from other Member States; Ireland also partially did so and partially used international credits from the Clean Development Mechanism.

Conclusion: The 2020 EU target was delivered. Fairness was primarily achieved through the differentiation of targets for Member States based on GDP *per capita* and on the partial redistribution of auctioning revenues under the EU ETS. Flexible arrangements facilitated compliance by individual Member States.

6.3 Differentiation and Flexibilities Allowed for 2021–2030

The basic strategy developed for the period prior to 2020 was replicated for 2030. A separate target of a 30%[17] reduction for the Effort Sharing sectors was agreed for 2030 compared to 2005, while allowing differentiation among Member States. The contribution of the Effort Sharing sectors was later increased to −40% compared to 2005 in view of being consistent with the reinforced overall target included in the Climate Law. This share was determined based on projections of cost-efficient emission reductions, where some sectors such as buildings show a similar level of mitigation potential as the power and industry sectors driven by increased energy efficiency and stepping up of fuel switching, while in contrast, transport shows a smaller reduction potential.

6.3.1 Continuation of the Differentiated Target Approach

The methodology of defining an Effort Sharing target for each Member State based on its GDP *per capita* as followed for 2020 was continued. For 2030, the target range was initially defined between 0 and −40% compared to 2005 emission levels. A similar range was kept when the Effort Sharing target was increased to −40%, in such a way that the least wealthy Member State has to reduce its emissions by 10% by 2030, while the wealthiest ones have to reduce theirs by 50%, compared to 2005. The initial target setting for 2030 required an update of the 2005 GDP *per capita* data as some Member States suffered significantly during the economic recession that started from 2008. Therefore, GDP *per capita* data from 2013 were used and this resulted in a differentiation as represented in the orange dots in Figure 6.5.

For some Member States, this clearly shows the impact of the economic downturn. For instance, using 2005 GDP *per capita*, Spain was very close to the EU average GDP *per capita*, resulting in a target like the overall EU

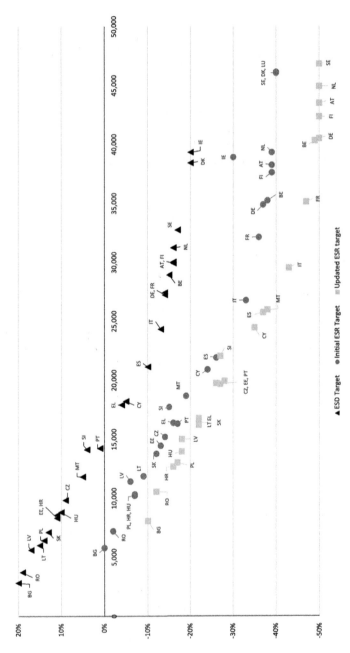

FIGURE 6.5 Comparison between 2020 targets and 2030 targets applying updated methodology

Source: European Commission[18]

ambition level for 2020. However, when setting the initial 2030 targets using 2013 GDP *per capita*, the impact of the economic recession resulted in Spain having a GDP *per capita* below the EU average. This, therefore, resulted in a lower 2030 target for Spain compared to the EU's overall ambition level for 2030. A contrasting example is Germany, which for 2020 received a target equal to France, but which, based on 2013 GDP *per capita*, received a target 1% more ambitious than France for 2030, underlining the stronger economic performance of Germany compared to France over the period 2005–2013. When determining the increased 2030 targets updated GDP data (2017–2019 average) was used and this brought about some more changes, as represented in the grey dots in Figure 6.5.

6.3.2 More Differentiation among Member States

As it was recognised that some Member States within the higher income group had a bigger challenge than others to achieve a target based on a GDP *per capita* basis, more differentiation was applied without changing the target of this group. Different scenarios were constructed comparing projections of potential emission reductions under "cost-efficient and with existing policies" situations with the proposed targets based on GDP *per capita*.

Higher income Member States could be grouped in different categories based on the size of the gap of what they were likely to achieve cost-effectively and with existing policies, and targets were, therefore, adjusted. In the initial Effort Sharing Regulation, the targets were reduced for Ireland and Luxembourg by 9 percentage points and for Austria, Denmark, Belgium, and the Netherlands, by a much smaller amount of 3 percentage points. For Sweden and Finland, no target adjustment was made, while for the UK, Germany, and France the target was increased by 1 percentage point.

During the 2023 revision of the Effort Sharing Regulation, following a similar approach, the targets were reduced by 9 percentage points for Ireland, and by 3 percentage points for Austria and Denmark. Those for France, Luxembourg, and Sweden were increased by 0.5 percentage point and those for Belgium, Finland, Germany, and the Netherlands were left unchanged. Figure 6.6 shows the results for the high-income Member States. A positive number indicates that cost-effective, current policy baseline projections show a gap between emissions and the proposed targets, while negative numbers indicate that there would be an over-achievement of the respective target by 2030.

In the 2023 revision of the ESR, a similar gap was witnessed for some lower income Member States and, therefore, the following adjustments were made: the target for Malta target was reduced by 19 percentage points, for Estonia and Cyprus by 3 and for Lithuania and Latvia by 1 percentage point.

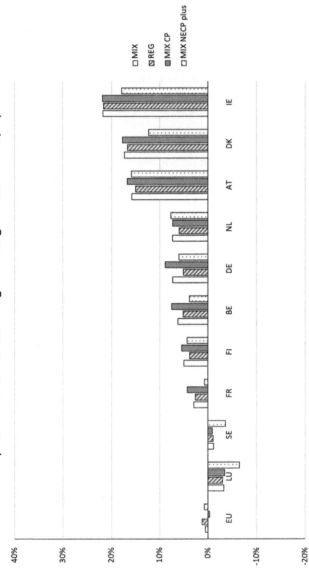

FIGURE 6.6 Gap between GDP-based 2030 targets and cost-efficient emission reductions for high income Member States (as a % of 2005 emissions)

Source: European Commission

Due to the size of the adjustments and the countries, those adjustments did not have any impact on the overall environment integrity at EU level.

6.3.3 Towards More Convergence among Member States by 2030

While the 2030 target increased overall with the 2023 revision by 11%, several Member States would have seen an even higher increase in their individual targets with the application of the initial methodology and the update of GDP data. It was, therefore, decided to limit the maximum target increase to 12%. This impacted five Member States which required an increase of 0.7% in the target of nine other Member States in view of maintaining the overall ambition level. Such a target setting approach resulted in improved convergence of Member States' targets.

The finally adopted targets were based on the differentiation elements developed in the previous section. They resulted in a balanced outcome and considered the differences in capacity to act between the diverse EU Member States (Table 6.1).

Crucial to note is that analysis shows the negotiated outcome of the ESR leads to a stronger convergence between the levels of allowed *per capita* emissions by 2030 compared to 2020. By 2030, 21 Member States are projected to have an allocated emissions level *per capita* within a range of 1 tonne above or below the EU average (see lower part in Figure 6.7). The negotiated outcome on the ESR delivered not only a political agreement but also fairness over time by opening a path towards significant convergence in *per capita* emissions within the EU.

TABLE 6.1 2030 targets compared to 2005 emission levels for ESR sectors *per Member State*

	Initial target	Updated target		Initial target	Updated target		Initial target	Updated target
DK	−39%	−50%	IT	−33%	−43.7%	SK	−12%	−22.7%
DE	−38%	−50%	IE	−30%	−42%	LT	−9%	−21%
LU	−40%	−50%	ES	−26%	−37.7%	MT	−19%	−19%
FI	−39%	−50%	CY	−24%	−32%	HU	−7%	−18.7%
SE	−40%	−50%	PT	−17%	−28.7%	PL	−7%	−17.7%
NL	−36%	−48%	SI	−15%	−27%	LV	−6%	−17%
AT	−36%	−48%	CZ	−14%	−26%	HR	−7%	−16.7%
FR	−37%	−47.5%	EE	−13%	−24%	RO	−2%	−12.7%
BE	−35%	−47%	EL	−16%	−22.7%	BG	0%	−10%

Source: EU Regulation (2018)[19]

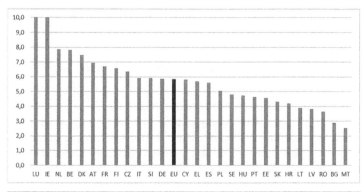

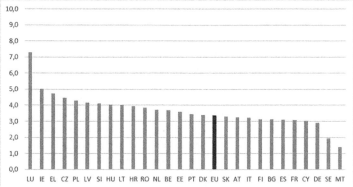

FIGURE 6.7   *Per capita* emissions in the Effort Sharing sectors in 2005 and projected *per capita* allowed emissions in the Effort Sharing sectors by 2030

Source: European Commission[20]

6.3.4   Starting Point and Trajectories

Based on the above methodology, specific emissions reductions are set for every year, expressed as Annual Emissions Allocations,[21] starting in the year 2021. The starting level is expressed in tonnes of CO_2-equivalent which is the average of 2016, 2017, and 2018 emissions in the Effort Sharing sectors, these being the most recent emissions known in the year 2020 when the absolute amounts of Annual Emissions Allocations were determined. It was decided that the precise starting point of the trajectory over time would be between 2019 and 2020.[22]

This starting point was a difficult compromise between two positions as represented in a stylised fashion in Figure 6.8.

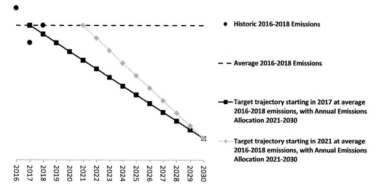

● Historic 2016-2018 Emissions

– – Average 2016-2018 Emissions

─■─ Target trajectory starting in 2017 at average 2016-2018 emissions, with Annual Emissions Allocation 2021-2030

─♦─ Target trajectory starting in 2021 at average 2016-2018 emissions, with Annual Emissions Allocation 2021-2030

FIGURE 6.8 Stylised representation of possible extreme options to set the starting point in 2021 for the Annual Emissions Allocation and the subsequent linear target trajectory to the 2030 target.

Source: Delbeke and Vis (2019)[23]

One school argued that as climate policies take time to have their full effect, emissions will continue to decrease below their average level in the years 2016–2018. If the starting point is set in 2020 at the average of 2016–2018 emission levels as represented by the red line, then one would expect targets in the early years of the decades to be overachieved. Member States would then be allowed to build up surpluses that would reduce the incentive to take further action to effectively achieve their 2030 target. Indeed, through the banking of Annual Emissions Allocations, they could deviate from their target later in the period 2021–2030. Therefore, it was proposed to start the target trajectory earlier, for instance, in 2017 as represented by the green line in the figure below. This would guarantee a gradual reduction of emissions and reduce the risk for a build-up of surpluses early in the period 2021–2030.

However, others pointed out that this approach would be flawed if, for some reason, emissions increased or did not decrease sufficiently over the period 2017–2021. In such a case, the non-ETS sectors would immediately start the period with a deficit in 2021, even in situations where the Member State was fully in-line with its targets for the period up to 2020.

Although this would not normally be expected to happen to the EU as a whole –though note that emissions did rebound in 2015, 2016, and 2017 – this situation could arise for some Member States individually and confront them with a circumstance whereby they would need to acquire surplus Annual Emissions Allocations early in the period from other Member States. However, these other Member States may either not have been able to build up any surpluses or may not feel confident enough to sell any surpluses already.

This school argued that this formulation of the starting point would put unreasonable pressure on the system.

Under the initial Effort Sharing Regulation, Annual Emissions Allocations in the period between 2021 and 2030 were defined, by a linear interpolation, on a straight line between the starting point and the 2030 end point.

During the 2023 revision of the Effort Sharing Regulation, an approach had to be found to reflect the increased ambition in the annual limits, as shown in Figure 6.9. As the negotiations took place during 2021 and 2022, the Annual Emission Allocations for these years were left unchanged. The Annual Emissions Allocations for the years 2023, 2024, and 2025 were defined, by a linear interpolation, on a straight line between the 2022 Annual Emission Allocations and the increased 2030 target (see the dark blue line in the same Figure). It was decided to define the Annual Emission Allocations for the years 2026, 2027, 2028, and 2029 in 2025, as the trajectory following the evolution of emissions after the COVID crisis was unknown at the time of the agreement. The starting level denominated in number of tonnes of CO_2-equivalent will be the average of emissions of 2021, 2022, and 2023 emissions. Again, different views were expressed regarding the starting point, which de facto defines the stringency of the emission budget available for each Member State.[24]

6.3.5   Flexibility with the Emissions Trading System

For higher income Member States, some flexibility related to the EU ETS has been introduced. They would transfer a limited number of EUA's from the EU ETS,[25] which they would normally auction, into the Effort Sharing sectors and swap for Annual Emission Allocations. As such, the Member States concerned would see their auctioning revenue decrease. The total amount of this flexibility was limited to 100 million allowances over the period of ten years, which equates to the equivalent of less than 0.5% of the expected initial Annual Emissions Allocations in the Effort Sharing sectors over the period 2021–2030.

The initial distribution of access to this flexibility provision within the group of higher income Member States followed the same reasoning as the adjustments of targets within this group. Ireland and Luxembourg, countries with the biggest projected gap with their targets, were allowed the highest extent of access to this flexibility, equivalent to 4% of 2005 emissions *per annum*.[26] The UK, Germany, and France had no gap in the projections, or a limited one, and got no access to this flexibility. All other higher income Member States (Netherlands, Belgium, Austria, Denmark, Finland, Sweden) got access equivalent to 2% of 2005 emissions *per annum*.

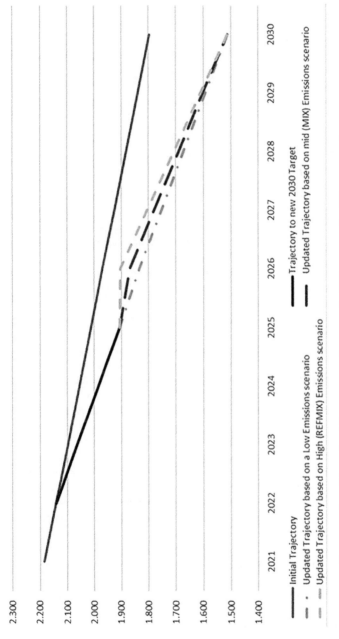

FIGURE 6.9   Representation of the updated linear target trajectory to the 2030 target under different scenarios

Source: European Commission

Malta is the only lower income Member State that can use this flexibility, at a rate of 2% of 2005 emissions *per annum*. The reason is that Malta is the Member State with the lowest *per capita* emissions in the Effort Sharing sectors and this would result in emissions of below 2 tonnes per person in 2030. Together with the fact that it is the most densely populated Member State, Malta sees its mitigation target as potentially challenging. This rate was increased to 7% in the 2023 revision given the structure of Malta's economy, and the projected gap between its target and cost-effective reduction potential.

6.3.6 Flexibility to Land Use Change and Forestry Sectors

The second innovative flexibility establishes a link between the Effort Sharing sectors and the specific sectors covered by the Regulation on the inclusion of greenhouse gas emissions and removals from land use, land use change, and forestry (LULUCF) in the 2030 climate and energy framework.[27] The LULUCF Regulation provides that from 2021 to 2025 Member States should ensure the absorptions and removals of emissions in the LULUCF sectors are not deteriorating, while a net removal target of 310 million tonnes CO_2 eq. was set for 2030. Overall, it is expected that these sectors will absorb carbon, reducing atmospheric concentrations. If Member States perform better than expected this gives rise to the generation of LULUCF "credits", for instance, due to the planting of new forests (afforestation) or due to the adaption of agriculture practices that improve the carbon retention of soil.

The legislation for 2021–2030 allows for flexibility between the LULUCF and ESR for a maximum number of credits set at 280 million tonnes CO_2 eq.[28] for the EU over the ten-year period 2021–2030, or on average 28 million per year. This will ensure that there is still need for strong reductions in the Effort Sharing sectors. All Member States have access to this flexibility, but they are grouped into three categories according to their size of agriculture emissions. Member States with a historic share of agriculture emissions in the non-ETS sectors of more than 25% have potential access to LULUCF credits equivalent to 15% of historic agriculture emissions. Only four countries qualify for this degree of access: Ireland, Lithuania, Denmark, and Latvia. Member States with the lowest share of agriculture emissions (below 15%) in the Effort Sharing sectors only have potential access to the equivalent of 3.75% of their agriculture emissions,[29] and the middle category to 7.5% of agriculture emissions (see Table 6.2).

If used to its maximum extent, this flexibility represents the equivalent of 1% of the annual emissions of the Effort Sharing sectors in 2005. In the 2023 ESR revision, the maximum amount for each Member States was equally split

TABLE 6.2 Maximum allowed LULUCF credits for potential use to comply with effort sharing targets; million tonnes of CO_2 equivalent

E	3.8	BG	4.1	CZ	2.6	DK	14.6
DE	22.3	EE	0.9	IE	26.8	EL	6.7
ES	29.1	FR	58.2	HR	0.9	IT	11.5
CY	0.6	LV	3.1	LT	6.5	LU	0.25
HU	2.1	MT	0.03	NL	13.4	AT	2.5
PL	21.7	PT	5.2	RO	13.2	SI	1.3
SK	1.2	FI	4.5	SE	4.9		

Source: European Commission (2018)[30]

in each of the periods 2021–2025 and 2026–2030, to respect the Climate Law, which caps the net removals to 225 million tonnes Co2 eq. Furthermore, these LULUCF credits cannot be traded between Member States in the fulfilment of their obligations under the Effort Sharing Regulation and can only be considered if a Member State would otherwise not be in compliance. These conditions further limit the extent to which LULUCF credits may be used, thereby reinforcing the safeguards of ensuring sufficient action is taken in the Effort Sharing sectors to reduce emissions.

Finally, any debit (i.e., excess emissions) under the LULUCF Regulation in the period 2021 to 2025 will be automatically deducted from Member States' Annual Emission Allocations, in the absence of a dedicated governance system under the LULUCF Regulation for these years. Therefore, Member States being unable to achieve their LULUCF targets may make the achievement of Effort Sharing targets more difficult.

6.3.7 Flexibility Linked to Earlier Over-Achievement

One final additional flexibility provision was introduced in the Effort Sharing Regulation to recognise early action in limiting emissions for Member States with income levels in 2013 below the EU average. It applies only to Member States that over-achieved their targets in the period 2013–2020, often generating considerable surpluses.[31] The Regulation does not allow "carry over" of such surpluses to ensure the overall environmental integrity of the policy. Instead, a limited "safety reserve" was created of a maximum of 105 million tonnes of CO_2-equivalent for the whole period 2021–2030 to be distributed to those lower income Member States that do not achieve their 2026–2030 targets, proportional to their over-achievement in the period 2021–2030.

This "safety reserve" can, however, only be used if the Effort Sharing sectors across the EU meet the target for 2030. As this will be known only at the end of the period, it would be hazardous for any Member State to rely too much upon using previous over-achievements (prior to 2020) in the period 2021–2030.

6.3.8 The 2030 Targets as Adopted

The combined flexibilities described in this chapter reduce the extent to which certain Member States would need to depend on transfers from other Member States. Each Member State knows its 2030 target as well as the maximum amount of EU ETS and LULUCF credit flexibilities it is allowed to access. Figure 6.10 summarises the finally allocated 2030 targets and the access each Member States has to the LULUCF and EU ETS flexibility (expressed as an annual percentage of annual emissions *per annum*).

> Conclusion: The Effort Sharing target for 2030 is set at 40% reduction below 2005 levels. Effort per Member State continues to be differentiated according to GDP *per capita* while limited flexibilities are introduced from 2021. The new ETS for road and heating fuels will create additional emissions reductions.

6.4   An Energy and Climate Governance System

Ensuring that the EU meets its climate and energy policy targets calls for a reliable and transparent governance system. All levels of government, whether European, regional, national, or local should contribute to this task, and the main tool to coordinate policies are integrated climate and energy plans to be prepared by each Member State. A governance system developed over time, starting from the international obligations to report and monitor greenhouse gas emissions to the development of integrated planning tools and the setting up of an encompassing high-level framework in the European Climate Law.

6.4.1   Integrated Energy and Climate Governance and the Climate Law

The Monitoring Mechanism Regulation[32] was the first policy decision to be adopted at EU level on climate action in the early 1990s and has been considerably developed since then. It determined the EU's internal reporting rules on greenhouse gas emissions, based on internationally agreed obligations under the UNFCCC and the Kyoto Protocol.

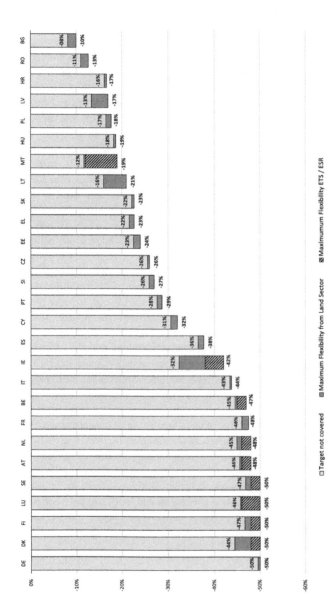

FIGURE 6.10 Member States 2030 reduction targets in the non-ETS sectors as well as maximum amount of EU ETS flexiblity and LULUCF credit flexibility *per* Member State

Source: European Commission

It was incorporated into the Regulation on the Governance of the Energy Union and Climate Action,[33] which in 2018 brought together existing requirements for planning, reporting, and monitoring in the climate and energy fields. The legal framework recognised that climate and energy policies are interlinked. Energy efficiency and renewable energy policies are key to promoting the achievement of greenhouse gas emissions reduction targets. By combining previously separated planning and reporting processes, the Governance Regulation reduced the administrative burden for Member States and the EU and prepared for the reporting obligations under the UNFCCC and the Paris Agreement.

The Climate Law adopted in 2021 further consolidated the governance framework by enshrining into legislation the EU's commitment to reach climate neutrality by 2050 at the latest and the intermediate target of reducing net greenhouse gas emissions by at least 55% by 2030, compared to 1990 levels. While EU targets so far had been agreed at political level the Climate Law enshrines them in legislation. Long-term certainty for investors and predictability to economic operators and citizens is provided while a strong political message, both at home and internationally, is being given on the EU's strategic direction to climate neutrality. In addition, the Climate Law strengthened the EU framework for climate action on aspects such as the establishment of the European Scientific Advisory Board on Climate Change, stronger provisions on adaptation and the need for strong coherence across policies.

With the Governance Regulation and the Climate Law, a framework is in place to support the development, implementation, and delivery of climate and energy policies. They enable the EU to have accurate annual information on greenhouse gas emissions and climate action. Member States are requested to report on past emissions from all economic sectors, projections of how emissions are expected to develop in the future, policies and measures to cut greenhouse gas emissions, climate adaptation measures, financial and technical support to developing countries, as well as Member States' use of revenues from the auctioning of EU Emissions Trading System allowances. By making this information publicly available, the system serves as a transparent basis for further research work and policy development. Planning instruments are also required towards the mid-term and long-term time horizons, with national energy and climate plans and national long-term strategies. A five-yearly assessment of progress towards the long-term targets aligned with the Paris Agreement cycle was also designed.

6.4.2   National Climate and Energy Plans

Integrated national energy and climate plans are central tools of the governance system. Member States adopted such plans for the first time in 2019 for the years 2021–2030. These integrated national energy and climate plans lay out projections and objectives for the five dimensions of the Energy Union,[34] together with the policies and measures intended to achieve them. These plans should be comprehensive and include transport, environmental, research, and competitiveness aspects as well as removals through sinks. The draft plans provide the EU and other Member States with an early indication of whether national efforts are sufficiently ambitious to meet the Energy Union objectives, in particular the EU 2030 climate and energy targets. Templates have been agreed both to assist the Member States and to make the plans comparable between them.

The draft plans are assessed by the Commission, including their collective contribution to the EU target. Furthermore, the Commission may make recommendations[35] to Member States. These recommendations are modelled on and complementary to those of the European Semester, which focuses on macro-economic and structural reforms, whereas the Governance Regulation addresses energy and climate-specific policy issues. After the increase of the 2030 targets, Member States had to provide an update to their plans in draft form by June 2023. The aggregation of the available projections contained in these plans shows that emissions would decrease by 33.8% in 2030 (compared to 2005 levels) which is insufficient to reach the required 40% target.[36] Member States have to commit to further action and strengthen their plans before their publication due by June 2024.

The Commission is also assessing annually the progress made by Member States towards their Effort Sharing target based on actual emission reductions achieved.[37] In case of insufficient progress, Member States will have to submit a corrective action plan, consisting of additional actions complementing its national energy and climate plan, or reinforcing its implementation. The formal compliance check under the Effort Sharing Regulation will take place every five years: in 2027 for the years 2021 to 2025 and in 2032 for the years 2026 to 2030. The Effort Sharing Regulation provides for a sanction mechanism to encourage compliance: if excess emissions remain after the use of available flexibilities, they would be added to the following year's emission figure multiplied by a factor of 1.08.

Conclusion: Member States are required to prepare comprehensive and integrated energy and climate plans. These plans include projections and provide the basis for monitoring progress towards meeting the 2030 targets. Member States are strengthening their plans in view of their publication due by June 2024.

Conclusion

A comprehensive climate strategy for the EU required the incorporation of fairness and the accommodation of distributive impacts between the Member States. This has been a complex task, both politically and technically, for which the EU has been a pioneer as no other countries have such legally binding targets in place. Fairness is itself not simple to ensure, yet it has been introduced through the differentiation of obligations, as well as with respect to the flexibilities allowed. As a result, 27 sovereign Member States have agreed on one common climate policy, despite their different levels of economic development, different industrial strategies, and different energy systems with varying degrees of dependence on fossil fuels.

Alongside the EU ETS which is based on the notion of cost-effectiveness in emissions reductions according to harmonised conditions in the power and manufacturing sectors, the Effort Sharing Regulation is based on the notion of fairness and differentiates efforts between Member States according to GDP per capita for the emissions related to transport, buildings, agriculture, and waste. Additionally, flexibilities are developed driven by the need to take account of specific circumstances of Member States, as well as recognition of efforts in the land use sectors, while limiting the risks to environmental integrity.

At the same time, the overall level of ambition was increased substantially, in line with the contribution under the Paris Agreement, but still underpinned by solid considerations of cost-efficiency. The sharing of obligations was informed and refined based on economic modelling and factual analysis. In addition, as of 2027, Member States' efforts to cut emissions will be supported by a new adjacent ETS2 system covering transport and heating fuels as well as small industrial heating systems.

Within the EU, the Climate Law and the Regulation on the Governance of the Energy Union and Climate Action set a solid framework from planning of policies to reporting of emissions and monitoring of progress. Member States must design national integrated climate and energy plans, which are crucial to outline the national and local policies required to reach the targets for the Effort Sharing sectors.

The bottom-up nature of the Paris Agreement allows for significant differentiation. The EU's example of differentiation could be informative for other big nations with a federal structure to develop internal policies in a similar manner. Equally, groups of nations could act together and differentiate their efforts, but this requires political trust and a common governance system to provide solid and comparable data.

Notes

1   An earlier version of this chapter was written by Artur Runge-Metzger and Tom van Ierland. The contribution of Ronald van de Ven for tables and figures in this chapter is acknowledged.

2 Decision No 406/2009/EC of the European Parliament and of the Council of 23 April 2009 on the effort of Member States to reduce their greenhouse gas emissions to meet the Community's greenhouse gas emission reduction commitments up to 2020. OJ L 140, 05.06.2009, pp. 136–148. See: http://data.europa.eu/eli/dec/2009/406/oj.

3 Regulation (EU) 2018/842 of the European Parliament and of the Council of 30 May 2018 on binding annual greenhouse gas emission reductions by Member States from 2021 to 2030 contributing to climate action to meet commitments under the Paris Agreement and amending Regulation (EU) No 525/2013. OJ L 156, 19.06.2018, pp. 26–42. See: http://data.europa.eu/eli/reg/2018/842/oj.

4 European Environmental Agency (2023) "EEA greenhouse gas projections- data viewer". Available at: https://www.eea.europa.eu/data-and-maps/data/data-viewers/eea-greenhouse-gas-projections-data-viewer.

5 Council Decision 2002/358/EC of 25 April 2002 concerning the approval, on behalf of the European Community, of the Kyoto Protocol to the United Nations Framework Convention on Climate Change and the joint fulfilment of commitments thereunder. OJ L 130, 15.5.2002, pp. 1–3. See: http://data.europa.eu/eli/dec/2002/358/oj.

6 These limits were specified in Article 5 of Decision No. 406/2009/EC.

7 See endnote 2.

8 The year 2005 was selected as a base year because it is the first year for which data is available for installations covered by the EU ETS, thus the first year for which the split can be made between ETS and Effort Sharing greenhouse gas emissions in the EU at Member State level.

9 GDP *per capita* measured at market prices.

10 IMPACT ASSESSMENT Proposal for a REGULATION OF THE EUROPEAN PARLIAMENT AND OF THE COUNCIL on binding annual greenhouse gas emission reductions by Member States from 2021 to 2030 for a resilient Energy Union and to meet commitments under the Paris Agreement and amending Regulation No 525/2013 of the European Parliament and the Council on a mechanism for monitoring and reporting greenhouse gas emissions and other information relevant to climate change {COM(2016) 482 final} (2016). Available at: https://eur-lex.europa.eu/LexUriServ/LexUriServ.do?uri=SWD:2016:0247:FIN:EN:PDF.

11 Impact Assessment accompanying the Package of Implementation measures for the EU's objectives on climate change and renewable energy for 2020 (SEC (2008) 85/3).

12 Capros, P., Mantzos, L., Papandreou, V., and Tasios, N. (2008) "Model-based analysis of the 2008 EU policy package on climate change and renewables". Report to the European Commission DG ENVI. Primes Model - E3MLab/NTUA. Available at: https://climate.ec.europa.eu/system/files/2016-11/analysis_en.pdf.

13 Most recent being Directive (EU) 2018/844 of the European Parliament and of the Council of 30 May 2018 amending Directive 2010/31/EU on the energy performance of buildings and Directive 2012/27/EU on energy efficiency. OJ L 156, 19.6.2018, pp. 75–91.

14 European Commission (no date) Ecodesign and Energy Labelling: Directive 2009/125/EC and Regulation (EU) 2017/1369 https://single-market-economy.ec.europa.eu/single-market/european-standards/harmonised-standards/ecodesign_en

15 European Commission report: "Two years after Paris – progress towards meeting the EU's climate commitments". COM(2017) 646 final of 07.11.2017, p. 5.

16 REPORT FROM THE COMMISSION TO THE EUROPEAN PARLIAMENT, THE COUNCIL, THE EUROPEAN ECONOMIC AND SOCIAL COMMITTEE AND THE COMMITTEE OF THE REGIONS Accelerating the transition to climate neutrality for Europe's security and prosperity EU Climate Action Progress Report 2022; COM (2022)514 Final. Available at: https://eur-lex.europa.eu/legal-content/EN/TXT/?uri=CELEX:52022DC0514.

17 Compared to 2005. The 30% target was established for 28 Member States and translates into a 29% target without the UK.

18 Impact Assessments accompanying the proposals for the Effort Sharing Regulation and its update (SWD (2016)247 final of 20.7.2016 and SWD (2021)611 of 14.7.2021).

19 REGULATION (EU) 2018/842 OF THE EUROPEAN PARLIAMENT AND OF THE COUNCIL of 30 May 2018 on binding annual greenhouse gas emission reductions by Member States from 2021 to 2030 contributing to climate action to meet commitments under the Paris Agreement and amending Regulation (EU) No 525/2013 (2018). Available at: https://eur-lex.europa.eu/legal-content/EN/TXT/?uri=CELEX:32018R0842

20 IMPACT ASSESSMENT REPORT Accompanying the document REGULATION OF THE EUROPEAN PARLIAMENT AND OF THE COUNCIL amending Regulation (EU) 2018/842 on binding annual greenhouse gas emission reductions by Member States from 2021 to 2030 contributing to climate action to meet commitments under the Paris Agreement (2021).

21 An AEA represents 1 tonne of CO_2-equivalent.

22 The European Commission had proposed a trajectory starting in the year 2020 and the compromise finally adopted by the European Parliament and the Council put the starting point at "five-twelfths of the distance from 2019 to 2020 or in 2020, whichever results in a lower allocation for that Member State".

23 Delbeke, J., and Vis, P. (Eds.) (2019) *Towards a Climate-Neutral Europe: Curbing the Trend* (1st ed.). London Routledge. Available at: https://doi.org/10.4324/9789276082569.

24 The European Commission had proposed a trajectory starting in the year 2024 and the compromise finally adopted by the European Parliament and the Council put the starting point at nine-twelfths of the distance from 2023 to 2024.

25 An allowance represents 1 tonne of CO_2-equivalent.

26 So, the flexibility is equivalent to ten times 4% of their 2005 emissions in the Effort Sharing sectors.

27 Regulation (EU) 2018/841 of the European Parliament and of the Council of 30 May 2018 on the inclusion of greenhouse gas emissions and removals from land use, land use change and forestry in the 2030 climate and energy framework and amending Regulation (EU) No 525/2013 and Decision No 529/2013/EU. See: http://data.europa.eu/eli/reg/2018/841/oj.

28 The amount of 280 million tonnes CO_2 eq. was established for 28 Member States and translates into an amount of 262 million tonnes CO_2 eq. without the UK.

29 Hungary, Slovakia, Croatia, Austria, Belgium, Germany, Czechia, Italy, Malta, and Luxembourg.

30 REGULATION (EU) 2018/842 OF THE EUROPEAN PARLIAMENT AND OF THE COUNCIL of 30 May 2018 on binding annual greenhouse gas emission reductions by Member States from 2021 to 2030 contributing to climate action to meet commitments under the Paris Agreement and amending Regulation (EU) No 525/2013 (2018). Available at: https://eur-lex.europa.eu/legal-content/EN/TXT/?uri=celex%3A32018R0842.

31 16 Member States would be able to benefit from the reserve if it becomes available, see Commission Decision (EU) 2023/863 of 26 April 2023 on setting out the amounts corresponding to 20% of the overall overachievement of certain Member States in the period from 2013 to 2020 pursuant to Regulation (EU) 2018/842 of the European Parliament and of the Council, OJ 112, 27.4.2023, pp. 43–45. See: http://data.europa.eu/eli/dec/2023/863/oj.

32 Regulation (EU) No 525/2013 of the European Parliament and of the Council of 21 May 2013 on a mechanism for monitoring and reporting greenhouse gas emissions and for reporting other information at national and Union level relevant to climate

change and repealing Decision No 280/2004/EC. Available at: http://data.europa. eu/eli/reg/2013/525/2018-12-24.

33 Regulation (EU) 2018/1999 of the European Parliament and of the Council of 11 December 2018 on the Governance of the Energy Union and Climate Action, amending Regulations (EC) No 663/2009 and (EC) No 715/2009 of the European Parliament and of the Council, Directives 94/22/EC, 98/70/EC, 2009/31/EC, 2009/73/EC, 2010/31/EU, 2012/27/EU and 2013/30/EU of the European Parliament and of the Council, Council Directives 2009/119/EC and (EU) 2015/652 and repealing Regulation (EU) No 525/2013 of the European Parliament and of the Council. Available at: http://data.europa.eu/eli/reg/2018/1999/2023-05-16.

34 These five dimensions are decarbonisation, energy efficiency, internal energy market, energy security, and research, competitiveness and innovation.

35 Such recommendations are non-binding, but Member States must take due account of them or provide and make public the reasons why they do not.

36 European Commission EU wide assessment of the draft updated National Energy and Climate Plans, COM (2023)796 final of 18.12.2023.

37 In 2021, EU-wide emissions in the Effort Sharing sectors remained 3.3% below the aggregated emissions limit, see European Commission Climate Action Progress Report 2023, COM (2023)653 final of 24.10.2023.

7

CLIMATE-RELATED REGULATIONS IN THE FIELD OF ENERGY, TRANSPORT, F-GASES AND METHANE

Edoardo Turano and Tom Van Ierland[1]

Introduction

Energy and transport policies are of crucial importance for EU climate policy as some three quarters of greenhouse gas emissions originate from the use of fossil fuels in these sectors.

Although energy policy has been at the core of the European project since the establishment of the European Coal and Steel Community (ECSC) and European Atomic Energy Community (EURATOM), both in the late 1950s, it was not until the amendments to the Treaty of Rome agreed in Lisbon in 2009 that a specific provision on energy was included.[2] EU energy policy at EU level focuses on the functioning of the energy market, security of supply, interconnections and the promotion of energy efficiency, energy savings and renewable energy. In principle these policies can be advanced with qualified majority. This, together with the competences related to the environment, means that the EU can develop a coherent climate policy for the energy sector using qualified majority voting. Decisions related to the energy mix are subject to the discretion of each Member State and EU legislation on this issue requires unanimity.

More recently, concerns were raised regarding the EU's dependence on imported energy. Over the last two decades, the rate of EU energy import dependence has hovered at around 60% on average, with the import dependence on oil being over 90% while for natural gas it increased from 66% in 2000 to 84% in 2020.[3] Saving energy and developing renewable energy allows the EU to reduce its overall import dependency, and at the same time bring down the emissions of greenhouse gases. As of 2007, the EU adopted combined climate and energy targets in the field of renewable energy and energy savings.[4] These were reinforced through the Green Deal aiming to make the EU the first

DOI: 10.4324/9781003493730-10

climate-neutral continent by 2050. The energy crisis following the Russian invasion of Ukraine highlighted even more how climate policy can contribute to enhancing the EU's energy security.

Transport is a major user of fossil fuels and has proven to be one of the hardest sectors to decarbonise. As standards of living improve, private transport demand increases and more goods are being transported. In 2021, transport accounted for around 29% of the European Union's greenhouse gas emissions.[5] Since 1990 emissions from all main sectors have been declining except in transport. The EU makes important decisions based on the internal market such as on regulations related to vehicles, but Member States bear the legal responsibility for reducing the emissions from the transport sector.

This chapter reviews the state of regulations in the field of renewable energy, energy efficiency, biofuels, passenger cars, heavy duty vehicles, methane and fluorinated gases.

7.1   Renewable Energy

7.1.1   A Binding EU-Wide Target

Along with its target for greenhouse gas emissions, the European Union set itself in 2007 a target of 20% renewables by 2020, defined as a share of gross final consumption of energy. It was also agreed that this target should be translated into a binding renewable energy target for each Member State, "taking account of different national starting points and potentials, including the existing level of renewable energies and energy mix".[6] This policy worked and the EU achieved a share of 22% of renewable energy in gross final energy consumption by 2020.

The Commission's approach considered Member States' capacity as the starting point for defining a fair distribution of effort between them. First, the "gap" was calculated between the renewable share at the time (8.7% in 2005) and its target of 20% in 2020. Half of this gap of 11.3% would be shared equally across all Member States (a flat rate of 5.75% was used) and the other half was shared among Member States on a GDP *per capita* basis. This implemented "fairness" insofar as every Member State had an element of the same flat-rate increase, seen by some as fair, combined with each country having a GDP *per capita* component that reflected its relative wealth, seen by others as fair. In this approach, richer Member States had to do more.

Mindful that the national renewable targets had not been determined in a manner that aimed at distributing the effort cost-efficiently, the Renewable Energy Directive of 2009 created cooperation mechanisms,[7] whereby Member States would be able to re-allocate over-achievement by one in favour of an under-achievement by another. The most used mechanism was statistical transfers, in which in the end 11 Member States participated.

In 2023, the EU adopted a target for renewable energy of 42.5% by 2030, while striving for 45% to contribute to the 55% greenhouse gas reduction target for 2030.[8] It was the result of a process that started with a 2030 target for renewable energy of 32% to contribute to the 40% greenhouse gas reduction target by 2030.[9] The strong ambition level was required to meet the higher greenhouse gas reduction target of 55% and was also influenced by the Russian invasion of Ukraine. A faster shift towards renewable energy was not only imperative to address the fight against climate change, but also to address the energy crisis and to reduce the fossil fuel imports from Russia, notably of natural gas. The EU had already implemented a ban on coal and maritime oil imports, but to do so for gas requires the deployment of alternatives, including a ramping up of renewable energy.

Whereas the 42.5% target is binding at the EU level, it is not for the Member States individually which are only required to define national contributions. The directive refers to an indicative formula for calculating the planned national contributions, considering a flat rate contribution, the cost-efficient potential, differences in GDP per capita and availability of interconnections for each of them.

Member States wanted to take benefit of the market dynamics as significant cost reductions occurred (see Figure 7.1). This cost reduction happened due to learning effects in a rapidly expanding market, not least kickstarted by the substantial national support mechanisms that were required to reach the binding 2020 national targets agreed at the EU level. Since then, the deployment of increasing amounts of renewable energy became less dependent on support mechanisms and increasingly attractive from a commercial perspective.

The emergence of competitive renewable electricity challenged the business model of fossil and nuclear generators and Member States needed to take a range of steps to integrate renewables, while maintaining the continuity of electricity supply. By 2014, renewable energy had become a significant player instead of an isolated future-oriented niche, adding the bulk of new additional capacity into the EU market. The regulatory focus shifted from questions about optimal support structures to questions relating to the organisation of the energy market and how to accommodate increasing amounts of intermittent renewable energy production.

The reinforced focus towards renewable energy will result in less natural gas in the energy mix by 2030 than initially expected, while the consumption of coal is expected to go down significantly. It is important to note that to achieve decarbonisation, not only solar PV and wind energy will require a dramatic increase in roll out, but also technologies that allow the increased use

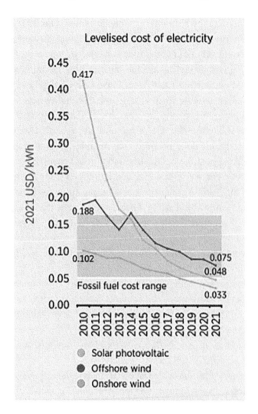

FIGURE 7.1   Global weighted average levelised cost of electricity (2010–2021)

Source: IRENA (2022)[10]

of renewable energy in end-use sectors. Of particular importance is the electrification of the transport and heating sector, allowing for renewable electricity to penetrate these sectors. The deployment of heat pumps also contributes directly to the renewables target by the captured ambient heat which is categorised as renewable energy.

7.1.2   Biomass

Biomass as a fuel plays an important role in the delivery of the renewable energy targets and is covered by the EU ETS with a zero-emissions factor. In 2021, it was still the largest source for renewable energy, with bioenergy produced from agricultural, forestry and organic waste feedstock accounting for about 59% of renewable energy consumption.[11] The 2018 review of the Renewable Energy Directive introduced additional sustainability criteria, as doubts were raised about the possible negative impact on the net savings of greenhouse gases as well as on the implications for biodiversity. In 2023 accounting rules under the Land Use, Land Use Change and Forestry (LULUCF) Regulation include for the first-time national targets for the total net removals and emissions of the land use sector (see Chapter 9). This implies that emissions related to the use of biomass are recorded on the side of the land use sector, and if done properly, sustainable forest management and afforestation make a positive contribution to climate change.

There is, however, a risk that biomass is sourced from a country that is not committed to the Paris Agreement's accounting rules for forestry emissions. Therefore, the Renewable Energy Directive foresees that the import of biomass material must come from countries with LULUCF accounting in place. In the future, one can also expect satellite monitoring to play an increasing role in the overall accounting of this most important sector, not least at the international level.

Still, doubts remain related to the sustainability of biomass for energy.[12] Therefore, a set of minimum requirements have been introduced, in relation to restriction on the type of land that can be used to produce the biomass, or the required greenhouse reductions achieved over the lifetime. These have been determined to at least 80% greenhouse gas savings, with a later entry into force for existing installations.

The future use of biomass also needs to be considered in conjunction with newly emerging carbon capture and storage technologies which over time can help to achieve the goals of the Paris Agreement. With the so-called "BECCS" technology, which stands for "Bio-Energy with Carbon Capture and Storage", carbon can be absorbed out of the atmosphere using biomass and has the potential to produce "negative" carbon dioxide emissions. By doing so the theoretical potential of the bioeconomy can be turned into a worthwhile contribution to the stabilisation of climate change globally.

Conclusion: The EU achieved a share of 22% of renewable energy in gross final energy consumption in 2020 and adopted a target of 42.5% by 2030. For solar PV and wind, significant cost reductions were achieved. Biomass is still the predominant source of renewable energy and is subject to strict sustainability criteria.

7.2 Electricity and Gas Market Integration and Climate Policy

Electricity and gas market regulation is of key importance to climate policy. When electricity markets react to pricing incentives, the EU ETS can play its role, by making electricity produced with high emissions more expensive and incentivising investment in low-carbon production. Energy market regulation is equally important in creating opportunities for new entrants that focus on renewable energy, as well as in assuring grid stability in a context where intermittent electricity production from solar and wind has become mainstream.

7.2.1 The Challenge of Integrating Renewable Energy

The first steps of the EU energy policy focussed on opening EU energy markets, allowing for cross-border energy flows and genuine competition on electricity and gas markets. In the electricity sector, price formation on the wholesale market was let free and determined by the marginal cost conditions for operating installations of the last producer entering the market to meet demand. These changes facilitated access for new entrants to the market but did not necessarily favour renewable energy because of its initial higher total costs, including investments. The focus was, therefore, on subsidising renewable energy to compensate for their higher costs and on ensuring access for them in the grid.

Subsidies at first typically took the form of feed-in tariffs at national level, providing certainty for investors but also creating rigidity in price setting. EU competition policies from 2014 onwards started to require a shift towards the use of tendering to support renewable energy.[13] This enabled the driving down of the subsidies per unit of installed capacity.

In 2009 the electricity market reform introduced "priority dispatch", where Transmissions System Operators had an obligation to first take the renewable energy that was available. The consequence was that over time other production capacity had to be used in a more flexible manner. Wind availability tends to be uncorrelated with demand and is prone to unpredictable fluctuations in its intensity, requiring other producers to operate more flexible and related interventions by the electricity system operators. While solar energy is more predictable, the sunrise and sunset effects as well as cloud formation require significant adjustment across the network, bringing other types of generation on-line to satisfy demand.

These adjustments had impacts on conventional generation assets, many of which were built to operate at relatively constant levels throughout the day, without fast-ramping capabilities. There can also be relatively long periods with very little wind and sun. In such cases, other sources of energy are needed to replace missing generation, whereas during periods when renewable energy is abundant, conventional assets may be standing idle.

In addition, when abundant wind and solar is available, the marginal cost of variable renewable energy is zero, and this has led to very low and increasingly even negative wholesale market prices. In combination with the subsidies for renewable energy, as well as relatively low gas prices, the wholesale market revenues of power companies came under pressure. The economic viability of new investments was adversely affected, putting at risk the resilience of the electricity system. To maintain investment in capacity needed to meet peak demand at times when renewable energy is limited due to weather conditions, Member States resorted to so-called capacity mechanisms that unfortunately also contributed to the fragmentation of European electricity markets.

These interventions continued to distort electricity markets and led in 2016 to the discontinuation of the mandatory "priority dispatch" for renewable energy.[14] Instead, it was decided that all wholesale market participants should face the same responsibilities in terms of grid balancing to ensure an improved integration of renewable energy supply, demand response, storage solutions, as well as reserve capacity waiting on stand-by in the case of unplanned events. The emphasis was on regional co-operation, a more efficient use of interconnectors and the procurement of reserve needs. This wider view ensured that the electricity supply system remained strong and resilient while allowing more renewables.

Some of these market dynamics changed abruptly with the onset of the Russian war in Ukraine in 2022, which saw gas prices multiply from the very low levels at the start of the COVID crisis. The electricity market experienced long periods of very high electricity prices, driven to a significant extent by gas-based electricity production being at the margin and setting the price. This in turn meant that producers with a lower marginal cost than the one determined by gas (based on so-called inframarginal technologies which includes solar and wind), experienced temporarily high windfall profits. This raised a critique on the market functioning, in that it did not allow consumers to benefit from the relative low cost of renewables in times of high electricity prices.

Instead of abandoning the market functioning based on marginal price setting, it was decided to introduce a temporary limit of €180 per MWh on the market revenues of such inframarginal producers. The 2023 review of the Electricity Market Regulation[15] does not continue this revenue cap, but instead requires that future public support for new generation capacity is based on two-way contracts for difference (CfDs), while encouraging the market at large to use more Power Purchasing Agreements. This not only avoids windfall profits but also guarantees that renewable energy producers receive a minimum level of revenues in times that electricity prices are low. This is expected to occur more frequently with ever higher rates of renewables penetrating the market. A major benefit of this market design is that the carbon price signal remains intact in the electricity price setting on the wholesale market.

In the gas market the introduction of renewable energy has been more limited, presently focussed on the production of biogas for local consumption and biomethane for mixing into the gas grid. The 2023 gas market reform[16] aims to ensure this market can open up further to injection into the existing grid of biomethane and to some extent hydrogen and other low-carbon gases, as defined by the regulation, while promoting cross-border trade. The review also agreed to the development of a separate cross-border hydrogen-only infrastructure and of a competitive hydrogen market, including by setting up an EU entity for Network Operators for Hydrogen.

7.2.2 *The Combined Effects of Electricity Market Reform and Carbon Pricing*

A well-functioning electricity market, in combination with a well-functioning EU ETS, can give sufficient price signals for the long-term investments consistent with Europe's decarbonisation goals.[17] Current carbon and electricity prices already make renewable energy cost competitive in many cases and one can expect this to become the driver for the energy transition in the power generation sector. The auction prices of renewable energy tenders for photovoltaics, onshore and even offshore wind suggest that this is already happening as more and more project developers are paying to be allowed to build new capacity. It is crucial, however, that the massive amount of investment in renewable electricity is effectively being generated in view of reaching the climate neutral goal of the EU.

For consumers to be incentivised to save energy, the Commission proposed to phase out retail price regulation, still present in several Member States. Social tariffs will still be allowed, subject to some requirements and emergencies, such as the 2022 high energy price crisis. Carbon pricing revenues are more and more utilised to compensate for energy poverty. Fairness is not only about managing the cost of energy for those who cannot afford it, but it is also about expecting those who can afford it to pay a price that takes externalities – such as its effects on climate and the environment – into account.

Finally, subject to strict conditions, it is still possible for Member States to introduce capacity mechanisms to address security of energy supply. To date, at least 11 Member States have introduced and had a variety of capacity mechanisms approved by the European Commission. These are generally technology neutral[18] and mostly ensure that gas and coal power stations, or other types of storage and flexibility – notably demand reduction but more and more also batteries – are available in the event of shortages of electricity supply.

Payments from national capacity mechanisms are in principle only possible for generation plants below a maximum threshold of 550 grams CO_2/ KWh, though some temporary exceptions can apply. This threshold excludes conventional coal-fired generation and for this reason it has been heavily criticised by certain Member States. However, the main aim is to avoid support being given to investments in high emitting generation assets that are inconsistent with the EU's long-term decarbonisation policy. Avoiding "stranded assets" in the power system is a rational policy objective, as otherwise plants need to be retired earlier due to their incompatibility with overriding goals.

7.2.3   Strengthened Role for Consumers

Recognising the importance of energy choices made by citizens, the opportunities for consumer choice and engagement with energy retail markets are being reinforced. The electricity market design aims to provide consumers relevant information, such as on electricity bills. The aim is to allow consumers to participate in energy markets directly or through companies that represent them. Moving from one energy supplier to another is facilitated, creating more price competition at the retail level.

The roll out of smart meters allows consumers to better manage energy consumption and benefit from dynamic price contracts. The 2023 proposal for electricity market reform stressed the need for greater contract choice and more direct access to renewable energy for end consumers. The installation of smart meters is also important for promoting the participation of consumers as generators of electricity for their own consumption, or for selling, storing, or offering to change consumption patterns as part of a demand-response programme, receiving remuneration either directly or through aggregators. Such measures contribute to energy security and enhance energy efficiency, while potentially enabling consumers to save money.

Conclusion: In combination with a reinforced EU ETS, the energy market reforms are crucial to incentivise renewable energy, demand response, fuel switching, as well as grid stability. The 2022 energy crisis has provided an even stronger call for a fast roll out of renewable energy.

7.3   Energy Efficiency

7.3.1   *Energy Dependence, the Import Bill and Barriers to Energy Efficiency*

Limiting the demand for energy through energy efficiency is an important way to reduce greenhouse gas emissions as well as energy dependence. In 2007, the EU agreed on an energy efficiency target in addition to the ones related to greenhouse gas emissions reduction and renewable energy. The aim was to reduce primary and final energy consumption by 20% compared to the baseline projections at that time. As a result, the trend of increasing energy consumption was reversed, with 2021 final and primary energy demand being down by, respectively, 10% and 16% compared to their peak in 2006. Still, concerns persist that this energy efficiency improvement is below the economic and technological potential in the EU and that more can be done.[19] For instance, it was recognised that compliance with the 2020 targets was triggered in part because of the exceptional drop in energy consumption in 2020 due to the COVID-19 crisis.[20]

In 2023, an ambitious energy efficiency target for the EU was agreed that translates into an absolute amount of primary energy consumption of 992.5 million tonnes of oil equivalent (Mtoe) and final energy consumption of 763 Mtoe by 2030.[21] This compares to a primary energy consumption in 2021 of 1309 Mtoe. The target is based on the "Energy Efficiency First" principle and intends to address Europe's energy vulnerability following the Russian invasion of Ukraine. It will require a significant stepping up of efforts, as is indicated in Figure 7.2. Annual savings rates will need to more than double and energy consumption will have to be reduced by around 20% in one decade. Critical in this context will be an increase in renovation rates, in the electrification of heating and of road transport as well as of some industrial processes.

Energy efficient investments with relative short payback time up to four or five years are often not undertaken in both the private and public sectors. Market and behavioural barriers such as imperfect information, split incentives, or up-front investment costs hinder consumer uptake, notwithstanding lower energy bills and other societal benefits. Governments and public sector actors may have been reluctant to undertake more ambitious energy efficiency programmes due to the need to consolidate public finances.

The recent energy crisis caused by the Russian invasion of Ukraine increased the risk of gas and electricity shortages and led to several emergency measures in view of ensuring security of supply over the winter period. A voluntary gas reduction target of at least 15% compared to historic consumption was set over the period from August 2022 to March 2023. This target was met and also extended for the period 2023–2024. Similarly for the electricity

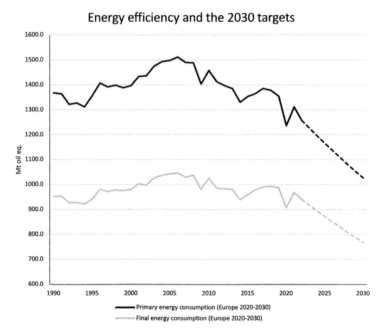

FIGURE 7.2   Energy efficiency trends and the 2030 targets

Source: EUROSTAT

market, a mandatory target was applied in the winter of 2022–2023 to reduce peak demand by at least 5%, while also an indicative target of 10% was set for overall consumption. A first assessment based on Member States reporting indicated that peak consumption was reduced by 5%, but the 10% reduction of the overall monthly consumption was not everywhere achieved. Given the stabilisation of the electricity market, it was decided not to prolong this measure.[22]

The price effect was the most important driver for these rapid reductions in energy consumption. Some reductions have been generated through new energy efficiency investments as, for instance, the sale of heat pumps increased by 40% in 2022.[23] But most other reductions have been associated with a cut in utility or production, which is in the longer term a suboptimal outcome.

7.3.2   The EU's Bottom-up Approach and the Energy Efficiency Directive

The EU's overall target on energy efficiency is not translated into legally binding targets for Member States but is realised through a bottom-up governance system. The Energy Efficiency Directive[24] sets out the overall ambition and enabling framework, while the Governance Regulation[25] captures the monitoring and reporting obligation of Member States in view of assessing whether collectively the EU ambition is being met (see Chapter 6).

The Energy Efficiency Directive requires Member States to plan and specify measures and define their overall contribution to the EU's primary and final energy consumption target in a bottom-up manner. A combination of criteria should be considered reflecting national circumstances such as energy intensity, GDP per capita, energy savings potential and fixed energy consumption reduction. Also, a wide range of facilitative measures is elaborated, including provisions relating to preventing energy poverty, smart meters, home energy management, energy audits in the commercial sector, heat planning at city level, retrofitting of public buildings, efficient district heating as well as demand response measures.

In addition, common sectoral policies at EU level are driving change within key sectors benefitting from scale effects through the single market. This approach is implemented through a combination of policies, such as the Eco-design Directive,[26] the Energy Labelling Directive[27] and the Energy Performance of Buildings Directive.[28]

7.3.3 Regulating the Energy Use and Labelling of Products and Devices

The "Eco-design Directive" sets common environmental performance standards of energy-consuming goods sold in the European Union. Many different categories of electrical and electronic equipment are covered, including heating equipment. The rationale for this legislation is to save energy and reduce emissions, but also to avoid differences in national laws that would obstruct intra-EU trade. The Commission estimates that the Eco-design Directive contributed around half of the energy savings target for 2020.

The Eco-design Working Plan for 2020–2024[29] includes a regular updating of existing standards such as for heating and cooling appliances and a comparable rescaling of energy labels. This is critical for the decarbonisation of buildings, guiding a shift away from inefficient "stand-alone" fossil fuel boilers towards heat pumps and hybrid-based systems. The plan also includes new product groups not yet regulated such as smartphones, tablets and photovoltaic solar systems. A recent review of the Eco-design Directive aims to significantly expand the scope, going beyond energy efficiency in the use phase of the products but to also contribute to improve the overall environmental performance of products over their lifetime.[30]

The Energy Labelling Directive has already provided, since 1992, information to consumers when purchasing household appliances, such as washing machines and dishwashers. The categories "A+++" to "D" show the energy performance of the product, enabling lower energy bills and ultimately fewer CO_2 emissions.

7.3.4 *Addressing the Energy Efficiency of Buildings*

Residential and commercial buildings account for some 40% of energy consumption in the EU, be it directly by heating the building using oil or gas or indirectly through the building's electricity consumption. The Energy Performance of Buildings Directive requires Member States to establish and apply minimum energy performance requirements for new buildings as well as for renovations of existing ones, to ensure the certification of the energy performance to inform owners and tenants and provides for the regular inspection of boilers and air-conditioning systems in buildings.

The Directive aims at increasing building renovation rates and fosters the delivery of smart building technologies, for instance, measures to allow for the installation of charging points for electric vehicles. The 2023 revision of the Directive[31] focusses on upscaling ambition. It bans incentives for boilers only based on fossil fuels, aims to ensure that all new buildings have a zero-emissions standard and include as much as possible solar energy installations. Certification is foreseen with an energy label from A to G, and Member States must ensure that the overall energy efficiency of the building stock improves, with the most important improvements in the worst categories.

The Directive could become an important driver for increasing effective renovation rates and some Member States have already started to implement these policies. An interesting addition is that the certification process for new buildings should not only inform how much energy they consume, but also reflect the greenhouse gas emissions performance over the entire life cycle, thus capturing the production of building materials. This is one of the first concrete policies developing a lead market for low-carbon industrial manufacturing products.

Decarbonising a building often also depends on local planning. The impact of the roll out of large amounts of heat pumps on the grid or the construction of heat networks require local authorities to be closely involved. The 2023 revision of the Renewable Energy Directive has transformed the indicative target for renewable energy in heating and cooling at national level into a binding one, requiring an increase by at least 1.1 percentage points as an annual average calculated for the period 2026 to 2030. Furthermore, the 2023 revision of the Energy Efficiency Directive also requires local heating and cooling plans at least in municipalities having a total population higher than 45,000. To set the examples, the revised Directive also expects the public sector to annually renovate at least 3% of the total floor area of heated/cooled buildings owned by all levels of public administration.

The proposed change in the building sector will require a considerable investment effort. The 2018 revision of the Energy Performance of Buildings Directive was accompanied by a Smart Finance for Smart Buildings Initiative. It consists, for example, of support for the aggregation of dispersed small-scale investments and a de-risking pillar for investors.[32] Funding possibilities to address this investment challenge have increased at the EU level, for example, in cohesion policy. The Recovery and Resilience Fund created after the pandemic has a strong green dimension and buildings figure high on the agenda in some Member States. Also, the creation of the Social Climate Fund linked to the EU Emissions Trading System will include the building sector.

Conclusion: To deliver its climate targets, the EU embraced the Energy Efficiency First principle in view of reducing its energy consumption by 20% in the coming decade. Member States implement various policies including higher renovation rates of buildings and encouraging electrification of heating and transport.

7.4   Emissions from Road Transport

Transport has been one of the hardest sectors to decarbonise. Since 1990 all sectors reduced their emissions while those of transport increased some 24% by 2019. In 2020, emissions from transport dropped as an effect of the COVID-19 pandemic, to around 7% higher than 1990 but, as of 2021, they resumed the old path[33]. Road transport represents approximately three-quarters of those emissions[34] and also represents a major concern in terms of air quality (Figure 7.3).[35]

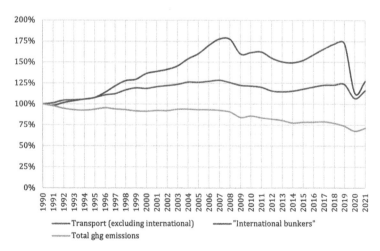

FIGURE 7.3   Evolution of EU greenhouse gas emissions from transport, 1990–2021

Source: EEA (2023)[36]

In 2020, the "Sustainable and Smart Mobility Strategy"[37] contained a long-term vision with the objective to reduce transport emissions by 90% by 2050. Member States have the primary responsibility for reducing transport emissions as these constitute the most important part of their mandatory target under the Effort-Sharing Regulation (see Chapter 6).[38] This encompasses a wide menu of options such as encouraging the use of cycling or encouraging public transport. In addition, the new EU emission trading system (EU ETS2) covering fuels from road transport and buildings provides for an EU-wide cap for emissions from these sectors. Respecting these mandatory emissions caps is facilitated by EU-wide regulations, including on biofuels, cars, vans and heavy-duty vehicles.[39]

7.4.1 Biofuels and Renewable Energy in the Transport Sector

In the early 2000s, the use of biofuels in the transport sector was considered a low cost and potentially large-scale solution to bring down the rapidly rising emissions from road transport. The assumption was that the carbon in the plants or trees had been absorbed from the atmosphere, and burning the fuel was only putting carbon back into the atmosphere where it had come from. However, this vision disregarded the emissions impact in forestry, agriculture and land use change. Without full consideration of all possible impacts, the EU rushed into biofuels while the benefits for climate change were exaggerated at the outset. Over time, legislators have increasingly concentrated their initiatives on fuels where there is greater consensus on their being beneficial for the environment.

The European Union introduced a blending target in 2003 with the aim to reach a 5.75% share of renewable energy (essentially biofuels) in the EU's transport sector by 2010.[40] As part of the EU's 2020 objectives, the target was increased to 10% and it was made mandatory for each Member State[41] and sustainability criteria were introduced. The criteria required biofuels not to be grown on land with a high carbon stock or high biodiversity, such as primary forestland. In addition, greenhouse gas savings compared to fossil fuel of at least 35% were required from 2009 and 50% from 2017, calculated during their life cycle and so including cultivation of raw materials, processing and transport. In 2015, new legislation was introduced to take account of emissions resulting from Indirect Land Use Change (ILUC) effects.[42] The use of food- and feed-based biofuels was capped at 7%.[43] In addition, biofuel production from new installations needed to ensure a greenhouse gas saving of at least 60%.

The legislation agreed in 2018 proposed a 14% sub-target for renewable energy in transport, expressed as a share of renewable energy within the final energy consumption in this sector. This target was further increased to a level of 29.5%, or more than a doubling of the target in view of contributing to the increased greenhouse gas reduction target of 55%. The 2023 review of the legislation also allowed Member States to implement this target as a greenhouse gas intensity reduction target, of at least 14.5% by 2030 compared to a baseline.

Several "multipliers" are applicable to favour certain advanced biofuels, as well as renewable electricity used by the rail and road sectors.[44] This is potentially an important shift as the largest amount of additional renewable energy in the transport sector is no longer expected to come from biofuels, but rather from the penetration of electric vehicles using increasingly renewable-based power production.

The renewable transport target reconfirmed that not more than 7% can be realised through so-called first-generation biofuels produced by the agricultural sector, such as from rapeseed.[45] In addition, a greenhouse gas saving of 65% is required of sustainable biofuels from 2021. A combined sub-target of at least 1% in 2025 and 5.5% in 2030 is set for advanced biofuels as well as synthetic fuels (now called "renewable fuels of non-biological origin").[46] The latter must represent a share of at least 1%.

Member States are required to translate the target as obligations towards fuel suppliers. The emphasis is explicitly to increase the production of advanced biofuels from the recycling of waste material, or from cellulosic wood material, and gradually also renewable fuels of non-biological origin.

Finally, a process has been agreed for the establishment of a certification process that is intended to certify food-crop biofuels that are deemed to have a low "indirect land use change", or displacement, effect. Food-crop biofuels that are deemed to have a high risk of indirect land-use change will be completely phased out by 2030. Palm oil, for example, is claimed to be such a high-risk feedstock. This certification process has begun and is being completed. Overall, the legislative framework seeks to ensure that biofuel use unequivocally contributes to emission reductions.

Despite all the environmental safeguards, the added value of biofuels is still disputed on the argumentation that they are energy intensive to produce, used in inefficient internal combustion engines and throw a lifeline to the fossil fuel-based products, with which biofuels are blended. From an air quality perspective, biofuels are of no benefit. From a climate change perspective, their production can be worse than fossil fuels if their production encourages deforestation through land-use displacement effects. This can happen not only within the EU but also, more importantly, in Asia, Latin-America or Africa, as food and feed commodity markets are truly global. In addition, biofuels produced from food and feed feedstock could increase food prices.

A consensus has been emerging that subsidies, incentives and research should be used to promote alternative powertrain technologies, in particular electric technologies. Production of sustainable liquid fuels, including synthetic fuels from renewable energy is promoted by EU legislation. However, their production will be limited in scale, at least for the next decade, and they should rather be reserved for uses where technological alternatives are not yet available, such as in aviation.

7.4.2 Regulating Zero CO_2 Emissions from Cars and Vans by 2035

Following agreement on the Kyoto Protocol, a Voluntary Agreement with car manufacturers was concluded in 1998, but it failed and as of 2009 emissions standards have been set in binding legislation.[47] All new passenger cars registered in the EU in 2015 and 2021 were required to emit on average not more than 130 and 95 gCO_2/km, respectively. In 2019, new targets were adopted for 2025 and 2030, which were set, respectively, 15% and 37.5% lower than the 2021 target.[48] In 2023, a further strengthening was adopted, and the percentage reduction has been increased to 55% for 2030 and zero CO_2 emissions for 2035.[49]

Similar binding CO_2 targets were adopted for light commercial vehicles (vans).[50] CO_2 emissions from new vans were limited to a fleet average of 175 gCO_2/km by 2017 and 147 gCO_2/km by 2020. These targets represent reductions of 3% and 19%, respectively, compared with the 2012 average of 180g CO_2/km. In 2019, new targets were adopted requiring average van emissions in 2025 and 2030 to be, respectively, 15% and 31% lower than the 2021 target. Like cars, a further strengthening for vans was adopted in 2023 and the percentage reductions have been increased to 50% for 2030 and zero CO_2 emissions for 2035. The 2023 revision of the Regulation also tasks the Commission to "*make a proposal for registering after 2035 vehicles running exclusively on CO_2 neutral fuels in conformity with Union law, outside the scope of the fleet standards, and in conformity with the Union's climate-neutrality objective*". This is currently being followed-up by the Commission.

The targets represent a historic policy decision, since it means that from 2035 onwards the emissions of new cars and vans in the EU should be 0 gCO_2/km, marking the ultimate shift from internal combustion engines to zero-emission technologies for new vehicles. This zero-emissions target does not set any restrictions for the circulation of the existing stock of vehicles in the EU, but it represents a clear signal to car manufacturers about the direction and speed of the required technological change. It also offers a clear perspective regarding the needed infrastructure to national and local authorities as well as to the reskilling of workers. Several elements facilitate compliance with the legislation. The 95 $gCO_2/$ km target in 2021 for cars allows for the use of so-called "super credits", which incentivise cars with emissions below 50 gCO_2/km, such as electric or plug-in hybrid cars. Such low-emitting cars are counted as two vehicles in 2020, 1.67 in 2021, 1.33 in 2022 and as one vehicle from 2023 onwards. This should accelerate the deployment of new technologies that could help realise future reductions. A similar facilitative element includes eco-innovations, providing manufacturers a bonus for CO_2 reductions through the application of innovative technologies not directly related to the engine performance.

The newly revised legislation includes a similar system for 2025–2029 to accelerate the uptake of zero- and low-emission vehicles (ZEV and LEV), which are defined as having CO_2 emissions between zero and 50 g/km. A manufacturer's specific CO_2 emissions target will be adjusted in case the share of zero- and low-emission vehicles in its fleet exceeds the benchmarks of 15% in 2025 and 35% (for cars) or 30% (for vans) in 2030. If a manufacturer exceeds the set benchmark by 1 percentage point, he will benefit from a 1% less stringent CO_2 target. This is allowed up to 5% of the target. For calculating that share, account is taken of the emissions of the zero- and low-emission vehicles, meaning that zero-emission vehicles are counted more than those with higher emissions.

As an initial result from the implementation of the CO_2 standards since 2009, the market registration of zero and low-emission vehicles in the EU is surging. Where manufacturers have fallen short of their specific emissions targets, significant penalties have been paid. According to provisional data for 2022, new electric cars already reached 23% of the market, up from 2% of new vehicles in 2018.

The CO_2 standards are based on the type-approval process and hence they can only be as good as the values coming from the underlying test procedure. In recent years, there has been evidence of growing discrepancies between test cycle results and emissions in real driving conditions. There has also been increasing media and regulatory interest around the use of "defeat devices" for air pollutants, or engine management systems, that manufacturers were hiding in their cars. In view of restoring consumer confidence, test procedures have been strengthened.

The performance of the vehicles is now measured according to a new regulatory test procedure carried out in laboratories. The type-approval legislation of 2017 introduces the World Harmonised Light Vehicles Test Procedure (WLTP) developed in the context of the United Nations Economic Committee for Europe (UNECE). This replaces the old procedure known as NEDC (standing for New European Driving Cycle) which had been designed in the 1980s. The new procedure is more representative of real-world driving in different conditions and reduces the risk of a creative use of the flexibilities that earlier legislation did not specifically prohibit.

In addition, a new market surveillance mechanism will improve the reliability and trustworthiness of the system.[51] Real-world fuel consumption data are starting to be collected and will be made public thanks to a standardised "on-board fuel consumption monitoring device" that must be installed in all new vehicles from 2021 on. Moreover, any significant deviations found during the verification of vehicle emissions in-service with the emissions determined in type-approval will be considered in the calculation of the average specific emissions of a manufacturer. The verification will also have to investigate the presence of any strategies that would artificially improve the performance of a vehicle during the type-approval procedure.

Furthermore, penalties are part of the overall compliance provisions and remain strict. If a manufacturer's average emissions exceed its specific emissions target, the manufacturer will have to pay an excess-emissions premium equal to €95 for each gCO_2/km above its target and for each new vehicle registered in that year.

The revised standards aim to decrease greenhouse gas emissions, to reduce pollutants with health benefits for EU citizens, as well as to decrease dependency on fossil fuels. Global markets are changing and the demand for fuel-efficient and electric vehicles is increasing. Major non-EU car markets such as China and the US are introducing ambitious policies, with stringency increasing and standards converging over time. However, the EU is a global leader in setting standards even if China has developed the most important domestic market for electric cars and buses over the past years (Figure 7.4).

7.4.3 Emissions from Heavy-Duty Vehicles (HDV), such as Lorries and Buses

As for passenger cars and vans, the emissions from heavy-duty vehicles, which represent a quarter of road transport emissions, continued to rise by around 28% in the period 1990–2021.[52] Until recently, no specific CO_2 policy was developed for HDVs. The claim made by road haulage companies was that they already did everything to keep down the fuel consumption of their fleet representing a substantial part of overall operating costs of HDVs.

Several market barriers have limited the adoption of emission reduction measures. Few transport companies had objective data to evaluate the fuel efficiency of new HDV before purchasing them. Split incentives exist between the owners of the vehicles such as leasing companies and the operators who

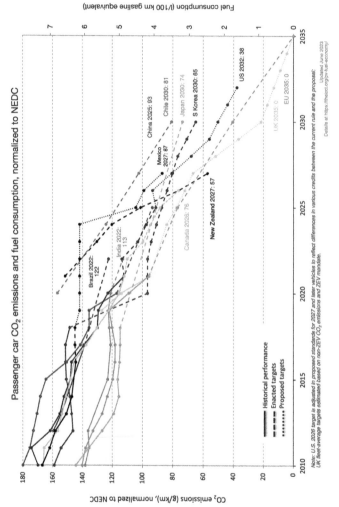

FIGURE 7.4 Average emission standards for new passenger cars

Source: ICCT (2023)[53]

would benefit from lower operating fuel costs. Furthermore, HDVs are not as standardised as passenger cars and vans, which makes the monitoring of the fleet emissions more complex. To overcome these barriers a simulation software, the Vehicle Energy Consumption Calculation Tool (VECTO),[54] was developed to calculate fuel consumption and CO_2 emissions of new HDVs for different vehicle types. Under the type-approval framework, a so-called "certification" Regulation was adopted in 2017 to define the methodology each manufacturer must use for calculating the CO_2 emissions and fuel consumption of new HDVs.[55]

These efforts also allow the monitoring and reporting of the CO_2 emission and fuel consumption of the sector as a whole and the data are published annually as of 2020. Equally, the certification of HDVs is of great importance for Member States who want to differentiate their road charging schemes according to CO_2 performance, as is made possible through the amendment of the "Eurovignette Directive" adopted in 2022,[56] which also allows for a widening of the system to encompass all vehicles.

Based on this groundwork the first EU CO_2 emission standards for HDVs were adopted in 2019. The specific CO_2 emissions of the EU fleet of new HDVs will have to be reduced by 15% in 2025 and 30% in 2030 compared to the emissions in the reference period, which is between 1 July 2019 and 30 June 2020. As a first step, these emission standards cover the largest vehicles accounting for 70% of the total CO_2 emissions from heavy-duty vehicles.

The legislation also includes a crediting system to incentivise the uptake of zero- and low-emission trucks. The incentive scheme aims at stimulating investment in all segments of the fleets. To reward early action, a super-credits scheme applies from 2019 until 2024. The credits gained can be used to comply with the target in 2025. A multiplier of two applies for zero-emission vehicles and a multiplier between one and two applies for low-emission vehicles, depending on their CO_2 emissions.[57] An overall cap of 3% is set on the use of super-credits to preserve the environmental integrity of the system. From 2025 to 2029 onwards, the super-credits system is replaced by a "bonus-only" benchmark-based crediting system, with a benchmark set at 2%. This means that the average specific CO_2 emissions of a manufacturer are adjusted downwards if the share of zero-emission vehicles in its entire fleet of new HDVs exceeds the 2% benchmark. The CO_2 emissions decrease is capped at a maximum of 3%.

The proposed legislation also contains flexibilities to ensure a cost-effective implementation of the standards. A "banking and borrowing" mechanism will allow manufacturers to balance under-achievement in one year by an over-achievement in another year. It also includes new elements such as exemptions for manufacturers responsible for less than 100 heavy duty vehicle registrations per year, or the possibility to "transfer" vehicles among manufacturers for compliance purposes to increase the cost-efficiency of the system.

For manufacturers failing to comply with their specific emission targets, the level of penalties proposed amounts to €4,250 per gramme of CO_2 per tonne kilometre (gCO_2/tkm) for the CO_2 emissions exceeding the specific targets. Several elements reinforce the effectiveness and the robustness of the legislation, such as verification of CO_2 emissions of vehicles in-service and measures to ensure that the certification procedure yields result representative of real-world CO_2 emissions.

A proposal to revise the targets has been adopted by the Commission in 2023[58] and it is currently being negotiated in Council and Parliament. The proposal extends the scope as of 2030 to cover all new heavy-duty vehicles whose emissions are certified, and also include accordingly buses, coaches, smaller lorries as well as trailers. Under the new proposal around 98% of the CO_2 emissions from the sector would be covered.

In addition, CO_2 emissions of the EU fleet of new HDVs will have to be reduced by 45% in 2030, 65% in 2035 and 90% in 2040. A specific sub-target is proposed for urban buses, so that the share of zero-emission vehicles in the manufacturers' fleet will have to be 100% as of 2030. By way of comparison, already in 2019, battery electric buses in China were accounting for 89% of newly procured buses. This choice reflects the specific use-case of such vehicles, which perform well on pre-defined routes, run in city centres with significant air quality impacts, and can recharge overnight in depots. While the penetration of zero-emission lorries and coaches in the EU remains limited, zero-emission urban buses are already a significant part of the market. According to the ICCT,[59] new battery electric buses reached around 30% of the market share in EU27 and UK, overtaking new diesel trucks.

In the new proposal most of the flexibilities for cost-effective implementation are maintained, while the incentive scheme for zero- and low-emission vehicles is stopped as of 2030, since the new targets are sufficient for an increased uptake of such vehicles.

Like the standards for cars and vans, multiple benefits arise in terms of improvement of air quality, reduction of fossil fuels dependency, and a clear signal for investments with positive impacts on innovation and industrial competitiveness. In fact, also for heavy-duty vehicles the global market is expected to change in future, with an increasing demand for zero-emission technologies. There is broader global action, evidenced, for example, by the Global Memorandum of Understanding (MoU) on Zero-Emission Medium- and Heavy-Duty Vehicles, with 27 countries including EU Member States, Canada, US and Turkey that committed to 100% zero-emission new truck and bus sales by 2040, and an interim objective of 30% zero-emission vehicle sales by 2030.[60]

> Conclusion: Passenger cars, vans and heavy-duty vehicles are regulated through CO_2 emissions performance standards. As of 2035, new cars and vans will be emission free. For large lorries, a CO_2 emissions standard has been set for 2025 and 2030, and a revision to strengthen the ambition is ongoing.

7.5   Phasing Down the Use of Fluorinated Gases

7.5.1   *Addressing the Hole in the Ozone Layer Internationally*

The Montreal Protocol on ozone-depleting substances was adopted in 1987 to counter the effects of chlorofluorocarbons (CFCs) and later the hydrochlorofluorocarbons (HCFCs) on the world's ozone layer. They focussed at first on phasing out the use of these gases, and it is presently estimated that the ozone layer will recover around 2066. However, these gases are also strong climate forcers.

The phasing out of CFCs was realised to a significant extent by substituting them with hydrofluorocarbons (HFCs) that became commonly used in the refrigeration, air-conditioning and heat-pump sectors as well as an extrusion agent in foams and aerosols. These fluorinated gases, also known as "F-gases", are harmless for the ozone layer but are very powerful greenhouse gases. The Kigali Amendment, which entered into force in 2019, agreed on a global phase down of the production and consumption of HFCs. A global target is set and developing country compliance is facilitated through a multilateral fund, which is a cost-efficient action to address climate change. This phase down will avoid up to 0.5°C of global warming this century.

7.5.2   *EU legislation Implementing the Montreal Protocol and the Kigali Amendment*

Hydrofluorocarbons (HFCs) represent around 90% of the EU's F-gas emissions and their use has been restricted as of 2006.

The main refrigerant used in mobile air conditioning, HFC134a, has a global warming impact 1,300 times higher than CO_2. The 2006 EU Mobile Air Conditioning (MAC) Directive[61] required all new types of passenger cars sold from 2011 to use cooling agents with a greenhouse warming potential of less than 150 times that of CO_2. The EU Directive on handling of end-of-life vehicles[62] regulated the collection and proper disposal of scrapped mobile air conditioners.

Perfluorocarbons (PFCs) released from primary aluminium production have been covered by the EU's Emissions Trading System since 2013. The small number of producers in the semiconductor industry that emit PFCs made a voluntary agreement to reduce their absolute PFC emissions by 10% in 2010 compared to 1995 and made a 41% reduction over this period.[63]

The 2014 F-gas Regulation[64] was reviewed in 2023[65] in view of phasing out the use of HFCs almost fully by 2050 and by 2030 around 70 million tonnes of CO_2-equivalent will be reduced compared to its peak in 2014.

The legislation is implemented via a quota system that allows a maximum annual amount of HFC gases to come to market in the EU. The quota is assigned to companies which can trade them. The latest revision included the sector for Medical Dose Inhalers under the quota system. The F-gas regulation includes use restrictions for those product categories where low or no global warming potential alternatives exist. This has led to the de facto elimination of F-gases in household refrigeration. The 2023 revision sets important bans for heat pumps and air condition systems, where high growth is expected. To smoothen the temporary shortage caused by the goal to more than double heat pump deployment in the EU, the quota system was extended with a limited and temporary "Heat Pump Reserve".

The F-gas regulation stimulates innovation and boosts European companies' leadership in the sector allowing the international community to increase global ambition. Data from the first years of the phase down[66] show the target being achieved. This is also expected to make the EU less dependent on imports, notably from China, which is the largest HFC producer. In addition, the Commission has published several reports addressing an enabling environment allowing rapid F-gas reductions. These include barriers caused by standards that do not allow global warming potential alternatives to HFCs to come to the market[67] and the availability of qualified personnel to ensure the effective installation and servicing of equipment.[68]

Conclusion: The Kigali Amendment to the Montreal Protocol will reduce global warming by 0.5°C by the end of the century. The EU has put in place legislation to almost phase-out the use of fluorinated gases by 2050 and to incentivise the deployment of low-carbon alternatives.

7.6 The EU Methane Strategy

Methane contributes around 20% to the anthropogenic greenhouse effect, making it the second biggest contributor after carbon dioxide. On a molecular level, it is more potent than carbon dioxide, as it traps more heat in the atmosphere. At the same time, methane has a relatively short lifetime in the atmosphere of around a decade. Over a 20-year period, its global warming potential (GWP20) is around 80 times that of CO_2, while over a 100-year period (GWP100) it is around 28 times more potent. The EU continues to base its climate policy on GWP100 following the UNFCCC guidelines but recognises that reducing the total amount of methane emissions is having a more immediate effect.

The sources of methane are both natural and anthropogenic. Natural sources include wetlands and freshwater, while anthropogenic sources are typically agriculture, waste management, and the energy sector. Methane emissions from agriculture arise mostly from livestock, caused by enteric fermentation in cattle and sheep, as well as from animal manure management. In the waste sector, methane emissions come from the decomposition of organic matter in landfill sites under anaerobic circumstances and wastewater infrastructure such as municipal wastewater treatment plants. Energy sources of methane result from venting, flaring and leakages in the oil, gas and coal sectors (i.e., "fugitive emissions", with natural gas largely being composed of methane), as well as from incomplete fuel combustion, especially in the residential sector.

In 2021, more than half of all methane emissions in the EU came from agriculture (44% enteric fermentation, 11% manure management), followed by waste management (18% landfill sites, 4% wastewater) and the energy sector (10% fugitive emissions, 6% fuel combustion).[69] The EU reduced its methane emissions by over 37% between 1990 and 2021, respectively, with 22% in agriculture, 43% in waste management, and 61% in the energy sector. This reduction has been driven largely by existing sectoral policies delivering emissions reductions accounted for under the Effort Sharing Regulation and will be reinforced by the Methane Strategy adopted under the Green Deal[70] (see Figure 7.5).

The Common Agricultural Policy (CAP) is the central framework for agricultural mitigation measures. Member States need to submit Strategic Plans demonstrating how their national implementation of the CAP will contribute to climate mitigation and adaptation. In this context, the European Commission encourages Member States to support measures mitigating methane emissions from both enteric fermentation by ruminant animals and manure management, including through feed additives and supplements as well as anaerobic digestion. The latter can produce biogas and biomethane, thus also

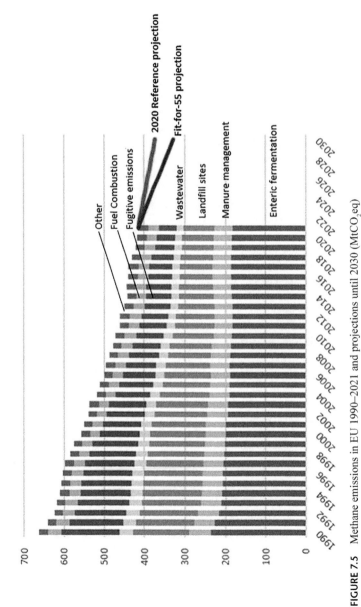

FIGURE 7.5 Methane emissions in EU 1990–2021 and projections until 2030 (MtCO$_2$eq)

Source: European Environment Agency and policy scenarios for delivering the European Green Deal

improving the EU's energy security. The review of the Industrial Emissions Directive[71] does not include the proposed scope extension to cattle farming which would have required the use of Best Available Techniques. This reduces the efficiency related to methane emissions considerably, though a review clause is foreseen for 2026.

The Waste Framework Directive seeks to reduce the generation of food waste and establishes a separate collection target for biogenic municipal waste. The Landfill Directive, in turn, requires Member States to reduce the amount of biodegradable waste going to landfill sites and several of them introduced a ban. Landfill sites that accept biodegradable waste need to monitor and control their landfill gas requiring the use of methane to produce energy, or where this is impossible, flaring.

The Urban Wastewater Treatment Directive requires so-called secondary and tertiary treatment as well as sewage sludge management, which reduces methane emissions. The review of the Directive[72] includes additional provisions aimed at greening the energy usage of urban wastewater treatment plants.

In the energy sector, fugitive methane emissions have substantially decreased mainly due to the reduced extraction of coal, and a lesser extent oil and gas. To reduce fugitive methane emissions further, a Regulation[73] will be implemented that obliges these sectors to monitor, report and verify methane emissions, to carry out leak detection and repair surveys, and to limit venting and flaring. The Regulation also contains provisions that require importers to provide transparency on methane emissions in their supply chain and allows the Commission to take further steps which will potentially impact methane emissions beyond the EU's jurisdiction.

The EU is also active internationally. It is one of the initiators of the Global Methane Pledge launched in 2021. The pledge aims to reduce methane emissions globally and collectively by 30% by 2030 compared to 2020, which could reduce global warming by at least 0.2°C by 2050. As methane also affects air pollution, the EU participates in the Gothenburg Protocol[74] which stresses that methane reductions are necessary for achieving cleaner air and that increasing concentrations could offset the reductions of other pollutants.

Conclusion: The EU reduced its methane emissions – the second largest climate forcer – by 37% between 1990 and 2021 through existing policies in agriculture, waste management, and the energy sector. The EU supports international ambitions, especially under the Global Methane Pledge.

Conclusion

The European Green Deal has taken a major step towards integrating climate change into policies in the field of energy and transport. A point of no return seems to be reached in the low-carbon transition, building less on fossil fuels and more on energy efficiency and renewable energy. This also helps to address the very high dependence of Europe on the import of coal, oil, and gas, an issue that has become a high political priority following the Russian invasion in Ukraine. The case in favour of renewable energy is overwhelming and this is expressed in the renewable target of 42.5% the EU adopted for 2030. The issue has become less about supporting schemes but more about adapting the functioning of electricity markets not least to deal with the intermittency of wind and solar in a cost-effective manner.

Of key importance is the price signal. Well-functioning electricity markets combined with well-functioning carbon markets can bring forward the ambitious emission reductions the EU adopted for 2030 and 2050. Equally, overcoming the barriers to improving energy efficiency is critical not least in light of the energy dependence of Europe. Grid resilience of the electricity system with increasing amounts of variable renewable energy needs to be further enhanced, as does the development of new technologies such as energy storage or the rapidly spreading digitalisation.

It remains a huge challenge to reduce transport emissions of greenhouse gases. The EU has established mandatory legislation imposing CO_2 performance standards for cars, vans, and high-duty vehicles. By 2035 all new cars and vans put on the market will be CO_2 free, predominantly through electric vehicles. For lorries, buses and ships, a solid database has been elaborated serving as the basis for strengthened EU standards that have been proposed for 2025 and 2030.

Member States have an important role to play to reduce the greenhouse gas emissions. Emissions from transport and heating represent the most important part of their mandatory target for 2030 under the Effort Sharing Regulation. They have important tools at their disposal such as tax incentives (e.g. zero-energy houses being subject to lower property taxes) and subsidies (e.g. for better housing insulation), energy audits for private households, or the installation or upgrading of district heating systems. Emissions from transport and heating fuels are gradually being brought under the EU ETS as of 2027, in view of establishing more economic incentives towards decarbonisation, through a carbon price as well as by using revenues from auctioning.

Technology undoubtedly plays an important role in bringing down emissions. One of the recurring themes is that electricity has the potential to be a significant game-changer both in transport and heating. That is good news, as power generation is on its path to full decarbonisation over the next two decades to come.

Notes

1 This chapter is the review of the previous one co-authored by Damien Meadows, Alex Paquot and Peter Vis.
2 In Article 194 of the Lisbon Treaty, energy policy has been linked with the "need to preserve and improve the environment".
3 Statistical Pocketbook (2022) Available at: https://energy.ec.europa.eu/data-and-analysis/eu-energy-statistical-pocketbook-and-country-datasheets_en.
4 COM (2007) 2 final and in 2014 with the adoption by the Commission of "A resilient Energy Union with a forward-looking climate change policy".
5 According to GHG Inventories reported to the UNFCCC, publicly available on the website of the European Environment Agency. Not including aviation's non-CO_2 climate impacts.
6 See p. 21 of http://www.consilium.europa.eu/ueDocs/cms_Data/docs/pressData/en/ec/93135.pdf.
7 The Renewable Energy Directive foresaw four different types of cooperation mechanisms: statistical transfers, joint projects between Member States, joint projects between Member States and third countries and joint support schemes.
8 Directive (EU) 2023/2413 amending Directive (EU) 2018/2001, Regulation (EU) 2018/1999 and Directive 98/70/EC as regards the promotion of energy from renewable sources, and repealing Council Directive (EU) 2015/652.
9 Directive (EU) 2018/2001/EC of the European Parliament and of the Council of 11 December 2018 on the promotion of the use of energy from renewable sources (recast). OJ L 328, 21.12.2018, pp. 82–209.
10 IRENA (2022) "IRENA renewable power generation costs in 2021", p. 17. Available at: https://www.irena.org/publications/2022/Jul/Renewable-Power-Generation-Costs-in-2021.
11 COM (2023) 650 final, ANNEX 1, *Union Bioenergy Sustainability Report.*
12 Searchinger, T. D. et al. (2018) "Europe's renewable energy directive poised to harm global forests." Available at: https://www.nature.com/articles/s41467-018-06175-4.pdf.
13 State aid guidelines for environmental protection and energy (EEAG).
14 Regulation (EU) 2019/943 of 5 June 2019 on the internal market for electricity.
15 Council of the EU (14 December 2023) Reform of electricity market design: Council and Parliament reach deal. Available at: https://www.consilium.europa.eu/en/press/press-releases/2023/12/14/reform-of-electricity-market-design-council-and-parliament-reach-deal/
16 https://www.consilium.europa.eu/en/press/press-releases/2023/12/08/gas-package-council-and-parliament-reach-deal-on-future-hydrogen-and-gas-market/.
17 SWD (2016) 410 final, "Impact assessment accompanying the market design initiative proposals."
18 The ECJ, however, recently found that the UK capacity mechanism was not neutral and risked discrimination against demand-side response solutions.
19 Energy Efficiency Financial Institutions Group (EEFIG) (February 2015) *Final Report* (see https://ec.europa.eu/energy/sites/ener/files/documents/Final%20Report%20EEFIG%20v%209.1%2024022015%20clean%20FINAL%20sent.pdf) and COMMISSION/DG ECFIN, Note to the Economic Policy Committee Energy and Climate Change Working Group (19 April 2016) Investment in Energy Efficiency by Households.
20 COM (2022) 641 final.
21 Directive (EU) 2023/1791 of 13 September 2023 on energy efficiency and amending Regulation (EU) 2023/955 (recast).
22 COM (2023) 302 final.

23 https://www.iea.org/commentaries/global-heat-pump-sales-continue-double-digit-growth.

24 Directive (EU) 2018/2002 of the European Parliament and of the Council of 11 December 2018 amending Directive 2012/27/EU on energy efficiency. OJ L 328, 21.12.2018, pp. 210–230.

25 Regulation (EU) 2018/1999.

26 Directive 2009/125/EC of the European Parliament and of the Council of 21 October 2009 establishing a framework for the setting of eco-design requirements for energy-related products. OJ L 285, 31.10.2009, pp. 10–35.

27 Regulation (EU) 2017/1369 of the European Parliament and of the Council of 4 July 2017 setting a framework for energy labelling and repealing Directive 2010/30/EU. OJ L 198, 28.7.2017, pp. 1–23.

28 Directive (EU) 2018/844 of the European Parliament and of the Council of 30 May 2018 amending Directive 2010/31/EU on the energy performance of buildings and Directive 2012/27/EU on energy efficiency. OJ L 156, 19.6.2018, pp. 75–91.

29 Communication "Ecodesign and Energy Labelling Working Plan 2022–2024", (2022/C 182/01)

30 https://www.consilium.europa.eu/en/press/press-releases/2023/12/05/products-fit-for-the-green-transition-council-and-parliament-conclude-a-provisional-agreement-on-the-ecodesign-regulation/.

31 https://www.consilium.europa.eu/en/press/press-releases/2022/10/25/fit-for-55-council-agrees-on-stricter-rules-for-energy-performance-of-buildings/.

32 www.eefig.com/deep.

33 European Environment Agency (2023) https://www.eea.europa.eu/data-and-maps/data/data-viewers/greenhouse-gases-viewer

34 EEA GHG data viewer (http://www.eea.europa.eu/data-and-maps/data/data-viewers/greenhouse-gases-viewer), extracted on 20/07/2023.

35 European Environment Agency (28 Feb, 2023) Air quality in Europe 2022 Available at: https://www.eea.europa.eu/publications/air-quality-in-europe-2022.

36 European Environment Agency (2023) "EEA greenhouse gases - data viewer." Available at: https://www.eea.europa.eu/data-and-maps/data/data-viewers/greenhouse-gases-viewer.

37 COM (2020) 789 final, of 9.12.2020 "Sustainable and smart mobility strategy – putting European transport on track for the future".

38 Regulation (EU) 2018/842 of the European Parliament and of the Council of 30 May 2018 on binding annual greenhouse gas emission reductions by Member States from 2021 to 2030 contributing to climate action to meet commitments under the Paris Agreement and amending Regulation (EU) No 525/2013 (OJ L 156, 19.6.2018, pp. 26–42).

39 https://taxation-customs.ec.europa.eu/green-taxation-0/revision-energy-taxation-directive_en.

40 Directive 2003/30/EC of the European Parliament and of the Council of 8 May 2003 on the promotion of the use of biofuels or other renewable fuels for transport. OJ L 123, 17.5.2003, pp. 42–46.

41 Directive 2009/28/EC of the European Parliament and of the Council of 23 April 2009 on the promotion of the use of energy from renewable sources and amending and subsequently repealing Directives 2001/77/EC and 2003/30/EC. OJ L 140, 5.6.2009, pp. 16–62.

42 Directive (EU) 2015/1513 of the European Parliament and of the Council of 9 September 2015 amending Directive 98/70/EC relating to the quality of petrol and diesel fuels and amending Directive 2009/28/EC on the promotion of the use of energy from renewable sources. OJ L 239, 15.9.2015, pp. 1–29.

43 Seven percent was the estimated installed capacity of EU biofuel production at the time.

44 For example, the share of renewable electricity used in road vehicles can be multiplied by four and the share of advance biofuels by two.

45 Directive (EU) 2018/2001/EC of the European Parliament and of the Council of 11 December 2018 on the promotion of the use of energy from renewable sources (recast). OJ L 328, 21.12.2018, pp. 82–209.

46 These are so-called synthetic e-fuels produced with renewable electricity, meeting certain requirement related to the additionality of the renewable electricity production and requiring overall 70% greenhouse gas emission savings over the life time compared to a fossil fuel comparator.

47 Regulation (EC) No 443/2009 of the European Parliament and of the Council setting emission performance standards for new passenger cars as part of the Community's integrated approach to reduce CO_2 emissions from light-duty vehicles. OJ L 140, 5.6.2009, pp. 1–25. Available at: http://eur-lex.europa.eu/legal-content/EN/TXT/PDF/?uri=CELEX:02009R0443-20130508&from=EN and Regulation (EU) No 333/2014 of the European Parliament and of the Council of 11 March 2014 amending Regulation (EC) No 443/2009 to define the modalities for reaching the 2020 target to reduce CO_2 emissions from new passenger cars. OJ L 103, 5.4.2014, pp. 15–21. Available at: http://eur-lex.europa.eu/legal-content/EN/TXT/PDF/?uri=CELEX:32014R0333&from=EN.

48 Regulation (EU) 2019/631 of the European Parliament and of the Council of 17 April 2019 setting CO2 emission performance standards for new passenger cars and for new light commercial vehicles, and repealing Regulations (EC) No 443/2009 and (EU) No 510/2011.

49 Regulation (EU) 2023/851 of the European Parliament and of the Council of 19 April 2023 amending Regulation (EU) 2019/631 as regards strengthening the CO2 emission performance standards for new passenger cars and new light commercial vehicles in line with the Union's increased climate ambition.

50 Regulation (EU) No 510/2011 of the European Parliament and of the Council of 11 May 2011 setting emission performance standards for new light commercial vehicles as part of the Union's integrated approach to reduce CO_2 emissions from light-duty vehicles. OJ L 145, 31.5.2011, pp. 1–18. Available at: http://eur-lex.europa.eu/legal-content/EN/TXT/PDF/?uri=CELEX:32011R0510&from=EN; and Regulation (EU) No 253/2014 of the European Parliament and of the Council of 26 February 2014 amending Regulation (EU) No 510/2011 to define the modalities for reaching the 2020 target to reduce CO_2 emissions from new light commercial vehicles. OJ L 84, 20.3.2014, pp. 38–41. Available at: http://eur-lex.europa.eu/legal-content/EN/TXT/PDF/?uri=CELEX:32014R0253&from=EN.

51 Scientific Advice Mechanism (SAM) (2016) Closing the gap between light-duty vehicle real-world CO_2 emissions and laboratory testing. High Level Group of Scientific Advisors, Scientific Opinion No. 1/2016. Available at: https://ec.europa.eu/research/sam/pdf/sam_co2_emissions_report.pdf#view=fit&pagemode=none.

52 ICCT (2023) "Passenger vehicle greenhouse gas emissions and fuel consumption." Available at: https://theicct.org/pv-fuel-economy/.

53 For more information on VECTO, please see Annex 4 of the Impact Assessment accompanying the document Proposal for a Regulation of the European Parliament and of the Council on the monitoring and reporting of CO_2 emissions from and fuel consumption of new heavy-duty vehicles, Commission Staff Working Document Impact Assessment SWD/2017/0188 final. Available at: http://eur-lex.europa.eu/legal-content/EN/TXT/?uri=SWD:2017:0188:FIN.

54 http://www.eea.europa.eu/data-and-maps/data/data-viewers/greenhouse-gases-viewer.

55 Commission Regulation (EU) 2017/2400 of 12 December 2017 implementing Regulation (EC) No 595/2009 of the European Parliament and of the Council as regards the determination of the CO2 emissions and fuel consumption of heavy-duty vehicles and amending Directive 2007/46/EC of the European Parliament and of the Council and Commission Regulation (EU) No 582/2011. Available at: https://eur-lex.europa.eu/eli/reg/2017/2400/oj

56 Directive 1999/62/EC on the charging of heavy goods vehicles for the use of certain infrastructures

57 A low-emission vehicle is defined as heavy-duty vehicle with emissions below 50% of the reference CO2 emission of the sub-group to which the vehicle belongs.

58 Proposal for a Regulation amending Regulation (EU) 2019/1242 as regards strengthening the CO$_2$ emission performance standards for new heavy-duty vehicles, COM (2023)88.

59 https://theicct.org/electric-buses-europe-may23/.

60 https://globaldrivetozero.org/mou-nations/.

61 Directive 2006/40/EC of the European Parliament and of the Council relating to emissions from air-conditioning systems in motor vehicles and amending Council Directive 70/156/EEC. OJ L 161, 14.6.2006, pp. 12–18. Available at: http://eur-lex. europa.eu/legal-content/EN/TXT/PDF/?uri=CELEX:32006L0040&from=EN.

62 Directive 2000/53/EC of the European Parliament and of the Council on end-of life vehiclesOJ L 269, 21.10.2000, pp. 34–43. Available at: http://eur-lex.europa. eu/resource.html?uri=cellar:02fa83cf-bf28-4afc-8f9f-eb201bd61813.0005.02/ DOC_1&format=PDF.

63 http://www.eeca.eu/esia/public-policy/sustainability-esh/pfc-gases.

64 Regulation (EU) No 517/2014 of the European Parliament and of the Council of 16 April 2014 on fluorinated greenhouse gases and repealing Regulation (EC) No 842/2006. OJ L 150, 20.5.2014, pp. 195–230. Available at: http://eur-lex.europa.eu/ legal-content/EN/TXT/PDF/?uri=CELEX:32014R0517&from=EN.

65 https://www.consilium.europa.eu/en/press/press-releases/2023/10/05/fluorinated-gases-and-ozone-depleting-substances-council-and-parliament-reach-agreement/.

66 European Environment Agency (17 Feb, 2023) Fluorinated greenhouse gases 2021 https://www.eea.europa.eu/publications/fluorinated-greenhouse-gases-2021

67 http://eur-lex.europa.eu/legal-content/EN/TXT/?uri=CELEX:52016DC0749.

68 http://eur-lex.europa.eu/legal-content/EN/TXT/?uri=CELEX:52016DC0748.

69 European Environmental Agency (2023) *Annual European Union Greenhouse Gas Inventory Report 2023.*

70 COM (2020) 663 final.

71 https://www.consilium.europa.eu/en/press/press-releases/2023/11/29/industrial-emissions-council-and-parliament-agree-on-new-rules-to-reduce-harmful-emissions-from-industry-and-improve-public-access-to-information/.

72 https://www.consilium.europa.eu/en/press/press-releases/2023/10/16/council-adopts-position-on-new-rules-for-a-more-efficient-treatment-of-urban-wastewater/.

73 https://www.consilium.europa.eu/en/press/press-releases/2023/11/15/climate-action-council-and-parliament-reach-deal-on-new-rules-to-cut-methane-emissions-in-the-energy-sector/.

74 Economic Commission for Europe (2023) Report on the review of the Protocol to Abate Acidification, Eutrophication and Ground-level Ozone, as amended in 2012.

8

REMOVALS AND EMISSIONS FROM AGRICULTURE AND FORESTRY

Christian Holzleitner, Artur Runge-Metzger and Sevim Aktas[1]

Introduction

Agriculture and forestry not only contribute to emissions but also have the potential to capture and store carbon dioxide from the atmosphere. The range of "climate smart" measures available to agriculture and forestry[2] surpasses that of many other sectors, highlighting their unique role in addressing climate challenges.

Since 2012, agricultural emissions from livestock management and use of fertilisers have been included in the Effort Sharing Regulation (ESR), while emissions from land use, land use change and forestry (LULUCF) promoting net carbon sequestration from agricultural land and forestry within its borders are covered under the LULUCF Regulation.

The Paris Agreement, adopted in December 2015, emphasised the need to achieve "a balance between anthropogenic emissions by sources and removals by sinks of greenhouse gases in the second half of the century." Moreover, it calls upon Parties to conserve and enhance the capacity of greenhouse gas sinks, including those in forests.

In 2021, the European Union significantly increased its initial Paris pledge and now aims to reduce its greenhouse gas emissions by at least 55% by 2030 compared to 1990, including a maximum of 225 million tonnes of net removals. For the EU to move to climate neutrality by 2050, emissions from agriculture, forestry and land use will have to become net zero by around 2035.

As a consequence, in 2023, the EU further strengthened its legislation by setting for the first time a separate 2030 target of 310 Mt of net removals from land use, land use change and forestry (LULUCF). This EU-wide target is then allocated to individual Member States. This requires active involvement of the agriculture and forestry sectors, which have the unique ability to

DOI: 10.4324/9781003493730-11

both contribute to emissions reductions and remove carbon dioxide from the atmosphere. This dual role holds global significance, as these sectors account for approximately 20–25% of global emissions, largely driven by tropical deforestation.

This chapter provides an understanding of the evolution of policies for these sectors, their key features, and the recent updates. It also addresses the current status of existing initiatives, discusses strategies to overcome sector challenges and examines the enabling environment for climate action in forestry and agriculture.

8.1 The Role of the Land Use Sector in Mitigating and Removing Greenhouse Gas Emissions

The land use sector encompasses the management of various land categories such as cropland, grassland, wetlands, forests and settlements. Additionally, it includes land use change activities such as afforestation, deforestation, the draining of peatlands and the utilisation of harvested wood products. Covering more than three-quarters of the EU's territory, the agricultural and land sector offers ample opportunities to reduce agricultural emissions and to remove carbon dioxide (CO_2) from the atmosphere.[3]

The greenhouse gas cycles associated with agriculture and forestry are complex, encompassing both non-CO_2 and CO_2 emissions, as illustrated in Figure 8.1. In agriculture, non-CO_2 greenhouse gases, primarily nitrous oxide (N_2O) from nitrogen fertilisers and methane (CH_4) from livestock digestion, contribute to more than half of the EU's non-CO_2 emissions. These emissions accounted for 10.9% of the total emissions in 2021, while net LULUCF removals made up 6.6% showing that overall the agriculture, forestry and land use sector remained a net emitter.[4]

Most of the nature-based avenues for the removal of CO_2 are reversible. When trees are cut down or grassland is converted to arable land or regenerative soil management practices are reverted, the carbon stored in them is released back into the atmosphere. Still, implementing effective carbon removal strategies in the EU becomes essential to counterbalance residual emissions and, beyond climate neutrality in 2050, to generate the required net negative emissions. To evaluate the role of land use and forestry in climate protection, it is crucial to annually monitor the balance between emissions and removals from agriculture and forestry. Increasing CO_2 storage in trees and reducing CO_2 emissions from agricultural land through improved soil protection will enhance their contribution to climate protection. Additionally, well-managed agriculture and forestry can provide sustainable and domestic raw materials for industry, energy and transport sectors transitioning away from fossil fuel dependency.

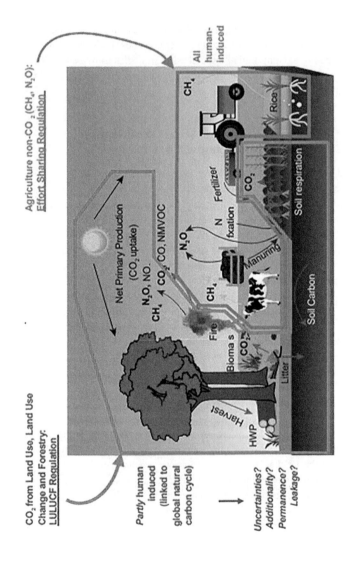

FIGURE 8.1   Land use and agriculture in EU climate policies

Source: IPCC (2006)[5]

One notable advantage of climate action in forestry and agriculture is their positive impact on agricultural productivity, climate adaptation and biodiversity conservation, particularly in a long-term perspective. Increasing soil organic matter in intensively farmed soils protects productivity, reduces erosion and fosters beneficial microorganisms while promoting sustainable agriculture and biodiversity conservation.[6] Sustainable land management is crucial for climate resilience as healthy ecosystems provide vital services such as flood protection, desertification prevention, air pollution reduction and urban heat mitigation. Recognising the interconnectedness of carbon sinks, biodiversity and climate change adaptation, the EU emphasises the significance of sustainable land management in reversing biodiversity loss and addressing climate change impacts effectively.

Conclusion: Emissions reductions and carbon removals in agriculture and forestry are vital for achieving the EU's climate goals. Significant additional efforts are needed to properly manage complex greenhouse gas cycles, monitor emissions and promote sustainable land management.

8.2   The LULUCF Carbon Sink in the EU

The LULUCF sector, as shown in Figure 8.2, in the EU acts as a net carbon sink, absorbing CO_2 through afforestation and forest management, but emitting CO_2 due to deforestation, cropland management, draining of peatlands and land-use changes. The sector's performance fluctuates from year to year mainly due to natural disturbances like storms, wild fires and droughts

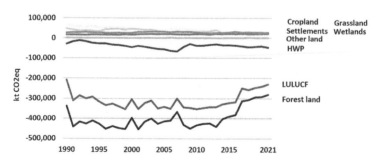

FIGURE 8.2   LULUCF emissions and removals by source and emissions

Source: European Union (2023)[7]

and also changes over time due to management changes as a result of, for example, increasing adverse effects of climate change, the age structure of forests, or market signals induced by renewable energy and biofuels policies. Important challenges remain for the sector in view of the ambitious 2030 target. Firstly, forest ecosystems' carbon sinks have been steadily deteriorating since 2000. Secondly, non-forest land uses continue to show overall net emissions. Particularly, the reduction of the significant emissions from the use of drained peatlands for arable crops or grasslands remains challenging for several northern European Member States including Germany, Poland, Ireland, the Netherlands, Finland and Sweden.[8]

Since 2012, the EU has implemented specific legislation to address land and agricultural emissions focusing on sustainable land use practices. Two significant developments are the Effort Sharing Regulation (ESR) and the Regulation on Land Use, Land-Use Change and Forestry (LULUCF). As illustrated in Figure 8.1, these policies are designed to address specific aspects of emissions reduction and land use management within the EU.

The ESR[9] (see Chapter 6) sets individual binding emission reduction targets for Member States, including non-CO_2 emissions from agriculture, while the LULUCF Regulation focuses on land and forest management, recognising their potential for carbon dioxide removals through sustainable land use practices. The ESR Regulation aims to achieve a collective reduction of 40% by 2030, relative to the emissions recorded in 2005. The LULUCF Regulation sets a net carbon dioxide removal target of 310 Mt CO_2eq by 2030.

8.2.1 Evolution of LULUCF: From Kyoto Protocol to Ambitious EU Targets

The EU's policy related to land use started with the implementation of the Kyoto Protocol, which sets out that LULUCF activities had to be included in the accounting framework for greenhouse gas emissions and removals. Participating nations were required to set binding national targets for reducing their greenhouse gas emissions, including emissions and removals from the land use sector.

In 2012, the EU took a significant step towards implementing the Kyoto Protocol by developing accounting methodologies and systems to track emissions and removals from LULUCF activities within its Member States. This process required establishing transparent and consistent procedures for monitoring, reporting, and verifying emissions and removals associated with land use, land use change and forestry.

However, during the period from 2013 to 2020, the LULUCF sector was not included in the EU's domestic climate commitment. Nonetheless, EU Member States recognised the importance of monitoring agricultural land and improving management practices on croplands and grazing lands. The Decision No 529/2013/EU[10] on LULUCF accounting rules generated valuable information, identifying emission hotspots and promising mitigation actions across the Member States, laying the groundwork for future inclusion of the LULUCF sector in climate action initiatives.

Following the ratification of the Paris Agreement, the EU adopted a 2030 target of reducing emissions by 40% compared to 1990, including the LU-LUCF sector for the first time, recognising the importance of addressing emissions and enhancing sinks to achieve its climate goals. Subsequently, the LULUCF Regulation (EU) 2018/241[11] was created.

With the enactment of the 2021 European Climate Law, a binding target was set of at least 55% net emission reduction by 2030 compared to 1990 levels, necessitating the upgrade of the LULUCF Regulation. As a result, the revised EU LULUCF Regulation establishes a new target of removing 310 million tonnes of CO_2eq by 2030 at EU level and sets individual net removal targets for Member States from 2026 onwards as shown in Figure 8.3. For each Member State, this represents an increase of approximately 15% in removals compared to the reference period from 2016 to 2018.

8.2.2 Building Further on the 2018 LULUCF Regulation

The 2018 LULUCF Regulation introduced accounting rules and provisions for the monitoring and reporting of greenhouse gas emissions and removals in the land use and forestry sector. It includes specific guidelines for different land use categories, such as cropland, grassland, deforested and afforested land, managed forestland and harvested wood products. Member States must adhere to best practice principles such as accurate, complete, consistent, comparable and transparent accounting. It positions LULUCF as a stand-alone pillar alongside the EU ETS (Emissions Trading System) and the Effort Sharing Regulation, emphasising its significance in achieving climate goals. It incentivises the conservation, restoration, and expansion of forest and soil carbon sinks to work towards carbon neutrality in line with the goals of the Paris Agreement.

The revised Regulation[12] introduces key changes to address inconsistencies, ensuring more accurate accounting of emissions and removals and improved transparency in reporting. For the first time, net carbon removals targets are set for each Member State. Equally important, with the end of the last commitment period under the Kyoto Protocol, the Regulation moves away from the previous Kyoto accounting rules, no longer requiring double reporting and making accounting now fully consistent with the UNFCCC reporting rules.

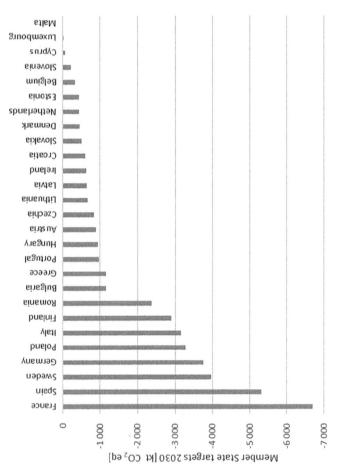

FIGURE 8.3   Net removal targets for EU Member States

Source: EU Regulation (2018)[13]

The revised Regulation consists of two phases:

- Phase 1 from 2021 to 2025: Remains close to the 2018 LULUCF Regulation, including the "no debit" rule and the accounting rules for the different land use categories.
- Phase 2 from 2026 to 2030: This phase enlarges the territorial scope to cover all managed land, simplifies compliance rules, and enhances data monitoring using advanced technologies like remote sensing and Earth observation.

The revised Regulation improves governance and enhances the quality of monitoring, reporting, and verification of emissions and removals through to new land monitoring technologies, techniques, and datasets generated by the EU's Common Agriculture Policy[14] (CAP). Better information will help Member States adopt more effective policies and measures, and land managers take up new carbon farming schemes (ways of farming that sequestrate carbon in the soil) and land management practices. Besides, the Regulation promotes synergies between climate mitigation and environmental protection measures to contribute to addressing the climate and biodiversity crisis.

Member States' National Energy and Climate Plans (NECPs)[15] play a crucial role in achieving increased targets by identifying coherent policies and programmes across relevant policy areas, including land management and carbon sinks. They are responsible for caring for and expanding their carbon sinks to meet their national targets and creating synergies with other relevant policy areas. NECPs also need to explain how policies contribute to their increased ambition in the ESR, which includes agriculture non-CO_2 emissions. The role of NECPs has increased in importance, with the potential of the CAP and new CAP Strategic Plans[16] in funding and delivering meaningful change being essential factors for success.

Detailed features of the new Regulation with its two phases are shown in the Table 8.1 at the end of this chapter.

Conclusion: A separate EU LULUCF sector has been established alongside the EU ETS, with a target of removing 310 million tonnes of CO_2eq by 2030. The enhanced legal framework also focuses on improved monitoring and reporting and on maximising synergy between climate mitigation and environmental protection.

TABLE 8.1 LULUCF regulation

	1st compliance period (2021–2025)	2nd compliance period (2026–2030)
Target	No debit rule commitment (Article 4.1)	Increase of the net sink by 42 Mt CO_2eq, compared to the average of the period 2016–2018 (Article 4.2), distributed among Member States
Land categories	Afforested land, deforested land, managed cropland, managed grassland, managed forest land, managed wetland (optional), harvested wood products (Article 2.1)	Forest land, cropland, grassland, wetlands, settlements, other land, harvested wood products (Article 2.2)
Accounting vs Reporting approach	**Accounting approach:** Accounting rules go beyond reporting rules and involve comparing reporting values against reference values. Accounted values are assessed against the "no-debit" commitment.	**Reporting approach:** Simplified rules in comparison to accounting. Reporting involves documenting the level and development of GHG emissions and removals over time, encompassing anthropogenic and biological processes influenced by human activities, following international guidelines under the UNFCCC. Reported values are assessed against the target in the process of compliance check.
Natural disturbances accounting Emissions resulting from natural disturbances	x (Article 10) exempted from accounting under specific conditions	x (Article 13b) compensated for under specific conditions and subject to the EU achieving its target
ESR flexibility (Article 12) Member States failing to meet LULUCF targets can transfer remaining annual emission allocations under the ESR to LULUCF; and vice versa.	X	x

(Continued)

TABLE 8.1 (Continued)

	1st compliance period (2021–2025)	2nd compliance period (2026–2030)
General flexibility (Article 12) Member States exceeding LULUCF targets can transfer remaining LULUCF overachievement to another Member State needing it to meet its target.	X	x
Managed forest land flexibility (Article 13) Allows a Member State to compensate emissions from managed forest land under specific conditions.	X	
Additional compensation for Finland (Article 13a) An extra 5 Mt CO2eq of emissions may be compensated under specific land accounting categories under specific conditions.	X	
Land use mechanism (Article 13b) Applicable to Member States missing targets or budgets during 2026–2030 but conditional on the EU achieving its target.		x
Compliance deadlines	Member States must comply with the "no debit rule" for the period 2021–2025 and the compliance check will be carried out in 2027. (Article 14)	The compliance check for the 2030 target will be carried out in 2032. (Article 14)

Data Source: Regulation (EU) 2018/841[17]

8.3 Scaling Up Carbon Removals and Ensuring Credibility

The Commission proposal for a Framework Regulation on an EU-wide Certification Framework for Carbon Removals[18] aims to establish standards and procedures for certifying carbon removals, inter alia, achieved through land-use projects, such as afforestation, reforestation, forest management and sustainable agriculture practices. These certified activities can contribute to the overall mitigation efforts within the LULUCF sector. The Certification Framework also covers industrial removals, such as carbon capture and storage[19] as well as long-term carbon storage in products such as wooden buildings.

High-quality carbon removals, under this framework, are defined by stringent criteria that ensure their efficacy, long-term impact and environmental integrity. These criteria encompass:

- Quantification: Accurate measurement and quantification of carbon removals.
- Additionality: Demonstrating that carbon removal activities go beyond market practices and what is legally required.
- Storage duration: Certificates clearly account for the duration of carbon storage and distinguish permanent storage from temporary storage.
- Sustainability: Carbon removal activities should not harm the environment or should benefit other environmental objectives such as biodiversity.

Robust monitoring and accounting systems are essential to provide appropriate incentives to farmers and forest owners. To ensure adherence to EU quality criteria for carbon removals, operators of such activities must engage with recognised or Commission-approved certification schemes. Independent bodies will rigorously verify and certify the compliance of carbon removal operations with EU regulations, leading to the issuance of compliance certificates and the recording of removal units in publicly managed registries.

Based on the criteria for high-quality removals, the Commission, supported by an Expert Group,[20] will develop tailored certification methodologies for the different types of carbon removal activities.

The Carbon Removal Certification Framework's enduring potential lies in its capacity to drive widespread and impactful carbon removal practices across sectors, fostering innovative solutions and contributing significantly to the EU's climate neutrality objectives.

8.4 An Enabling Environment for Climate Action in Forestry and Agriculture

The land use sector often contributes to multiple environmental goals such as biodiversity, pollution reduction, and responsible resource management, all of which are central to the European Green Deal. Building upon its principles, a range of EU policy developments have been set in motion to address the interplay between environmental, social, and economic aspects of land use within the EU. These policies not only promote sustainable land use sector practices but also serve as a catalyst for further climate actions within EU Member States. The following ones are of particular importance:

- EU Energy Policy: The implementation of the RES Directive and biofuels quota continue to have a major impact on the demand for sustainable biomass, and hence on the management of cropland and forests.
- The Common Agricultural Policy (CAP): While the CAP encompasses various aspects of agricultural policy, it plays a crucial role in shaping the land sector by promoting sustainable land management practices, biodiversity conservation, climate change mitigation, and rural development. It is potentially able to provide financial incentives for farmers to adopt environmentally friendly practices, ensuring the long-term sustainability of European agriculture and rural areas.
- EU Strategy on Adaptation to Climate Change: It recognises that land-related activities are vulnerable to climate change, such as extreme weather events, rising temperatures, and changing precipitation patterns, and aims to support adaptive measures in the land use sector.
- EU Biodiversity Strategy for 2030: The strategy aims to restore and protect Europe's biodiversity by 2030. This strategy recognises the interdependence of biodiversity conservation and land-related activities. It seeks to integrate biodiversity objectives into these sectors for holistic and coherent implementation of EU measures.
- Circular Economy Action Plan: It seeks to transition the EU to a more circular and resource-efficient economy. It includes measures to reduce waste, promote recycling and reuse of, for example, wood products, and minimise the environmental footprint of land-related activities.
- Forest Strategy: The strategy aims to ensure the sustainable management of forests, enhance their contribution to climate change mitigation, and protect biodiversity. It focuses on promoting sustainable forestry practices, forest restoration, and the use of wood-based products.
- Farm to Fork Strategy: The strategy aims to make the EU food system more sustainable, from production to consumption. It promotes sustainable agricultural practices to enhance carbon sequestration, reduces the use of chemical pesticides and fertilisers, and enhances biodiversity conservation in agricultural landscapes.
- Carbon Cycles Communication: The communication presents an action plan to develop sustainable solutions for increasing carbon removals and addresses key challenges related to the carbon cycle. It promotes nature-based solutions, technological advancements, and the use of

long-lasting products like wooden buildings to enhance carbon removal and storage.

- Nature Restoration Law: The Commission proposal provides a legal framework and guidelines for promoting nature restoration activities, including the rehabilitation of degraded ecosystems, reforestation, wetland restoration, and the creation of green infrastructure.
- Soil Monitoring Law: The objective of this Commission proposal is to have all soils in healthy conditions by 2050. The proposal provides for a harmonised definition of soil health and puts in place monitoring framework.
- Forest Monitoring Law: The Commission proposal establishes a comprehensive forest knowledge base through enhanced monitoring, fostering cooperation among Member States, supporting long-term forest plans, and facilitating the marketing of ecosystem services. It aims to improve the accuracy and reliability of data on forest-related parameters, which are essential for assessing the carbon sequestration potential and emissions from the LULUCF sector.
- Sustainable Finance – EU Taxonomy Regulation: The EU Taxonomy is a classification system that helps companies and investors identify "environmentally sustainable" economic activities to make sustainable investment decisions. It includes the forest sector (afforestation, forest conservation, forest management and forest rehabilitation and restauration) and the restauration of wetlands.
- Deforestation-free supply chains Regulation: The law requires key goods like palm oil, soy, timber, and their derivatives to be deforestation-free when exported or placed on the EU. Companies must conduct strict due diligence, ensuring products are sourced sustainably and comply with human rights standards. The regulation applies globally, encouraging sustainable practices and supply chain transparency.

To accelerate climate action and support the agriculture and forestry sectors, it is crucial to establish direct incentives for the adoption of climate-friendly practices. One important approach is carbon farming, which can play a pivotal role in achieving a climate-neutral economy by capturing CO_2 from the atmosphere. Several measures can be implemented. The first is the Common Agricultural Policy (CAP) that supports farmers who commit to specific environmental and climate practices or investments, with income support. The Carbon Removal Certification Framework enables a business model that rewards land managers for carbon sequestration. A second element is the standardisation of monitoring, reporting and verification in view of providing a clear and reliable framework for carbon farming. The Soil and Forest Monitoring Laws put in place a solid and coherent monitoring framework for all soils and forests. These measures will ensure transparency and trust in the carbon farming process, enabling land managers to participate with confidence. Finally, improved knowledge and advisory services are important. Land managers need access to improved knowledge, data management tools and tailored advisory services to effectively engage in climate-friendly practices. By providing the necessary support and guidance, land managers can make informed decisions and maximise the potential of carbon farming.

In addition to direct incentives, funding opportunities from various EU programmes can further support climate action in the agriculture, land use and forestry sectors. The EU's research and innovation program, Horizon Europe, allocates a specific budget of €10 billion to support projects in food, agriculture, rural development and the bioeconomy. The Mission "A Soil Deal for Europe" is a key funding instrument to support the adoption and scaling up of carbon farming practices. The new European Bauhaus aims to transform the built environment into a sustainable, inclusive and enriching space through creative, participatory and transdisciplinary approaches. It emphasises the use of wood as a sustainable material for long-lasting products. Finally, there is the EU's environment and climate instrument, LIFE, that offers support for the agriculture and forestry sectors in activities such as biodiversity conservation, improvement of air and water quality, and climate change mitigation and adaptation. LIFE projects serve as testing grounds for innovative approaches and methods related to climate-smart agriculture and land use. Successful projects can be scaled up and integrated into larger EU policies, including the CAP or national policies.

By combining direct incentives, standardised frameworks, and funding opportunities, an enabling environment can be created to drive climate action, promote sustainable land management, and encourage the adoption of climate-friendly practices in agriculture and forestry.

> Conclusion: EU policies already promote sustainable practices in agriculture and forestry, with incentives under the Common Agricultural Policy (CAP), revenues from carbon farming and funding from programmes like Horizon Europe and the LIFE Program.

Conclusion

The agriculture and forestry sectors represent a growing area of attention for climate policy around the world. One reason is that they not only emit greenhouse gases but can also become an important source of removals of carbon dioxide from the atmosphere. Globally, a quarter of the planned emission reductions by 2030 will come from the land use sector, mainly through the reduction of deforestation in developing countries.

Further reductions in greenhouse gas emissions and increasing removals will become more challenging in the EU, especially where farmers and foresters experience hotter summers and scarcer water resources. While other sectors in the EU will substantially decarbonise by 2050, a large part of agricultural emissions are due to biological processes that are difficult to be reduced to the same extent. They will constitute one-third of total EU emissions and remain inevitable residual emissions largely driven by demand for specific agricultural products especially beef and milk. In the second half of the century, when global and EU emissions will have to reduce to net zero and below, the agriculture, forestry, and land use sectors will be key to balancing the remaining emissions with sufficient removals.

The LULUCF emissions are part of the overall EU target of a greenhouse gas reduction of "at least 55%" by 2030. This sector constitutes a reinforced pillar alongside the EU Emissions Trading System and the Effort Sharing Regulation, with a specific target of 310 Mt CO_2eq of carbon removals by 2030.

It is now high time to develop appropriate policies to improve the uptake of carbon into Europe's soils and forests. As there are still many uncertain elements about the fluxes of CO_2 the land use sector generates, much attention has been paid to how to better monitor and account for these emissions. For that reason, an EU-wide certification regulation of carbon removals is being developed and will ultimately allow for rewarding of efforts by farmers and foresters to remove carbon from the atmosphere.

Notes

1 This is a review of the chapter originally drafted by Artur Runge-Metzger and Peter Wehrheim.
2 This includes introducing leguminous crops, reducing fertiliser and fuel use through precision farming, improving manure storage, enhancing livestock breeding practices, and implementing conservation agriculture techniques to improve soil carbon content, preserving grasslands, transforming wetlands and peatlands, combining agriculture with trees, afforestation on marginal lands, optimising forest use and utilising biomass for wooden buildings.
3 Eurostat (May, 2021) Land use statistics https://ec.europa.eu/eurostat/statistics-explained/index.php?title=Land_use_statistics (2018).
4 EEA (2023) "Annual European Union Greenhouse Gas Inventory 1990–2021 and Inventory Report 2023." Submission to the UNFCCC Secretariat. EEA/PUBL/2023/044, Copenhagen.
5 IPCC Guidelines for National Greenhouse Gas Inventories (2006) *Volume 4 Agriculture, Forestry and Other Land Use.* Available at: https://www.ipcc-nggip.iges.or.jp/public/2006gl/vol4.html.
6 Reviewing the contribution of the land use, land-use change and forestry sector to the Green Deal (2021).

7 European Union (2023) *National Inventory Report (NIR)*, p. 590. Available at: https://unfccc.int/documents/627851.

8 In 2019, land with organic soils occupied just 4.2% of the total land area but emitting 108 MtCO2.

9 Commission Implementing Decision (EU) 2023/1319 of 28 June 2023 amending Implementing Decision (EU) 2020/2126 to revise Member States' annual emission allocations for the period from 2023 to 2030. Available at: https://eur-lex.europa.eu/legal-content/EN/TXT/?uri=CELEX%3A32023D1319&qid=1688028580045.

10 Decision No 529/2013/EU of the European Parliament and of the Council of 21 May 2013 on accounting rules on greenhouse gas emissions and removals resulting from activities relating to land use, land-use change and forestry and on information concerning actions relating to those activities (europa.eu).

11 https://eur-lex.europa.eu/legal-content/EN/TXT/?uri=CELEX%3A32018R0841.

12 Consolidated text: Regulation (EU) 2018/841 of the European Parliament and of the Council of 30 May 2018 on the inclusion of greenhouse gas emissions and removals from land use, land use change and forestry in the 2030 climate and energy framework, and amending Regulation (EU) No 525/2013 and Decision No 529/2013/EU. Available at: https://eur-lex.europa.eu/legal-content/EN/TXT/?uri=CELEX%3A02018R0841-20230511.

13 REGULATION (EU) 2018/841 OF THE EUROPEAN PARLIAMENT AND OF THE COUNCIL of 30 May 2018 on the inclusion of greenhouse gas emissions and removals from land use, land use change and forestry in the 2030 climate and energy framework, and amending Regulation (EU) No 525/2013 and Decision No 529/2013/EU (2018) Annex IIa. Available at: https://eur-lex.europa.eu/legal-content/EN/TXT/HTML/?uri=CELEX:32018R0841.

14 https://agriculture.ec.europa.eu/common-agricultural-policy/cap-overview/cap-glance_en.

15 https://commission.europa.eu/energy-climate-change-environment/implementation-eu-countries/energy-and-climate-governance-and-reporting/national-energy-and-climate-plans_en.

16 CAP Strategic Plans promote a shift to a smart, competitive, and diverse agriculture that ensures food security, while also supporting climate action, preserving natural resources, enhancing biodiversity, and boosting rural economies. See https://agriculture.ec.europa.eu/cap-my-country/cap-strategic-plans_en.

17 Consolidated text: Regulation (EU) 2018/841 of the European Parliament and of the Council of 30 May 2018 on the inclusion of greenhouse gas emissions and removals from land use, land use change and forestry in the 2030 climate and energy framework, and amending Regulation (EU) No 525/2013 and Decision No 529/2013/EU. Available at: https://eur-lex.europa.eu/legal-content/EN/TXT/?uri=CELEX%3A02018R0841-20230511.

18 COM(2022) 672 final 2022/0394 (COD). Available at: https://climate.ec.europa.eu/eu-action/sustainable-carbon-cycles/carbon-removal-certification_en.

19 Bioenergy carbon capture and storage (BECCS) and direct air carbon capture and storage (DACCS).

20 https://climate.ec.europa.eu/eu-action/sustainable-carbon-cycles/expert-group-carbon-removals_en.

9

ACCELERATING THE GREENING OF EU INDUSTRY

Stefaan Vergote and Christian Egenhofer

Introduction

From the very beginning, the development of climate policy has been closely scrutinised for its potential impact on overall economic development and welfare. At EU level, this has been most prominent by using cost-effectiveness as a central guiding principle for the overall climate strategy to deliver 2020 and 2030 targets.[1] In combination with specific instruments to deal with distributional and social aspects, broad political acceptance was obtained. Gradually, a wider policy approach emerged not only to create low-carbon technologies, but more importantly to deploy these at scale and to make them competitive on global markets. The new geopolitical context has accelerated this process and the EU is now implementing a policy of 'open strategic autonomy'[2] in which the low-carbon industry plays a central role. This chapter describes how several key elements of this policy emerged over the last decade.

9.1 The New Policy Context

Along with the deployment of carbon pricing, policy instruments were developed offering specific support to push certain technologies into the market. This approach has been most prominent in the field of renewable energy, where demand was supported through instruments such as feed-in tariffs for solar, wind and other renewable technologies. In the first decade of the 21st century, Germany offered considerable subsidies for solar PV equivalent to a premium of 500€/tonne CO_2. This was the result of a consensus between those that advocated a strong climate policy, and those that wanted Germany to become the global leader in PV technology. In 2008, the CEO of Q-Cells, a German PV manufacturer, was quoted in the *New York Times* saying, "*To develop a technology, you've got to create an industry. You can wait and wait and wait for costs to come down, but it takes too long*".

DOI: 10.4324/9781003493730-12

Fifteen years later, a few lessons have been learned. The costs of feed-in tariffs spiralled and the policy had to be adapted, for instance, through organising competitive auctions for renewable energy. As the sector was maturing and growing at record pace, manufacturing shifted almost completely to South-East Asia, China in particular. Having largely ignored the supply side of the equation, solar feed-in tariffs ended up in failure from an industrial policy perspective. At the same time, the CEO of Q-cells was right: the policy did create the industry, but not in Germany. Massive cost reductions were realised, beyond anyone's expectations, to the extent that solar PV is now the most competitive power generation technology in almost all parts of the world. As such, positive spillovers have made it a very successful global climate policy.

Ambitious climate targets necessarily involved larger parts of the economy and the production of materials such as steel, cement, non-ferrous metals, chemicals, and ceramics came into focus. Climate neutral[3] materials will require the deployment of new breakthrough technologies. Increasingly, these are being seen as an economic opportunity for the European industry, tapping into a growing market. This has been formulated in subsequent industrial strategies, ultimately leading to the Green Deal Industrial Plan in early 2023.

However, climate neutral technologies and industries face a cost gap, which sometimes is referred to as 'green premium'. Carbon pricing under the EU ETS has been able to narrow this cost gap. In some sectors such as cement production, a CO_2 price of €90 or more per tonne makes solutions for climate neutral technologies more economic compared to conventional production, provided carbon leakage protection is ensured. However, in other sectors additional policies are necessary to close the cost gap. The transformation of industrial processes, such as direct reduced iron (DRI) with hydrogen, electrified chemical processes or cement production with carbon capture and storage require high investments and they are unlikely to be paid back under current carbon price expectations. The industrial transition not only requires affordable low-carbon energy like renewable electricity, green hydrogen, or bio-methane, but also a shift in feedstock to biomass or recycled materials. This will require the further development of electricity, hydrogen or recycling infrastructure.

Green hydrogen is expected to be necessary for the decarbonisation of certain industries and could become a game changer for industries with a wide range of uses, e.g. as feed-stock in the chemical industry for the manufacture of ammonia, methanol and other chemicals, as well as for various refinery and metallurgical processes. A significant decline of the cost of green hydrogen would make a business case for the decarbonisation of some industries in a not-too-distant future. Similarly, carbon capture, utilisation and storage could open up new low-carbon business opportunities for energy-intensive industries.

Materials are often characterised by globally integrated value chains where feedstock is traded across borders, dependent on raw materials that are mostly not available in Europe. Dependencies and associated risks can be reduced through material efficiency, substitution with climate neutral inputs including recycling, re-use or industrial symbiosis, pointing to the importance of the circular economy. Already the 2018 Long-Term Strategy "A Clean Planet for All"[4] stated that net-zero target achievement necessitates more circularity of materials and feedstocks.

A final element of the decarbonisation of materials is the creation of lead markets for climate neutral and circular products supported by novel industrial processes and clean technologies. The most important materials value chains such as construction, steel, textiles and plastics are already covered both by the EU ETS as well as materials efficiency policies, notably the forthcoming Eco-design Regulation. These create a demand for low-carbon materials and it is only recently that the Commission came forward with measures to support the supply of such production, not least through the Net-Zero Industrial Act. While the demand factor was more dominant in Europe, in other jurisdictions such as the US and China, the emphasis has been much more on stimulating the production of low-carbon materials, compared to demand-driven policies.

Since 2020, the question of how to accelerate low-carbon innovation through a Green Industrial Policy has come prominently back to the fore. The COVID pandemic led to supply disruptions and made policymakers acutely aware of the risks associated with dependence on highly complex global supply chains. More recently, the vulnerability of Europe's energy system was demonstrated following the Russian invasion of Ukraine. The EU responded with the REPowerEU Plan to phase out dependence on Russian gas. At the same time the EU realised that policies are needed to avoid that the deployment of low-carbon solutions might enhance other dependencies on other trading partners, for instance, in terms of import of batteries, rare earth materials, or solar PV. Figure 9.1 illustrates to which degree China is dominating various supply chains in clean tech manufacturing. More importantly, it is estimated that the global market for key manufactured net-zero technologies is set to triple by 2030 to around €600 billion per year.

Finally, geopolitical tensions and trade disputes are on the rise, in particular between the US and China. In 2022, the US adopted the Inflation Reduction Act. It is so far the most comprehensive and ambitious effort by the US to tackle climate change and bring the US on an emissions path consistent

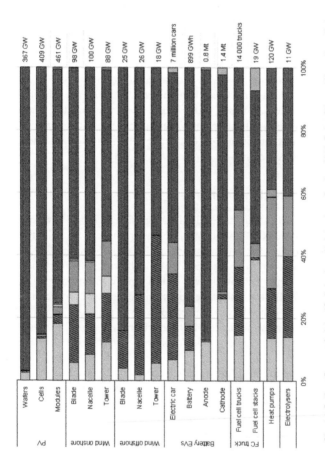

FIGURE 9.1   Regional shares of manufacturing capacity for selected clean technologies

Source: IEA (2023)[5]

with its pledges for 2030 and 2050.[6] But it is also a straightforward industrial policy, deploying (at times extremely generous) production and investment subsidies, accompanied by local content rules, aimed at attracting clean tech industries to the US and catching up with China. While the EU had mainly been relying on demand creation and innovation support focusing on early deployment, the US is now favouring domestic protection hoping that a cheap and abundant supply will lead to the creation of its demand.[7]

Figure 9.1 also shows that Europe does hold a substantial manufacturing base in the supply chains of wind, electric vehicles, electrolysers and heat pumps. However, a period of increased clean tech competition has started and the rules of the game, in the past contained in the context of WTO, are shifting rapidly. Through the Green Deal Industrial Plan, Europe formulated a strategic response called *open strategic autonomy*, a concept that aims to enhance Europe's self-sufficiency and independence in critical areas while staying open to global trade and cooperation. How that is enfolding in practice is outlined in the next sessions.

9.2   The Innovation Fund

One of the first EU initiatives specifically designed to accelerate low-carbon innovation was the NER300 programme.[8] The overwhelming majority of the revenues from the ETS auctioning are flowing to the Member States, but in 2013 it was decided to set aside 300 million allowances to fund innovative renewable energy technologies and carbon capture and storage projects. However, the low EU ETS allowance prices limited the overall budget and in total only some €2 billion was committed covering 39 projects. The NER300 was, nevertheless, a useful start in which experience was gained, such as the need for more mature projects and the importance of an effective governance system.[9]

As a follow-up to the NER300, the Innovation Fund was created.[10] In the 2023 ETS revision, an amount of 530 million ETS allowances was set aside for the period 2021–2030. At an average carbon price of €80, this corresponds to an overall budget of some €42 billion, one of the world's largest funding programmes for the commercial *demonstration* of innovative low-carbon technologies. It places itself in between on the one hand the research programmes of Horizon Europe, and on the other, full-scale commercial deployment of mature technologies, the demand for which is incentivised by other policies such as the ETS and the Renewable Energy Directive and co-financing instruments such as InvestEU[11] and structural funds (Figure 9.2). The demonstration phase is particularly challenging as many promising innovations fail in this so-called 'valley-of death'.[12]

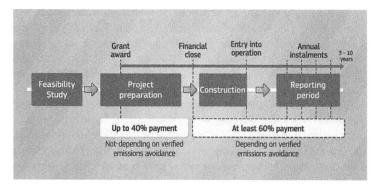

FIGURE 9.2   The Innovation Fund as part of the innovation value chain

Source: European Commission[13]

The European Commission has the overall responsibility for the Innovation Fund, including defining the budget and policy priorities of calls for proposals, adopting the award decisions and reporting to Council and Parliament.[14] An evaluation process by independent experts is a crucial governance element and ensures a selection based on excellence without political interference.[15]

The Innovation Fund focuses on the following areas:

- Industrial decarbonisation, including, amongst others, CCS, CCU and the substitution of carbon-intensive products
- Innovative renewable energy technologies, including the manufacture of equipment and components
- Innovative energy storage technologies, including the manufacture of equipment and components
- Innovative technologies in buildings and transport, maritime and aviation such as battery manufacturing, hydrogen applications, and the production of synthetic fuels (based on carbon capture and utilisation)

The Innovation Fund supports up to 60% of the relevant costs, i.e. generally covering capital and operational costs minus revenues, over the first ten years of operation. The fact that additional operational costs during the first ten years can be taken into account as eligible cost is essential for the financial viability of many projects, especially in the field of industrial decarbonisation. For instance, it has turned out that additional costs linked to the use of renewable electricity or hydrogen, as compared to conventional fossil fuel-based industrial processes, are of critical importance for the deployment phase.

In the first two calls, 23 large-scale and 46 small-scale projects were funded, for a total budget of more than €3 billion. As there was no firm knowledge on the potential project pipeline, the Commission did not indicate any prioritisation and followed a bottom-up approach in these initial calls. This gave flexibility to project promoters to come forward with their most promising projects. A broad portfolio of technologies was supported including clean hydrogen production and application, CCUS (carbon capture, storage and utilisation), recycling/reuse and renewable energy. Some important areas such as clean tech manufacturing and energy storage attracted less interest in the first calls. Blending, mixing public and private finance, has been important. On average, total capital investment have been four times higher than the support offered by the Innovation Fund. In addition, calls for proposals have been massively oversubscribed. For instance, the second large-scale call, with a budget of €1.5 billion, received 138 applications, with a total funding request of €12.1 billion. A large number of projects that were evaluated as being of high quality could unfortunately not be funded due to lack of budget.

Following the Russian invasion of Ukraine, the European Commission adopted the REPowerEU Plan, aiming to rapidly reduce the EU's dependence on fossil fuel imports from Russia. A range of measures was put forward to save more energy, substitute fossil fuels by renewable energy, and diversify supply routes for gas and oil. Consumers and producers reacted to the new situation: gas demand has been significantly lowered, additional LNG terminals have been built in record time notably in Germany, gas import from other countries such as the US has surged, and the deployment of renewables, in particular solar, has accelerated.[16] The REPowerEU plan also had an impact on the Innovation Fund, including the decision to double the funding available for the 2022 large-scale call to €3 billion. In addition, the Commission decided to move away from the pure bottom-up approach and defined four 'policy windows'.

1   **Innovative electrification and hydrogen applications in industry** focusing on demonstrating industrial applications that do not rely on fossil fuels, notably gas.
2   **Innovative clean tech manufacturing** aimed to foster the manufacturing of equipment in the field of renewable energy technologies (solar PV, wind), electrolysers, heat pumps and, most importantly, batteries, with a view to meet REPowerEU targets.
3   **Mid-sized pilot projects** that could attract smaller innovators and scale ups and seeking projects aiming to validate, test and optimise highly innovative solutions, prior to the first commercial applications. This window aimed to focus on earlier stage projects with high technical risk, in contrast to previous calls.

4 **General decarbonisation** covering the entire scope of the Innovation Fund, so as to continue to serve the existing pipeline of projects, as previous calls were continuously oversubscribed, with many high-quality projects previously not selected due to lack of budget.

As was the case in previous calls, the third large-scale call was oversubscribed, attracting applications to the tune of €18 billion. In total, 41 projects were selected across the four policy windows, with a budget of €3.6 billion. In the field of clean tech manufacturing, 11 projects were pre-selected, including four projects in electrolyser manufacturing, four on battery manufacturing (including recycling), and three on PV cells and modules, making a first significant contribution to the objectives of the Net-Zero Industry Act (see Section 9.6).

Conclusion: Project selection in the Innovation Fund is based on excellence, EU-wide competition and flexibility in programme management. The Innovation Fund supported a broad portfolio of industrial decarbonisation technologies (CCS, CCU, hydrogen applications, alternative process technologies) as well as clean tech manufacturing projects (batteries, solar PV, electrolysers). Private capital has been leveraged and a fair geographical balance was achieved.

9.3   The Battery Alliance

The EU is gradually tightening the average emissions of the new passenger car fleet in view of the phasing out of the internal combustion engine by 2035.[17] This will require the large-scale deployment of zero-emission vehicles, notably battery electric vehicles. A discussion unfolded on the consequences for the European automotive industry supply chain, the loss of employment linked to the manufacture of internal combustion engines, and the question in how far the European automotive industry would competitively transition towards electrification. The lack of any meaningful Li-ion battery production in Europe, TESLA's growing success, and China's Industrial Policy programme (Made in China 2025) all fuelled such concerns.

In the past five years, the Commission took a number of initiatives that can be seen as the industrial supply-side pillar of the CO_2 and car strategy. These include:

- The formation of a European Battery Alliance, a partnership with industry, Member States and research organisations to support the development of a competitive and sustainable battery value chain in Europe.
- A Strategic Action Plan for Batteries adopted in 2018, setting out a framework of regulatory and non-regulatory measures to support all segments of the battery value chain.[18]
- Launch of Important Projects of Common European Interest (IPCEI's) in the field of batteries.[19] Two IPCEI have been approved for a total amount of €6.2 billion of State aid from 12 Member States for research, development and innovation (RDI) and first industrial deployment (FID), expecting to unlock an additional €13.8 billion of private investment.
- A new European Batteries Partnership was established with a budget of €1 billion to strengthen and coordinate research on batteries, in collaboration with industry and research organisations.
- The Batteries Regulation[20] aims to control and improve the environmental performance of batteries sold on the EU market, including provisions for collection, re-use and recycling. The recycling provisions will become increasingly important to reduce dependence on the import of raw or refined materials, and enhance the security of supply of Europe's battery supply chain.

The combination of a strong demand side policy based on the single market (CO_2 and cars legislation) with supply-side measures coordinated at European level allowed the emergence of a manufacturing hub for batteries. By mid-2021, six giga factories with a total Li-ion cell production capacity of 62GWh were operational. Both home-grown companies, such as Northvolt, as well as foreign companies (China, South-Korea, Japan) are investing at substantial scale. Some are projecting a production capacity of more than 500GWh by 2025 in the EU.

Many questions about the future still remain. Will Chinese automotive companies succeed in further scaling up export of battery electric vehicles to Europe? What will be the effect of the Inflation Reduction Act, with the advanced manufacturing tax credit implying an unprecedented production subsidy for US based battery cell/component production[21]?

> Conclusion: A manufacturing hub on batteries is emerging in the EU based on a strong demand for electric vehicles combined with supply-side measures such as standard setting, recycling rules, and coordinated financial support by the EU and its Member States.

9.4 The Role of State Aid: The Temporary Crisis and Transition Framework (TCTF)

As part of the response to the US Inflation Reduction Act, the European Commission revised in 2023 the Temporary Crisis and Transition Framework to foster support measures in sectors which are key for the transition to a net-zero economy. This amends and prolongs in part the Temporary Crisis Framework, adopted in 2022 to enable Member States to support the economy in the context of Russia's war against Ukraine.

First, the new framework prolongs the possibility for Member States to further support measures needed for the transition towards a net-zero economy such as accelerating the rollout of renewable energy and energy storage, and schemes for the decarbonisation of industrial production processes. It also expands the options and flexibility for national aid, in terms of scope, aid ceilings and support mechanisms.

The biggest change, however, is the introduction of new guidelines, applicable until the end of 2025, enabling investment support for the manufacturing of strategic equipment, namely batteries, solar panels, wind turbines, heat-pumps, electrolysers and carbon capture usage and storage as well as for production of key components and for production and recycling of related critical raw materials. This marks a major change in a long-standing competition policy where aid for manufacturing, being at the heart of the single market, is severely restricted.[22] Specifically, Member States may design simple and effective schemes, providing support capped at a certain percentage of the investment costs and nominal amounts, depending on the location of the investment and the size of the beneficiary, as defined in the table below.

In exceptional cases, Member States can provide higher support to individual companies, where there is a real risk of investments being diverted away from Europe. In such situations, Member States may provide either the amount of support the beneficiary could receive for an equivalent investment in that alternative location (the so-called 'matching aid'), or the amount needed to incentivise the company to locate the investment in the European Economic Area (the so-called 'funding gap'), whichever is the lowest. This option is subject to safeguards. First, it can be used only for (i) investments taking place in assisted areas, as defined in the applicable regional aid map; or (ii) cross-border investments involving projects located in at least three Member States, with a significant part of the overall investment taking place in at least two assisted areas, one of which is an "a" area (outermost regions or regions whose GDP per capita is below or equal to 75% of the EU average). Second, the beneficiary should use state-of-the-art production technology from an environmental perspective. Third, the aid cannot trigger relocation of investments between Member States.

The revision of these State aid guidelines reflects a balance between those Member States with the desire and fiscal space to support and attract clean tech investments, responding to the US IRA, and others, mostly smaller and less wealthy Member States.

Conclusion: State aid rules have been adapted under the Temporary Crisis and Transition Framework to incentivise the manufacturing of strategic equipment such as batteries, solar panels, wind turbines, heat-pumps, electrolysers and carbon capture usage and storage.

9.5   The Hydrogen Bank and EU-Level Auctioning under the Innovation Fund

Hydrogen is currently widely used in the chemistry industry for activities such as oil refining or the production of ammonia (fertiliser) and methanol. Almost all hydrogen is produced globally through steam-reforming of methane or through gasification of coal,[23] both very CO_2-intensive processes. The role of hydrogen is likely to become more prominent in a fully decarbonised energy system. To play this role, clean, low-carbon hydrogen will have to be produced, by water electrolysis using carbon-free electricity, or from natural gas steam reforming using carbon capture and storage. Hydrogen could potentially contribute to decarbonise various sectors: as a storable energy carrier to provide dispatchable power complementing renewable electricity; as an energy carrier option where electrification is not possible or too expensive and/or as a feedstock for industry such as steel, chemicals and synthetic fuels in those sectors which are most difficult to decarbonise.

The role of clean hydrogen in the transition was first recognised in the 2018 'Clean Planet for All' Communication.[24] Following the launch of the Green Deal, the Commission developed a Hydrogen Strategy[25] in 2020, addressing the development of a full supply chain (production, infrastructure and demand) as well as international aspects. The Strategy set out the objective to produce up to 10 million tonnes of renewable hydrogen in the EU. The REPowerEU Plan proposed to complement this goal by facilitating 10 million tonnes of renewable hydrogen imports by 2030. A comprehensive legislative framework for the production, consumption, infrastructure development and market rules for a future hydrogen market was developed, as well as quotas for renewable hydrogen consumption in industry and transport.

The development of a hydrogen supply chain at a scale in line with stated policy ambitions will require very large and coordinated investments, in the order of several hundred billion Euros. It will also necessitate, at least in the short to medium term, substantial public funding in the knowledge that, even with current carbon and natural gas prices, the production of renewable hydrogen is still more expensive than fossil hydrogen without CCS. State-aid was approved for two rounds of Important Projects of Common European Interest (IPCEIs) to support the production and use of renewable and electricity-based hydrogen for a total amount of €10.6 billion in funding, expected to unlock an additional €15.8 billion in private investments.

With all these aspects in mind, the European Commission launched in 2023 the "European Hydrogen Bank".[26] This funding initiative has the objective of supporting the creation of a market for renewable hydrogen in Europe. It will be organised around four pillars: (i) domestic market, (ii) international imports, (iii) transparency, and (iv) coordination with existing European and international financing instruments. The domestic pillar of the Hydrogen Bank is being implemented through the Innovation Fund, making use of an EU-wide auction. Following the revision of the ETS, the Innovation Fund can now use such 'competitive bidding' instruments as a complement to the regular grant programme as described in Section 9.2.

The major financial risk for a project producing renewable hydrogen relates to the electricity supply price, which can represent approximately 70%[27] of the costs of producing hydrogen via electrolysis. Public funding can hedge this risk in the operational stage of projects to mobilise private investments more easily. An efficient manner of supporting the value chain of hydrogen would be tackling the "green premium", i.e. the difference between the costs of producing it and the project's sales revenues. A first pilot auction was launched by the end of 2023 with a budget of €800 million under the Innovation Fund. In this way, the Commission aims to develop a cost-efficient and market-based instrument at EU level, to de-risk projects, and to maximise leverage of private capital. It can lead to price discovery and market formation. In addition, as compared to a grant-based approach, it can reduce administrative burden and allow for a faster approval procedure. In parallel, Member States are also launching auctions for green hydrogen.

To organise a successful auction, it is essential that all 'terms and conditions' of the auction, including all qualification requirements, the specific design of the auction and all financial and legal rights and obligations of successful bidders are fully available at the time of the auction. The Commission has, therefore, invested heavily in developing robust terms and conditions,[28] and has consulted stakeholders and Member States extensively to fine-tune the auction design.

Key elements of the auction design:[29]

- The auctioned good is RFNBO hydrogen, in line with the definitions and requirements form the Renewable Energy Directive and its Delegated Acts.
- Remuneration: fixed premium, pay-as-bid, first ten years of operation
- Ceiling price for the bids: 4.5 €/kg of hydrogen produced.
- Maximum budget restriction for each bid: one-third of the total available budget.

Two qualification requirements are particularly important

- In order to discover true costs and safeguard a level-playing field across the EU, cumulation of support awarded through the auction with State Aid is restricted, with only few exceptions. This aims to avoid that the same costs are covered twice by public support and that the auction is distorted.[30]
- Winning bidders need to deposit a completion bond equivalent to 5% of the envisaged support, so as to prevent speculative bidding. It helps to ensure that only mature projects are bidding into the auction, that winning projects are actually implemented and substantially reduces the administrative burden, for project promoters and authorities, to prove and assess project maturity.

The Commission has also offered the pilot auction as a service to Member States (Auctions-as-a-service[31]). This means that Member States can use the auction platform with own financial resources to support projects that are outside the available Innovation Fund budget. This is being facilitated by defining standard rules for Member States to design their national auction window in a way that is fully compatible with State aid rules. This approach could help reducing administrative burden, and avoiding a fragmentation of support, with each Member State developing its own support scheme with its own rules and procedures.

For the first auction on renewable Hydrogen launched in November 2023, Germany has committed a budget of €350 million to support projects in Germany, in addition to the €800 million from the EU Innovation Fund already foreseen for projects across Europe (Figure 9.3).

Conclusion: An emerging clean hydrogen market is facilitated through an EU-level auction creating a fixed 'green premium'. Competitive bidding instruments at EU level hold significant potential to accelerate early deployment and can be extended to other areas. The concept of 'Auctions-As-A-Service' pools national and EU financial resources under one platform.

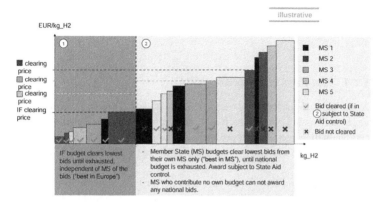

FIGURE 9.3   The role of the Member States in the EU hydrogen auction

Source: European Commission (2023)[32]

9.6   Towards a European Net-Zero Industry

The European Green Deal altered the functioning of the Innovation Fund, by including new 'competitive bidding instruments', such as 'carbon contracts of difference' and 'green premiums' offered through an auctioning mecha-nism. Such instruments can now be used as a complementary instrument to the regular Innovation Fund grant programme. While competitive bidding has been very successful to support the uptake of renewable energy in Member States, it is the first time that this kind of instrument will be used at EU level. It will support innovative low-carbon technologies, whose market penetra-tion is held back by lower costs of incumbent fossil-based technologies and high-risk perception by private investors. It is particularly suited for the scale up and early deployment of innovative technologies, where technical risks have been largely overcome. Particular advantages of this instrument include explicit price discovery, pursuing higher cost efficiency in awarding support (an issue particularly important at the stage of early deployment, when over-all investment figures climb rapidly) and thus minimise public support while maximising the leverage of private capital.

Within the context of the Green Deal Industrial Plan,[33] the Commission also made new proposals to accelerate the green transition and enhance the EU's competitiveness in net-zero technologies. The Net-Zero Industry Act (NZIA) aims to improve the regulatory framework for manufacturing of net-zero technologies with a focus on overcoming barriers to scale-up manu-facturing. The Critical Raw Materials Act is narrowly related to it and con-centrates on access to critical raw materials. The Strategic Technologies for

Europe Platform (STEP) focuses, as part of the upcoming review of the EU's multi-annual budget on how to better target strategic technologies, including clean ones.

9.6.1   Net-Zero Industry Act (NZIA)

NZIA aims to facilitate investments in net-zero technology manufacturing by addressing barriers such as streamlining administrative requirements and facilitating permitting, opening access to markets in public procurement procedures, auctions, and schemes aimed at supporting private demand by consumers.

The Innovation Fund made an important first contribution to the policy objectives of the Net-Zero Industry Act by expanding EU production capacity for clean tech equipment by 2030.[34]

The Act also sets an EU objective of 50 million tonnes of annual CO_2 injection storage capacity by 2030. This aims to address an emerging coordination failure: while industrial sectors such as cement are increasingly ready to invest in capturing CO_2, driven by the CO_2 price and the prospect of the phase out of free allocation due to CBAM, they face a significant risk of not being able to have access to CO_2 storage sites. For instance, CCS projects selected under the Innovation Fund alone are expected to capture more than 10 million tonnes of CO_2 per year. However, there is today only one CO_2 storage site commercially available. This is Northern Light in Norway with an initial CO_2 injection capacity 1.5 million tonnes of CO_2, although other projects in the Netherlands, Denmark and Norway are in preparation. However, without additional action, projections point towards a substantial shortage of storage capacity in the coming decade.

To meet this objective, EU Oil and gas producers would be legally required to contribute *pro rata* of their oil and gas production in the EU. Oil and gas producers are indeed best placed to make such investments, as they have the geological expertise, the property rights, and the financial resources to

TABLE 9.1   Innovation fund supported production capacities contributing to NZIA objectives

	Total capacities of IF projects	NZIA 2030 policy objective	Contribution to 2030 NZIA objective (%)
Solar	4 GW	24 GW	17
Batteries	38 GWh	549 GWh	7
Electrolysers	2.75 GW	25 GW	11
CCS	10.4 m tonne of CO2	50 m tonne of CO2	21

Source: European Commission.

invest in such projects. As oil and gas production is spread over a substantial number of countries in the EU, it is to be expected that this obligation will also spur storage projects beyond the North Sea, such as the Mediterranean Sea, the Black Sea or onshore, thereby ensuring cheaper access to CO_2 storage across the Union. The Act provides flexibility to oil and gas producers to meet this obligation through joint ventures and agreements with other producers or third parties investing in CO_2 storage.

By mandating this first industrial-scale storage capacity to be available by 2030, investments in the capturing of CO_2 emissions are de-risked, and the relevant sectors can better coordinate their investments towards a European Net-Zero CO_2 transport and storage value chain that energy-intensive industries can use to decarbonise their operations.

9.6.2 Critical Raw Materials Act

The Critical Raw Materials Act also aims at scaling up net-zero technologies and products. Strategic or critical raw materials are those that are required for manufacturing in sectors considered to be of strategic importance owing to their use in sectors such as renewable energy, digital, space and defence technologies. Generally, they are projected to see a high demand growth.[35] The proposal concentrates on the upstream and external side where Europe is dependent on critical raw materials, while the 'twin' proposal, the Net-Zero Industrial Act focuses on the internal situation and was triggered by COVID-induced supply chain disruptions. EU's dependence in critical raw materials was defined mainly but not only by China's dominance in the envisaged sectors.

Three pillars are defined: (i) development and strengthening of critical raw materials value chains via finance, skills and standards; (ii) diversification through a combination of new international partnerships and, if possible; (iii) measures to ensure sustainable sourcing and circularity. The following lines of action have been set out:

- to strengthen the different stages of the European strategic raw materials value chain, by setting benchmarks for domestic extraction, processing and recycling of strategic raw materials.
- to diversify the EU's imports of critical raw materials to reduce strategic dependencies.
- to improve EU capacity to monitor and mitigate current and future risks of disruptions to the supply of critical raw materials.
- to ensure the free movement of critical raw materials on the single market.
- to ensure a high level of environmental protection, by improving circularity and sustainability.

The circularity dimension is prominently present and includes rules for Member States to adopt and implement measures such as increasing the re-use of products and components, increasing the collection of waste, in particular with high critical raw materials recovery potential. Another focus is on standards such as assessing conformity, certification schemes and environmental footprint declarations.

9.6.3   Strategic Technologies for Europe Platform (STEP)

The US IRA showed a strategic focus and straightforwardness in implementation, which is often felt lacking in EU instruments. In response, the Strategic Technologies for Europe Platform (STEP) aims to "reinforce, leverage and steer EU funds" to co-finance public funds into deep and digital technologies (e.g., microelectronics, quantum computing and artificial intelligence), clean tech (e.g., renewable energy, manufacturing and advanced materials) and biotechnologies (e.g., pharmaceuticals and biomanufacturing).

STEP aims to increase synergies in the complex landscape of EU funding. To achieve this objective, the proposal includes a Sovereignty Seal. The Seal would be awarded to projects contributing to STEP objectives if they meet minimum quality requirements for calls under the Innovation Fund, Horizon Europe, the Digital Europe programme, the European Defence Fund, and the EU4Health programme. It would serve as a quality label to attract additional funding and facilitate cumulation or combined funding of several EU instruments.

This instrument would also enable Member States to fund high-quality projects in the Innovation Fund that did not receive EU funding due to lack of budget, for instance, with structural funds, or through the Modernisation Fund. As this approach would still require State aid approval, the Commission is also working on aligning State aid and Innovation Fund procedures, with the aim to achieve a simultaneous decision.

STEP also proposes an – albeit limited – reinforcement of funds that are targeted specifically to promote STEP objectives. The Innovation Fund would receive €5 billion, to be spent in Member States with a GDP/cap below the EU average, and €3 billion would go to InvestEU. The European Defence Fund would have an additional €1.5 billion and Horizon Europe €0.5 billion. Those budgetary reinforcements, if agreed by the co-legislators, could lead to additional investments of around €110 billion, geared towards critical industrial technologies. Member States are encouraged to reprioritise their programmes such as their Recovery and Resilience Plans and Cohesion Funds.

Conclusion: The Green Deal Industrial Plan identified ways to strengthen the European clean tech industry. The Net-Zero Industry Act addresses implementation barriers such as permitting procedures. The Critical Raw Materials Act aims to manage Europe's dependence through own minerals production as well as new international partnerships. The Strategic Technologies for Europe Platform (STEP) identifies synergies between various EU funds.

Conclusion

The geopolitical context, the urgency of tackling climate change and the desire to reap economic benefits in the transition, will keep the question of how to green EU's industry on the table. The concept of 'open strategic autonomy' was adopted which broadly means to enhance Europe's self-sufficiency while staying open to global trade and cooperation. The first steps in this direction have been made, but much of the practical implementation still needs to be developed. Based on the experience so far, a number of lessons can be learned.

First, a green industrial policy is part of a complex policy mix, whereby carbon pricing plays a critical role. Carbon pricing reduces, or even eliminates, the 'funding gap' necessary for large-scale deployment of green technologies. From a climate perspective it is essential that businesses and consumers internalise the cost of emitting CO_2 in their investment and purchasing decisions. In this context, it is important to note that the US Inflation Reduction Act is expected to reduce emissions by some 40% in 2030 as compared to 2005, substantially lower than the US pledge under the Paris Agreement of 50–52%. While in the short term the US Inflation Reduction Act will be effective in attracting investments in clean tech manufacturing, it will be more difficult for long-lived industrial decarbonisation projects, such as clean hydrogen applications and CCUS, to remain competitive once the subsidies have dried up.

Secondly, the Green Deal Industrial Plan and the subsequently proposed legislation represents an important step towards a coherent green industrial policy, potentially enabling the EU to stay competitive in the green tech race. A strongly coordinated industrial policy at EU level preserves, and can even strengthen, the single market, rather than risking to distort it, which matters in the face of fierce competition with economic blocks such as China and the US. As evidenced by the Innovation Fund, it can create EU-wide excellence-based competition, awarding the best projects from across the EU, and still respect geographical balance. An EU-level approach helps the efficient allocation of resources, e.g. select investments using the best and cheapest renewable resources, and create economies of scale.

Thirdly, experience with EU-wide competitive bidding applied in the first Hydrogen auction holds significant potential to be expanded and extended to other areas requiring industrial decarbonisation, provided sufficient funding at EU level is available. With the Temporary Crisis and Transition Framework (TCTF) for state aid expiring by the end of 2025 and the new Multi-Annual Financial Framework planned for 2028, the next European Commission will have to shape the next steps. The modifications proposed through the Strategic Technologies for Europe Platform (STEP), such as the reinforcement of the European Innovation Council, the Innovation Fund and InvestEU, all centrally managed EU instruments, point towards potential instruments that could play a stronger role and require more funding.

Fourthly, implementation matters a lot. While the conceptual and political case for a green industrial policy may be strong, in reality there are also many examples of failure. As information asymmetries are abundant, authorities will need to invest in in-depth knowledge of technologies, sectors and supply chains. Policy preparation is greatly helped through impact assessments that describe the problems, test specific objectives, assess different policy options, and deal with trade-offs. In terms of governance, experience points towards independence and flexibility in execution, extensive programme monitoring, while keeping administrative burden in check. As Europe is not blessed with abundant natural resources, including critical raw materials, cheap energy or labour, it will have to compete on the basis of better performance, higher added value, and superior environmental credentials.

Finally, an issue largely unaddressed so far is the external pillar of an open strategic autonomy. European self-sufficiency is unrealistic. The EU needs to continue to foster trade and cooperation with global partners. The approach should go beyond maximising free trade and foster sustainable development here as well as in partner countries. A revised EU geopolitical strategy will need to integrate the industries of the Global South into the value chains of green tech, and through that process facilitate worldwide solutions to climate change, as well as sustainable development in North and South.

Notes

1 The determination of EU GHG targets themselves has been mostly based on the EU's fair contribution to a global mitigation effort that is required to meet the 2°C target, and subsequently the goals of the Paris Agreement, i.e. below 2°C and making efforts towards 1.5°C above pre-industrial level.
2 According to the European Commission website, 'open strategic autonomy' means cooperating multilaterally wherever we can, acting autonomously wherever we must.

3   Climate neutral industrial products means (i) zero GHG emission energy for all industrial/manufacturing processes, (ii) zero emission raw materials and feedstock (e.g. necessary carbon no longer coming from oil or other fossil sources), (iii) as low as economically viable process emissions, and CCUS for any residual emissions, (iv) as low as possible emissions after the end of material/product life, incl. via as high as economically viable re-use/recycling/upcycling, or (v) developing novel products/materials that can store carbon that has been removed from the atmosphere – as permanently as possible.

4   COM (2018) 773.

5   IEA (2023) *Energy Technology Perspectives 2023*. Paris: IEA, p. 96. Available at: https://www.iea.org/reports/energy-technology-perspectives-2023, License: CC BY 4.0.

6   Various analysis project US Greenhouse gas emissions and the excepted impact of the IRA (and other existing policies). On average, they project a reduction of −40%, while the US pledge under the Paris Agreement is −50 to 52% in economy-wide net greenhouse gas emissions in 2030 compared to 2005.

7   For example, the US IRA includes fixed subsidy rates for both industrial decarbonisation (hydrogen, CCS, CCU, etc.) as well as clean tech manufacturing (batteries, solar PV, wind and related supply chains).

8   NER stands for New Entrance Reserve.

9   Lessons learned from the NER300 were used to change the governance under the Innovation Fund.

10 https://climate.ec.europa.eu/eu-action/funding-climate-action/innovation-fund/legal-framework_en.

11 A dedicated EU fund to support sustainable investment, innovation, and job creation.

12 The "valley of death" describes the difficulty for a start-up or new innovative technology to economically survive the period of negative cash flow in the early stages, before the new product or service is bringing in revenue from real customers.

13 "What is the innovation fund?" EU Climate Action. Available at: https://climate.ec.europa.eu/eu-action/eu-funding-climate-action/innovation-fund/what-innovation-fund_en.

14 The implementation of the Innovation Fund, including the launch of calls, evaluation, grant management and project monitoring has been delegated to the Executive Agency CINEA (European Climate, Infrastructure and Environment Agency). The European Investment Bank is responsible for providing and managing project development assistance (PDA), which consists of financial and technical advisory services to improve project maturity and quality of potential project proposals.

15 The five evaluation criteria are defined in the delegated act, and further specified in the call for proposals: (1) effectiveness of greenhouse gas emissions avoidance, (2) degree of innovation, (3) project maturity, (4) replicability and (5) cost efficiency.

16 EU installed about 20 GW of solar in 2021, 40 GW in 2022 and an expected 60 GW in 2023.

17 See Chapter 7.

18 COM (2018) 293 final.

19 European Commission (no date) Important Projects of Common European Interest (IPCEI)https://competition-policy.ec.europa.eu/state-aid/ipcei_en

20 https://data.consilium.europa.eu/doc/document/PE-2-2023-INIT/en/pdf.

21 Production subsidy of 35$/kwH until 2030, phasing out by 2030, for battery cells; 10$/kWh for battery modules.

22 Aid was allowed under specific conditions, for instance in the context of State Aid guidelines for regional aid, and in the context of guidelines for research & innovation, including specific guidelines for Important Projects of Common European Interest (IPCEI).

23 Global Hydrogen Review, IEA, 2022.

24 COM (2018) 773 final.
25 COM (2020) 301 final.
26 COM (2023) 156.
27 Assumption for electrolyser turnkey CAPEX of 800EUR/kW and electricity costs at 0.07 EUR/kWh. "Levelized Cost of Hydrogen", Agora Energiewende, 2023.
28 https://climate.ec.europa.eu/eu-action/eu-funding-climate-action/innovation-fund/competitive-bidding_en.
29 eur-lex.europa.eu/legal-content/EN/TXT/PDF/?uri=CELEX:52023DC0156.
30 A detailed description of which kind of national aid is allowed is included in the Terms & Conditions.
31 https://climate.ec.europa.eu/system/files/2023-11/policy_funding_innovation_conceptpaper_auctionsasaservice.pdf.
32 Communication from the Commission to the European Parliament, The Council, the European Economic and Social Committee and the Committee of the Regions on the European Hydrogen Bank (com (2023) 156 final) p. 9. Available at: https://eur-lex.europa.eu/legal-content/EN/TXT/PDF/?uri=CELEX:52023DC0156.
33 COM (2023) 62 final.
34 As defined in the policy scenario of the Staff Working Document of the Net-Zero Industry Act (NZIA)in the section on needs assessment.
35 Critical raw materials are listed in Section I of Annex I of the Proposal. Examples include cobalt, copper, lithium (battery grade) and natural graphite (battery grade).

10

THE GREENING OF EU FINANCE

Laura Iozzelli and Yvon Slingenberg

Introduction

Sustainable finance has become a key concern in the global policy agenda, particularly following the adoption of the UN 2030 Sustainable Development Agenda and the Paris Agreement. Under Article 2(1) (c), the Agreement calls for *"making financial flows consistent with a pathway towards low greenhouse gas emissions and climate resilient development."* The EU strongly supports this ambition.

The transition to a green and low-carbon EU economy requires large investments. According to Commission analyses,[1] the *additional* private and public investment needs in relation to the green transition are estimated at €477 billion per year between 2021 and 2030. On top of that the REPowerEU plan following the Russian invasion of Ukraine requires an estimated additional investment of up to €35 billion per annum between 2022 and 2027.[2] These are daunting figures. The EU is implementing a sustainable finance strategy towards the private sector while at the same time mainstreaming the climate dimension in its own budget. The latter debate is likely to get reinforced in the preparation of the next budget, commonly called the Multi-Annual Financial Framework (MFF), which will start with the Commission proposal that is expected for 2025.

10.1 The EU Sustainable Finance Strategy

The integration of sustainable development into financial activity has become a crucial policy priority for the EU. According to the European Commission, sustainable finance refers to "the process of taking environmental, social and governance (ESG) considerations into account when making investment decisions in the financial sector, leading to more long-term investments in sustainable economic activities and projects."[3] The aim is to significantly raise the amount of private capital finding its way into sustainable investment.

DOI: 10.4324/9781003493730-13

The 2018 Action Plan on Financing Sustainable Growth[4] focused on re-orienting capital flows towards sustainable investment, managing financial risks stemming from climate change, environmental degradation and social issues, as well as fostering transparency and long-termism in financial and economic activity.[5] Following the COVID outbreak and the Russian invasion of Ukraine, the Strategy was reconfirmed and focused also on issues related to the financing of interim steps in the transition towards the EU's climate neutrality and environmental objectives.[6] Progressive steps are being taken towards the transition, as it is unrealistic to expect that all companies can switch overnight towards low or zero carbon activities.

The aims of the Action Plan have been translated into three building blocks for a sustainable financial framework, which are: (1) a classification system, or 'taxonomy', of sustainable activities, (2) a disclosure framework for non-financial and financial companies and (3) investment tools, including benchmarks, standards and labels (see Figure 10.1).

10.1.1 The EU Taxonomy

The Taxonomy Regulation adopted in 2020 establishes a science-based, EU-uniform classification system directed at financial market actors such as companies and investors for determining whether an economic activity is environmentally sustainable and in line with a net-zero trajectory by 2050. It is expected to bring order to the array of standards and labels for sustainable financial products used in the European financial market, thereby contributing to scale up and facilitate access to cross-border capital markets for environmentally sustainable investment.[7]

The taxonomy is an important transparency tool, as it aims to protect investors from greenwashing practices, boosting their confidence that the activities in which they invest contribute to environmental objectives, as well as give to the companies in which they invest the right incentives to make their business models more sustainable and mitigate market fragmentation.

The EU Taxonomy establishes six broad environmental objectives, namely: (a) climate mitigation; (b) climate adaptation; (c) sustainable use of and protection of water and marine resources; (d) transition towards a circular economy; (e) pollution prevention and control and (f) protection and restoration of biodiversity and ecosystems.[8] To qualify as sustainable, an economic activity needs to 'contribute substantially' to one or more of these six objectives and cause no significant harm to any of the others, while at the same time meeting minimum social safeguards.[9]

Under the Taxonomy Regulation, the European Commission is tasked with the adoption of delegated acts setting the list of economic activities that can

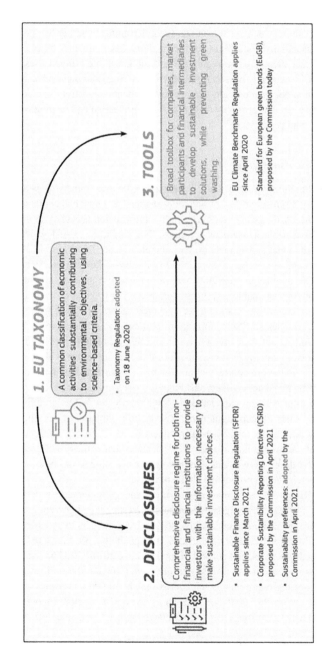

FIGURE 10.1   The pillars of the EU sustainable finance framework

Source: European Commission, 2021[10]

be classified as sustainable. This is done through the definition of technical screening criteria which set thresholds for determining when an economic activity substantially contributes to one or more environmental objectives. Four Delegated Acts have been adopted and the latest one brings forward a new set of EU taxonomy criteria for economic activities making a substantial contribution to one or more non-climate environmental objectives, including transition to a circular economy and control and protection and restoration of biodiversity and ecosystems.[11]

10.1.2 Disclosure Rules

The second building block of the EU sustainable finance framework is a set of mandatory disclosure rules for both non-financial and financial companies, which are meant to provide investors with the information necessary to make informed sustainable investment decisions. Two main pieces of legislation were adopted to that end, namely the Sustainable Finance Disclosure Regulation (SFDR) and the Corporate Sustainability Reporting Directive (CSRD).

The SFDR, applicable since 2021, was introduced to enhance transparency in the market for sustainable investments products. The Regulation introduces a set of requirements mandating asset managers and other financial market participants to disclose ESG information, particularly on the sustainability risks[12] and impacts of their investments.[13] The SFDR is intertwined with the EU Taxonomy, as it compels issuers to prove that their investments align with the taxonomy in the pre-contractual documentation phase and annual reporting. In case financial actors deem sustainability risks not to be relevant, they are obliged to provide an explanation.[14] Additionally, the SFDR establishes transparency rules concerning adverse sustainability impacts of investment decisions at both entity and financial products levels.[15] By July 2023, more than 50% of the assets under management disclosed under the SFDR, valued at around €5 trillion, were qualified as sustainable investments or investments promoting social or environmental characteristics.[16]

The CSRD covers both financial and non-financial undertakings. In line with the EU strategy to strengthen sustainable investment and prevent greenwashing, the CSRD aims to enable investors and stakeholders to assess companies' long-term value creation and their sustainability risk exposure. The CSRD extends the scope and content of the Directive 2014/95/EU on the disclosure of non-financial and diversity information (NFRD)[17] by setting more stringent reporting requirements for approximately 50,000 companies compared to the current 11,700.[18] The rules apply likewise to companies outside the EU with listed securities on an EU-regulated market. Companies will need to disclose detailed information on a 'double materiality' perspective, which means that they will be required to disclose information both on how sustainability issues affect their development, performance and position, and on the impact of their activities on sustainability.[19]

Additionally, to boost investors' trust the CSRD mandates a third-party assurance obligation on companies, requiring reporting to be certified by an accredited independent body. The CSRD mandates that reporting be consistent with the SFDR and the EU Taxonomy. In fact, the CSRD and the SFDR are closely linked: to fulfil their reporting requirements under the SFDR, financial market participants rely on adequate sustainability information from the companies in which they invest. In turn, the CSRD aims to ensure that investee companies provide the necessary information to financial market participants so that they can meet their obligations.

Corporations will have to report based on European Sustainability Reporting Standards (ESRS) which set out the details of what must be reported by companies as part of the CSRD, including their business strategy, climate targets (e.g., GHG emissions reduction targets), policies related to sustainability matters, actual or potential adverse effects connected with an entity's own operations and value chain, principal risks and how these are managed.[20] The standards are being adopted by the Commission via delegated acts after advice from the European Financial Reporting Advisory Group (EFRAG), a technical advisory body to the EC. The first set of standards are applicable as of 2024.

10.1.3 Benchmarks and Green Bonds

As a further element to finance sustainable growth, the EU has introduced a set of investment tools, including benchmarks, standards and labels designed to increase transparency for financial market participants and help them align their investment strategies with the EU's climate and environmental goals.

In the EU, green bonds are becoming prominent tools in financing assets needed for the low-carbon transition and are being increasingly employed to raise financing in sectors such as energy production and distribution, resource-efficient housing and low-carbon transport infrastructure. The issuance of green bonds based on the international Capital Market Association (ICMA) standard is rapidly increasing and is likely to exceed €1 trillion by the end of 2023.[21] Green bonds make up for 16% of total bond issuance in the EU, which is much more than in the rest of the world (2%). Meanwhile, in early 2023 a political agreement was reached between the European Parliament and the Council to develop the first EU Green Bond Standard (EUGBS).[22]

Once adopted, the EUGBS is expected to act as a high-quality voluntary standard for how companies, public authorities and issuers located outside of the EU can use green bonds to raise funds on capital markets to finance large-scale investments, while meeting stringent sustainability requirements and protecting investors.

The EUGBS is based on recommendations made by the Technical Expert Group on Sustainable Finance and focuses on three key elements. First, the totality of the proceeds raised by the bond should be allocated to finance economic activities that are aligned with the EU taxonomy. Second, there needs to be full transparency on how the bond proceeds are allocated through detailed reporting requirements. Third, all European green bonds must be checked by an external reviewer to ensure compliance with the Regulation and taxonomy alignment of the funded projects. External reviewers providing services to issuers of European green bonds must be registered with and supervised by the European Securities and Markets Authority. This will ensure the quality of their services and the reliability of their reviews to protect investors and ensure market integrity.

The EU has also developed sustainability benchmarks, which are useful tools for investors to create investment products, track and measure their performance and allocate assets accordingly. Following the need to establish more transparent and sounder sustainable indices' methodologies to reduce greenwashing, the EU Climate Transition Benchmarks Regulation became applicable as of 2020. The rules create a new category of benchmarks, comprising (1) the low-carbon benchmark or 'decarbonised' version of standard indices, whose underlying assets are selected, weighted or excluded such that the resulting benchmark portfolio is on a decarbonation path; and (2) the positive-carbon impact benchmark, whose underlying assets are selected in such a way that the resulting carbon emission reductions in the benchmark portfolio are aligned with the ambitious Paris Climate Agreement's long-term global warming target objective.[23] The Regulation helps defining the carbon footprint of companies and offers investors greater information on an investment portfolio. The Commission is empowered to adopt delegated and implementing acts to specify how competent authorities and market participants shall comply with the obligations laid down in the Regulation.

10.1.4 The EU and the International Approach to Sustainable Finance

The EU action on sustainable finance takes place within a rapidly evolving array of international initiatives, as national governments, financial institutions and financial regulators increasingly recognise the financial risks and opportunities associated with climate change and other sustainability issues.

At the global level, a vast array of initiatives exists in view of greening the global financial system in support of the Paris climate goals. In 2015, the G20 Financial Stability Board established the Task Force on Climate-related Financial Disclosures (TFCFD) who developed a disclosure framework of climate-related financial risks and opportunities through companies' existing reporting processes.[24] The recommendations developed by this task force aim to provide the financial market with high-quality information on the impact of climate-related matters on companies' performance. These recommendations are largely in line with the EU sustainable finance disclosure rules and can be used by companies in both the financial and non-financial sectors. In November 2022, the number of organisations endorsing the Task Force recommendations surpassed 4,000, from more than 100 countries, with a combined market capitalisation of USD 27 trillion.[25]

In the banking sector specifically, two initiatives stand out, namely the Sustainable Banking Network (SBN) and the Network of Central Banks and Supervisors for Greening the Financial System (NGFS). The former is a unique global platform set up by regulatory agencies, banking associations, environment and finance ministries and industry associations to provide support for initiatives aimed at promoting sustainable investing. The latter is a network of central banks recognising that climate-related risks constitute a source of financial risks. The NGFS works to strengthen the global response required to meet the goals of the Paris Agreement by improving the identification and measurement of the financial sector's exposure to climate-related risks, devising climate change stress tests for financial institutions and mobilising capital for green and low-carbon investments.[26] To this end, the NGFS defines and promotes best practices to be implemented within and outside of its membership and conducts or commissions analytical work on green finance.

The European Central Bank (ECB) followed up pro-actively on the activities of the NGFS and published in January 2023 a first set of climate-related statistical indicators to assess more effectively how climate risks affect monetary policy, price stability and the financial system.[27] The indicators developed by the ECB are experimental and analytical in nature. Experimental indicators focus on relevant green financial instruments and financial institutions' carbon footprint, while analytical indicators are based on carbon emissions and climate-related physical risks. These indicators include sustainable finance indexes that provide an overview of the issuance and holding of debt instruments with sustainability characteristics by residents in the euro area.[28] The analytical indicators include measures of financial institutions' carbon emissions that provide information on the carbon intensity of the securities and loan portfolios of those financial institutions. In addition, they include indicators focused on physical risks deriving from the impact of natural hazards, such as floods, wildfires, or storms, on the performance of loans, bonds and equities portfolios.

The development of statistical indicators is part of the ECB strategy to integrate climate change considerations in monetary policy. The ECB developed an economy-wide stress test to assess the resilience of corporates, households and banks to climate-related risks both in the short and long term. Three transition policy scenarios were analyzed namely an "accelerated transition" under which the green transition would start immediately; a "late-push transition" under which the green transition would start in 2025 and a "delayed transition" under which the transition would not start before three years.[29] The results show that banks, households and firms would clearly benefit from an accelerated transition[30] and that *"the benefits of a timely transition far outweigh the costs,"*[31] even if this would imply an increase in energy costs.[32]

In other countries similar sustainable finance activities are underway. In 2022, the US Securities and Exchange Commission (US SEC) proposed the adoption of new rules[33] to enhance and standardise climate-related disclosures for companies, with a view to promote transparency and protect investors from greenwashing. The new disclosure rules, yet to be adopted at the time of writing, will require companies to include certain climate-related information – including expected climate risks, greenhouse gas emissions and transition plans – in their registration statements and periodic reports. The goal of the proposal is to provide investors with consistent, comparable and useful information for making investment decisions and clear reporting obligations for undertakings. Similarly, the UK government adopted disclosure rules building on the TFCFD recommendations in its 2021 Roadmap to Sustainable Investing, which was updated in 2023.[34]

As the largest economy in the world, China's efforts to build sustainable finance markets and direct investment towards green activities are of great importance to meet global environmental objectives.[35] China has issued several legislative frameworks in relation to sustainable finance, particularly by adopting the "green bond catalogue" in 2015 which is usually referred to as the "Chinese taxonomy".[36] Furthermore, recent sustainable finance policies applied in China include improving the green finance standard system and strengthening regulation and disclosure requirements to enlarge its green finance market and attract global investors, as well as expanding international cooperation on sustainable finance efforts.[37]

Conclusion: The EU envisages enhanced transparency of its business sector in view of encouraging investment in the low-carbon economy. A taxonomy of sustainable activities and non-financial disclosure obligations for corporates and financial companies have been established, while a voluntary EU Green Bond Standard is imminent. The ECB has developed a climate stress test and is developing indicators to test the climate resilience of the EU financial system.

10.2 Mainstreaming Climate in the EU Budget

10.2.1 The Climate Mainstreaming Target

The EU mainstreams the climate dimension in its budget as it is a public good with a clear European added value. The 2014–2020 period included for the first time a climate spending target of 20% which was delivered mainly through expenditure in the fields of transport, cohesion, agriculture and research. The targets agreed under the Paris Agreement led to the decision to increase this percentage to 30% for the period 2021–2027. At the same time, the "do-no-significant-harm" (DNSH) principle was introduced, which implies that no EU funding should go against or undermine climate or environmental objectives.

According to the assessment of the Commission, the execution of the climate mainstreaming under the current EU budget is well on track, and is estimated to represent 32.6% of the overall budget. However, against the background of several critical reports of the European Court of Auditors (ECA), the European Parliament and several stakeholders expressed concerns over the methodology used in that assessment.[38] According to ECA, substantial overreporting of environmental expenditure happened especially under the Common Agricultural Policy (CAP). ECA found that whereas the Commission attributed over €100 billion of CAP funds during the 2014–2020 period to tackling climate change, this had little impact on reducing emissions from agriculture, which have not been altered significantly since 2010.[39] In fact, most mitigation measures supported by the CAP have been marginal in terms of mitigating climate change and the CAP rarely finances measures with high climate mitigation potential.[40] Additionally, according to ECA, the Commission's monitoring system does not provide data that allows for a proper monitoring of the impact of CAP climate funding on greenhouse gas emissions.

In response, the Commission partly adjusted its methodology and promised to come back on this issue in the review of the existing accounting rules under the CAP planned for 2025–2026. The Commission also seeks to ensure that the future Common Agricultural Policy (CAP) will guarantee the implementation of the DNSH principle by defining requirements attached to EU farm subsidies.[41] The methodology on the monitoring of the climate mainstreaming will remain an issue for the next MFF on which the Commission is expected to table a proposal in 2025.

10.2.2 The Specific Programme Targets

The EU budget's overall climate spending target is broken down into programme-specific targets. These include the Recovery and Resilience Facility (37%), InvestEU (30%), the European Regional Development Fund (30%) and the Cohesion Fund (37%), Horizon Europe (35%), the LIFE programme (61%) and the Neighbourhood, Development and International Cooperation Instrument (30%) and the Common Agricultural Policy (40%).

10.2.2.1 The Recovery and Resilience Facility

The "Recovery and Resilience Facility" (RRF), which has been politically baptised as NextGenerationEU (NGEU), supports the EU's recovery from the economic downturn induced by the pandemic. The RRF has a value of up to €723.8 billion and enables Member States to significantly increase climate investments. To qualify for the Facility's grants (€338 billion) and loans (€385.8 billion), Member States submit recovery and resilience plans setting out investments and policy reforms that contribute to the Facility's six policy objectives including the green transition. Each national plan must spend a minimum of 37% of its total allocation on measures contributing to climate objectives, such as initiatives promoting energy efficiency, sustainable mobility and renewable energy. Every measure must also comply with the "do-no-significant-harm" principle. Collectively, Member States dedicate 40% of their allocations to climate objectives (€203 billion) with some of them spending well over half of their allocation to fund climate policy.

During 2023 Member States complemented their recovery and resilience plans with new chapters on *REPowerEU*, a joint response to the energy crisis caused by Russia's invasion of Ukraine. New or scaled-up reforms and investments in Members States will help phase out the EU's dependence on Russian fossil fuels as well as accelerate the clean energy transition. These will be supported by €20 billion of new grants, transfers from other funds and use of remaining NGEU loans.

Member States submit Recovery and Resilience Plans (RRPs) to the Commission which approves them after a detailed screening on, inter alia, the mainstreaming target and the "do no significant harm" (DNSH) principle. A novelty introduced with the RRF is that it is implemented in direct management, where the funds are disbursed to Member States based on progress in implementing and reaching agreed milestones and targets. As far as the RepowerEU Plans are concerned, a derogation of the DNSH principle was included, allowing Member States to still finance gas (and in some cases oil)-related infrastructure but only where such investments are proven to be strictly necessary and proportionate to ensure security of energy supply, taking into account the abrupt disconnection from imports of these fuels from Russia.

10.2.2.2   InvestEU

The EU provides guarantees to help de-risking major investment programmes. At least 30% of the InvestEU programme of €372 billion for mobilising additional investment over the period 2021–2027 should contribute to meet the EU climate objectives. Under the Sustainable Infrastructure Window, 60% of the funding must be spent on climate and environment. Investments above €10 million are subject to sustainability proofing (identify, assess and mitigate climate, environment or social risks). All InvestEU-supported investment will be climate and environmentally tracked against the methodology issued by the Commission. Besides the EIB, 18 institutions have been selected to start negotiating Guarantee Agreements for them to become Implementing Partners. Guarantee Agreements have been signed with the European Bank for Reconstruction and Development (EBRD), Council of Europe Development Bank (CEB), Nordic Investment Bank (NIB), CDP Equity (CDPE), Caisse des Dépôts (CDC) in 2022. Financial products foreseen will help address market failures in providing access to finance projects in a broad area of policy priorities from transport, smart mobility, clean energy, digital connectivity, as well as energy efficiency, decarbonisation of industry, renewable energy and the circular economy.

10.2.2.3   European Regional Development Fund and Cohesion Fund (ERDF and CF)

Member States' planned allocations under Cohesion policy programmes for the period 2021–2027 exceed the climate expenditure targets of both the European Regional Development Fund (30.0%) and the Cohesion Fund (37.0%). Some €92 billion (36.3%) of the €253.3 billion envelope is expected to fund climate change mitigation and adaptation measures. In addition, about 24.9% of the €10.2 billion of Interreg funds financed by the EU are expected to fund climate-relevant measures (see Figure 10.2).

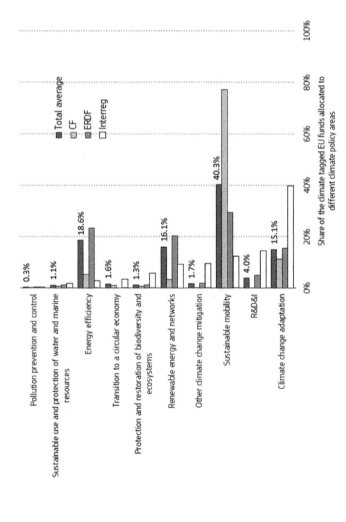

FIGURE 10.2 ERDF, CF and Interreg EU climate amounts by policy area

Source: European Commission (2023)[42]

10.2.2.4 Research and Innovation Framework Programmes (Horizon Europe)

Investments in research and innovation are essential for generating knowledge and solutions for the transition towards climate neutrality and resilience. Overall, Horizon Europe will contribute at least 35% of its €95.5 billion budget to climate objectives. By the end of 2022, over €8.5 billion had already been earmarked to R&I supporting climate action. A broad portfolio of ambitious European private-public partnerships is mobilising resources and developing solutions necessary to deliver on the EU's climate agenda across key economic sectors such as steel, process industries, hydrogen, batteries, bioeconomy, aviation, road and waterborne transport, buildings, water and more.

10.2.2.5 LIFE Programme

LIFE is the EU's funding instrument for the environment and climate action supporting demonstration, best practice, coordination, capacity building and governance projects. In 2022, more than €600 million was awarded to 200 projects supporting the Green Deal, including projects developing innovative solutions and sharing best practice to reduce GHG emissions, increase resilience to climate change and contribute to clean energy transition. In 2023, over €600 million will be awarded to projects supporting environment, climate action and the clean energy transition, including contributing to the objectives of REPowerEU and the Green Industrial Plan.

10.2.2.6 The Neighbourhood, Development and International Cooperation Instrument

International public climate finance plays an important role in helping developing countries to implement the Paris Agreement, together with climate finance from private sources. Climate spending targets have also been introduced in the EU's international finance instruments.

At least 30% of the Neighbourhood, Development, and International Cooperation Instrument (NDICI) – Global Europe with a total budget of €79.5 billion for the 2021–2027 period should be dedicated to climate action, directly supporting partner countries in the Global South. The Instrument for Pre-Accession Assistance (IPA III), providing support to the countries in the EU Neighbourhood, foresees a climate change spending target of 18%, growing to 20% by 2027. Furthermore, beyond the climate change spending targets the Commission committed an additional €4 billion for climate finance until 2027 to tackle climate change to reduce emissions and build resilience to the effects of climate change in developing countries.

10.2.2.7 Common Agricultural Policy

Regarding the bioeconomy, at least 40% of the EU's budget for the Common Agricultural Policy (CAP) should be related to climate action. Farmers should comply with a basic set of standards concerning climate and environment. In addition, as part of their CAP Strategic Plans, Member States can set up several types of incentive schemes to reward agricultural practices that are beneficial for the climate, for example, payments for the maintenance of and the conversion to organic land or for other types of interventions such as agroecology, conservation agriculture and integrated production.

10.2.2.8 European Social Fund (ESF+)

The green transition, as well as the digital transition, will require that workers become skilled in different activities, such as renewable energy, electrical vehicles, deep renovation and the installation of heat pumps. The enhanced European Social Fund is there to support Member States in the development of the necessary plans and programmes for (re)training and (re)skilling. Although there is no climate mainstreaming target for the ESF+, for the period 2021–2027 Member States programmed almost €6 billion or 6% of total ESF+ allocations[43] for green skills and green jobs, considerably more than in the previous programming period. In several Member States this share is even 20% or higher.

10.2.2.9 Technical Support Instrument (TSI)

To support the implementation of the Green Deal, the Technical Support Instrument provides support to governments in the development of plans and policies in new and particularly challenging areas, also called "flagships."

Whereas in the early years the focus was on the reforms needed in the context of the Recovery and Resilience Facility, lately a number of projects on adaptation, do-no-significant-harm, faster permitting, industrial eco-systems and skills, building renovation but also capacity building have been financed under the TSI. A Flagship on the preparation of the Social Climate Fund and the new ETS has also been developed to support Member States.

Conclusion: The EU's budget for 2021–2027 mainstreams climate in at least 30% of its expenditure. The principle of "do no significant harm" applies to the remaining 70% of the funding and requires that the EU's climate and environmental objectives are not thwarted.

10.3   The EIB becomes the EU's Climate Bank

As a multilateral development bank, the European Investment Bank (EIB Group) is one of the largest multilateral finance providers for climate-related and environmental sustainability projects globally.[44] A key supporter of the EU's climate policy objectives, the EIB Group has positioned itself as the 'EU climate bank' and works to increase investments in projects that contribute to climate action, environmental sustainability and inclusive development. The EIB has also been a pioneer in issuing bonds whose proceeds are earmarked for environmental projects that meet certain eligibility criteria.[45]

To support the European Green Deal, the EIB Group has launched a 'Climate Bank Roadmap' for the period 2021–2025 to step up action towards financing long-term green investments through the provision of a wide range of financial products and advisory services.[46] The Roadmap aims to align the Group's financing operations with the goals of the Paris Agreement and phase out lending for fossil fuel projects, and secondly, to take on the role of main implementing partner in the European Green Deal's investment pillar, the Sustainable Europe Investment Plan, which seeks to mobilise €1 trillion by 2030 from public and private sources.

To that end, the Group has made three specific commitments[47]

- to gradually increase the share of its financing dedicated to support climate action and environmental sustainability to over 50% of annual lending by 2025 and beyond
- to support €1 trillion worth of investments to accelerate climate action and environmental sustainability between 2021 and 2030, and
- align all new operations with the principles and goals of the Paris agreement

The EIB is on track to deliver on those commitments. The 50% target has already been reached in 2021 (51%) and in 2022 (58%),[48] potentially opening the perspective for a higher target after the mid-term review of the Climate Bank Roadmap. In 2022, the amount of EIB investments that went to climate action and environmental sustainability projects reached €36.5 billion (EIB, 2023), thereby supporting €222 billion of private investments, up from €75 billion in 2021. If the EIB sustains this acceleration, it has the potential to achieve its €1 trillion goal. The coming years, however, may present a challenge, as the Russian invasion in Ukraine has put the issue of financing a diversification of Europe's gas infrastructure back on the table.

As illustrated in Figure 10.3, to reach these goals the EIB strategy focuses on four key workstreams: (1) increasing green investment and supporting long-term innovation and new business models; (2) ensuring that the transition is "just for all" – particularly by supporting regions that currently rely

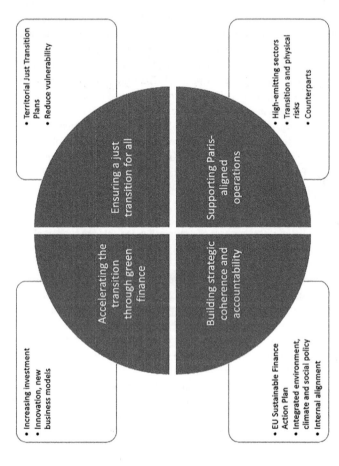

FIGURE 10.3 Main pillars of the EIB climate strategy

Source: EIB (2020)[49]

on carbon-intensive industries as a major source of local employment and income and working to support communities exposed to structural change or climate risks; (3) ensuring that all these activities are consistent with the path to low-carbon and climate-resilient development set by the Paris Agreement; and (4) guaranteeing that the various activities take place within a coherent policy approach towards supporting sustainable finance, in line with the EU Sustainable Finance Action Plan. The above figures show that the EIB is well advanced on workstream 1. The 2022 Progress report also details evidence on progress on workstreams 2 and 3. However, the EIB has not fully aligned its operations with the Taxonomy yet, as foreseen under Workstream 4. The EIB has been assessing applicability considerations for the DNSH criteria to non-climate environmental objectives, but new updates of the investment frameworks are yet to be taken.[50] Additionally, the EIB requires time to adjust its Roadmap to the increasing bulk of secondary legislation being agreed by the EU, including delegated acts of the Taxonomy Regulation, and to fully situate its green finance tracking methodology within the EU Taxonomy. Full alignment with the Taxonomy will be an important issue for the mid-term review.

As a further way to green its lending portfolio and contribute to the goals of the Paris Agreement, the EIB has also introduced a new energy lending policy, whereby as of end of 2021 it no longer finances unabated fossil fuel energy projects and commits to increase lending in renewable energy, energy efficiency, alternative fuels and infrastructure to help green technologies grow.[51] Additionally, the EIB Group aims to support the REPowerEU plan to reduce dependence on Russian fossil fuels and fast-forward the green transition, by providing up to €30 billion in additional loans and equity financing over the next five years.[52]

Conclusion: The EIB is a major multilateral development bank and has decided to become the EU's Climate Bank. The road map is a key tool that could be further reinforced in view of aligning with the EU sustainable finance agenda and reaching the EU's climate goals.

Conclusion

The low-carbon transition requires a major investment effort and is not going to materialise without the massive support of both public and private sources of finance. The EU agreed upon important structural changes in the field of sustainable finance. More than 30% of the spending under the EU's budget and the Recovery and Resilience Facility is directly in relation to reaching the climate objectives, while the remaining 70% will be used without doing no significant harm to them.

Equally, the EU is undertaking significant action to turn around the tanker of private finance towards sustainability. The EU taxonomy defines what is meant by green and sustainable finance, and the disclosure rules for corporates in the world of finance and industry will shed as of 2024 some clear light on the climate risks, the transition plans and the targets they are adopting. The European Central Bank is engaging in climate stress testing for the EU's financial system. And the European Investment Bank took it on itself to become the EU's Climate Bank.

These are all important structural changes. Their impact will become clearer as we move to the test of real-life implementation. A debate will undoubtedly unfold at the occasion of the MFF as of 2025. Questions are likely to arise about how to organise the low-carbon transition while maintaining core industries on the European continent. Has the EU been under-estimating the size of the necessary investment this entails? How should public money become a more active driver for greening private finance? Should the fiscal rules governing the euro area make more space for sustainable investments? Or should the Recovery and Resilience Facility be re-oriented and possibly expanded to rise to the climate challenge? These critical questions bode for a challenging policy debate during the new European policy cycle, but this debate will greatly benefit from the fact that fundamental decisions on the greening of the EU's finance have already been agreed upon.

Notes

1 SWD (2023) 68 final. Values reported in EUR 2022.
2 COM (2022) 230 final, p. 12.
3 European Commission, "Overview of sustainable finance," Official Website of the European Commission, web archived at https://finance.ec.europa.eu/sustainable-finance/overview-sustainable-finance_en#:~:text=Sustainable%20finance%20refers%20to%20the,sustainable%20economic%20activities%20and%20projects (accessed 20 July 2023).
4 Communication from the European Commission to the European Parliament, the Council, the European Central Bank, the European Economic and Social Committee and the Committee of the Regions – Action Plan: Financing Sustainable Growth (COM/2018/097 final of 08/03/2018).
5 European Commission (8 March 2018) *Action Plan: Financing Sustainable Growth*, p. 3.
6 Transition risks are defined as financially-material risks that relate to changes in the regulatory environment, technological development or consumer behaviour. Physical risks are defined as financially-material risks relating to the impacts of climate change on an undertaking.
7 Schuetze, Franziska and Stede, Jan, EU Sustainable Finance Taxonomy – What Is Its Role on the Road towards Climate Neutrality? (December 2020). DIW Berlin Discussion Paper No. 1923, Available at: http://dx.doi.org/10.2139/ssrn.3749900
8 Article 9 EU Taxonomy Regulation.
9 Article 3(b) and Article 17 EU Taxonomy Regulation.
10 COMMUNICATION FROM THE COMMISSION TO THE EUROPEAN PARLIAMENT, THE COUNCIL, THE EUROPEAN ECONOMIC AND SOCIAL COMMITTEE AND THE COMMITTEE OF THE REGIONS EMPTY Strategy

for Financing the Transition to a Sustainable Economy, COM (2021) 390 final (2021). Available at: https://eur-lex.europa.eu/legal-content/EN/TXT/HTML/?uri= CELEX:52021DC0390&from=BG

11 European Commission. Available at: https://finance.ec.europa.eu/regulation-and-supervision/financial-services-legislation/implementing-and-delegated-acts/ taxonomy-regulation_en.

12 According to the SFDR, Article 2(22), a sustainability risk is understood as "an environmental, social or governance event or condition that, if it occurs, could cause a negative material impact on the value of the investment."

13 Article 1 SFDR.

14 Article 6 SFDR.

15 Article 4 SFRD.

16 European Commission. *EU Climate Action Progress Report 2023*, COM (2023) 653 final, 24 October 2023, p. 38.

17 Directive 2014/95/EU of the European Parliament and of the Council of 22 October 2014 on the disclosure of non-financial and diversity information.

18 Companies under the scope of the CSRD will be large companies, defined by three criteria: (1) more than 250 employees; (2) more than EUR 40m turnover and (3) more than EUR 20m total asset. For more information, see European Commission, Corporate sustainability reporting https://finance.ec.europa.eu/ capital-markets-union-and-financial-markets/company-reporting-and-auditing/ company-reporting/corporate-sustainability-reporting_en and European Parliament (2022) Sustainable economy: Parliament adopts new reporting rules for multinationals https://www.europarl.europa.eu/news/en/press-room/20221107IPR49611/ sustainable-economy-parliament-adopts-new-reporting-rules-for-multinationals

19 Article 1(4), CSRD.

20 Articles 29(a) and 29(b), CSRD. For more information, see also https://www. bdo.global/getmedia/64b7ae4d-0188-4a0f-983b-8162b10dac3b/ISRB-2022-07-CSRD-finalised-and-first-batch-of-ESRS-delivered.pdf.aspx.

21 European Commission. *EU Climate Action Progress Report 2023*, COM (2023) 653 final, 24 October 2023, p. 36.

22 Council of the European Union (2023) https://www.consilium.europa.eu/en/press/ press-releases/2023/02/28/sustainable-finance-provisional-agreement-reached-on-european-green-bonds/

23 European Parliament (2020) *Sustainable Finance and Benchmarks*. Available at: https://www.europarl.europa.eu/RegData/etudes/BRIE/2019/640135/EPRS_BRI (2019)640135_EN.pdf.

24 See Ngo, T. et al. (2023) "Climate risk disclosures and global sustainability initiatives: A conceptual analysis and agenda for future research." *Business Strategy and the Environment*, 1–16.

25 TFCFD (2023) "About."Available at: https://www.fsb-tcfd.org/about/ (accessed 4 September 2023).

26 NGFS (2023) "Origin and purpose." Available at: https://www.ngfs.net/en/about-us/governance/origin-and-purpose (accessed 4 September 2023).

27 ECB (2023) "Towards climate-related statistical indicators." Available at: https://www. ecb.europa.eu/pub/pdf/other/ecb.climate_change_indicators202301~47c4bbbc92. en.pdf (accessed 6 September 2023).

28 Ibid.

29 ECB economy-wide climate stress test (2021). Available at: https://www.ecb. europa.eu/pub/pdf/scpops/ecb.op281~05a7735b1c.en.pdf.

30 ECB (2023) "Faster green transition would benefit firms, households and banks, ECB economy-wide climate stress test finds." Press Release. Available at: https:// www.ecb.europa.eu/press/pr/date/2023/html/ecb.pr230906~a3d6d06bdc.en.html.

31 Speech by Frank Elderson at the conference on 'The decade of sustainable finance: half-time and evaluation', 14 November 2023. Available at: https://www.

bankingsupervision.europa.eu/press/speeches/date/2023/html/ssm.sp231
114_1~98a5230732.en.html.
32 Ibid.
33 SEC.GOV (2023) "SEC proposes rules to enhance and standardize climate-related
disclosures for investors." Available at: https://www.sec.gov/securities-topics/
climate-esg.
34 De Francesco (2022) "Achieving the full potential of sustainable finance:
The role of national, European and international initiatives." Discussion Paper, European Policy Center. Available at: https://www.epc.eu/en/Publications/
Achieving-the-full-potential-of-sustainable-finance-The-role-of-natio~49da40.
35 OECD (2020) "Green finance and investment. Developing sustainable finance definitions and taxonomies." Available at: https://www.oecd-ilibrary.org/docserver/
134a2dbe-en.pdf?expires=1693835932&id=id&accname=ocid195734&checksum=
FBF250CA74A02EC093C83E4B7C9DA2B1.
36 Ibid.
37 Green Finance & Development Center (2023) "Green finance trends in China
(1): China's green finance policy landscape." Available at: https://greenfdc.org/
green-finance-trends-in-china-1-chinas-green-finance-policy-landscape/ (accessed
4 September 2023).
38 European Parliament (2022) "Climate mainstreaming in the EU budget: 2022
update."Availableat:https://www.europarl.europa.eu/thinktank/en/document/IPOL_
ATA(2022)732369.
39 ECA (2021) "Common agricultural policy and climate." Available at: https://
op.europa.eu/webpub/eca/special-reports/cap-and-climate-16-2021/en/#:~:
text=Overall%2C%20we%20found%20that%20the,potential%20to%20
mitigate%20climate%20change.
40 Ibid., p. 3.
41 European Commission (2021) *Replies of the European Commission to the European Court of Auditors Special Report.* Available at: https://www.eca.europa.eu/
Lists/ECAReplies/COM-Replies-SR-21-22/COM-Replies-SR-21-22_EN.pdf.
42 European Commission (2023) *Progress Report 2023: Climate Action*, p. 44. Available at: https://climate.ec.europa.eu/document/download/60a04592-cf1f-4e31-
865b-2b5b51b9d09f_en
43 European Commission (2023) "European social fund + performance." . Available at: https://commission.europa.eu/strategy-and-policy/eu-budget/performance-
and-reporting/programme-performance-statements/european-social-fund-
performance_en.
44 EP (2021) "Green and sustainable finance." Briefing. Available at: https://www.
europarl.europa.eu/thinktank/en/document/EPRS_BRI(2021)679081.
45 Mertens, D. and Thiemann, M. (2023) "The European Investment Bank: The EU's
climate bank?" In *Handbook on European Union Climate Change Policy and Politics*, edited by T. Rayner, K. Szulecki, A.J. Jordan and S. Oberthür. Cheltenham:
Edward Elgar Publishing.
46 EIB (2020) "EIB group climate bank roadmap 2021–2025." Available at: https://
www.eib.org/attachments/thematic/eib_group_climate_bank_roadmap_en.pdf.
47 Ibid.
48 "EIB group 2022 climate bank roadmap progress report," p. 3.
49 Data sourced from: EIB Group (2020) *The EIB Group Climate Bank Roadmap 2021–2025.* European Investment Bank. Available at: https://www.eib.org/en/
publications/the-eib-group-climate-bank-roadmap.htm.
50 "EIB group 2022 climate bank roadmap progress report," p. 12.
51 EIB (2023) "Climate action and environmental sustainability. Overview."
Available at:https://www.eib.org/attachments/lucalli/20220287_climate_action_
and_enviromental_sustainability_overview_2023_en.pdf.
52 Ibid.

11

CONCLUSION

Jos Delbeke

Scientists from all over the world in the forum of the IPCC have been delivering convincing climate research for decades. What they predicted is now happening in a manner visible to all, and even faster than anticipated.

The United Nations brought all countries of the world together in establishing the UNFCCC and adopting the Paris Agreement in 2015. COP28 in Dubai finally agreed to transition away from fossil fuels. This is a gigantic task, as the use of coal, oil and gas has permeated all facets of modern society and powerful vested interests are reluctant to change their business models. On top of that, the world's population keeps growing. However, it is a sober fact that despite all the warnings by the scientific community, as well as decades of meetings in the context of the UN, greenhouse gas emissions keep increasing at the global level. There is, nevertheless, hope that emissions will peak in the next few years, after which the decline can finally start.

The EU has reduced its emissions by 32.5% since 1990. By 2030, the EU is committed to reducing its greenhouse gas emissions by at least 55% below 1990 levels, and by 2050 will be climate neutral. Emissions per head are steadily declining from more than 12 tons per head in 1980 to around 7 tons today. A decoupling between economic growth and emissions has been realized. New economic activities are being created and low-carbon innovations continue to be brought to the market.

Agreeing targets is one thing, but implementing these through the development of policies remains challenging. Over the last five years, a European Green Deal has been rolled out, representing a comprehensive package of policies covering all sectors of the economy, not least in the fields of energy, transport, and industry. In addition to strengthening existing policies, new policies have also developed, such as the disclosure of climate risks incurred by companies and financial institutions. Finally, the EU has systematically started to mainstream climate and sustainability concerns in all its policy areas, not least the ones related to the use of its budget.

DOI: 10.4324/9781003493730-14

The EU has been and can remain a laboratory for an efficient and fair implementation of climate policy. Getting started, even in a less perfect manner, learning-by-doing and a gradual tightening of its policies have been central to its success. Starting slowly gave the chance to both public and private actors to learn how to tackle things in practice. The EU developed a common climate policy even though it is comprised of 27 sovereign Member States with very different economic, social, political and geographic conditions. Much attention has been given to maintain the collective 'willingness to pay' by searching for policies having the lowest economic costs combined with a due regard to fairness. While common EU targets were adopted, their implementation was always subject to differentiation taking account of fairness. In the coming years, more attention will have to be paid to social issues and the impacts of the transition on individual households.

At the heart of its policy the EU established a system of carbon pricing. In the sectors covered, emissions have been reduced the most. Having the economic incentives right and making polluters pay has proven to be effective. It also raised significant revenue that is being used to reinforce climate action and to address social impacts. Carbon leakage has been prevented through a system of free allocation under the EU ETS, that is now gradually being replaced by the introduction of a Carbon Border Adjustment Mechanism. Based on the EU's internal success in applying carbon pricing, it is now time to develop an outward-looking strategy. A start has been made by the 'Call for Paris-aligned Carbon Markets' in June 2023. Several critical deadlines on implementation are approaching such as the longer-term treatment of international civil aviation. A new wave of EU enlargement may generate innovative ways of using carbon pricing to accelerate the climate and energy transitions of candidate countries. Finally, the operational arrangements on Article 6 of the Paris Agreement should be brought to a close and this also requires an active engagement by the EU.

Changes in the energy sector have delivered the most significant emission reductions until now. Fuel switching away from coal to natural gas and renewable energy has been intensive and will continue. However, since the Russian invasion of Ukraine in 2022, the availability of abundant and cheap natural gas has come to an end. The high prices for energy encouraged the uptake of renewable energy as well as the improvements in energy efficiency, but the reality remains that today fossil fuels still account for a too high a share of the energy mix.

As part of the geopolitical re-balancing of the world, the EU must doubledown on the energy and climate transition and turn the ongoing challenges into an opportunity for the continent. One of the key challenges is to decarbonize energy-intensive manufacturing while maintaining a solid industrial base in Europe. This not only requires massive investment in low-carbon technologies but also needs a diversification of the EU's trade relationships. Europe should build further on its tradition of defending international trade and open markets but diversify the risks related to it. The climate transition should, therefore, be embedded in the development of a geopolitical industrial strategy in view of making Europe more resilient to external economic and political shocks. The energy and climate plan each Member State is developing should become the starting point of a pro-active governance system in view of helping to deliver the strategic autonomy the EU is aiming for.

Cost-efficiency combined with social corrections, accompanied by considerations of the long-term resilience of the EU's economy, must be at the center of future reviews of legislation. Delivery of climate neutrality by 2050 will require removals of CO_2 at scale through technology as well as nature-based solutions. Coherence between the multiple sub-targets adopted in recent years can be improved, and new pragmatic trade-offs will have to be found between economic, strategic and sustainability considerations – such as for securing critical raw materials. The EU should engage pro-actively in the climate and energy transition that many countries in the world are going through. Groups of like-minded countries should be brought together in climate clubs including on carbon pricing and on low-carbon technology exchange. These may become a precious help in preparing the next round of Nationally Determined Contributions due in 2025.

Even if there is a lot more to be done, EU climate policy has reached a point of no return. While the task ahead remains challenging, useful policy experience is now available. The EU has shown that bringing down emissions through policies and incentives for low-carbon technologies and behavioral change is possible without undermining economic growth. This should inspire confidence that it is still possible to deliver the global goals of the Paris Agreement.

INDEX

Note: **Bold** page numbers refer to tables; *italic* page numbers refer to figures and page numbers followed by "n" denote endnotes.

Action Plan on Financing Sustainable Growth (2018) 52, 236
advanced biofuels 181
afforestation 28, 170, 199, 208
agricultural productivity 201
agro-forestry 28
air pollution 78, 192, 201
air quality 13, 128, 179, 181, 187
annual emission allocations (AEAs) 141, 152–154, 157
Anthropocene 6, *7*
anthropogenic methane 190
Assigned Amount Units 37
Auctioning Regulation 74
'Auctions-As-A-Service' concept 226
Australia, national emissions trading system in 105
aviation emissions 109, 111–112, 114–120; CORSIA and ICAO (*see* Carbon Offsetting and Reduction Scheme for International (Civil) Aviation (CORSIA) and ICAO); EU ETS review (2023) 114–116; European airports under EU ETS 112, **113**, 114; international governance for 109, *110*, 111–112; sustainable fuels 116–117

backloading mechanism 65
banking and borrowing mechanism 186
banking crisis (2008) 13, 17, 64, 67, 68, 108
Batteries Regulation 222
Biden, Joe 42

biodiversity 6, 30, 125, 170, 180, 201, 205, 208, 209, 211, 236, 238
Bio-Energy with Carbon Capture and Storage (BECCS) technology 170
blue hydrogen 25
bonus-only benchmark-based crediting system 186
bottom-up approach 40, 176–177
Burden Sharing Agreement (2008–2012) 142

Caisse des Dépôts (CDC) 245
Call for Action for Paris Aligned Carbon Markets (2023) 17, 32, 256
Canada, national carbon pricing system in 107
cap-and-trade approach 14, 59
CAPEX support 24
Capital Market Association (ICMA) 239
Capital Markets Union, European Union 52
CAP Strategic Plans 190, 205, 213n16, 248
Carbon Border Adjustment Mechanism (CBAM) 51, 74, 76, 83, 84, 92–99, 104, 105; carbon price paid 95–96; design 92; liability 92–95, **94**, 99; monitoring 96–97; for policy cooperation 97–98
Carbon Border Adjustment Mechanism (CBAM) Regulation 15–18, 25, 32, 96, 228, 256; Article 2 98; Article 9 95; Recital 72 98
carbon budgets 5, 37

carbon capture, storage and utilisation (CCUS) 220, 231
carbon capture and storage (CCS) 17, 27, 76, 170, 208, 215–216
'carbon contracts of difference' 227
carbon credits 17, 62, 64–65, 67, 104, 105, 119
Carbon Cycles Communication 209–210
carbon farming 210, 211
carbon leakage 15, 27, 31–32, 78, 98, 99, 105, 215, 256
carbon leakage and EU ETS 83–100; Carbon Border Adjustment Mechanism 92–98; free allocation 84–85, 87–91; problems 83–84
carbon markets 37, 45, 47, 65–68, 104–105, 107–108, 129
Carbon Offsetting and Reduction Scheme for International (Civil) Aviation (CORSIA) and ICAO 16, 112, 114, 117–120, 129; governance arrangements and double counting 120; offsetting and crediting programmes 119; participation 118–119
carbon price paid 95–96
carbon pricing 14–18, 20, 24, 31, 32, 50, 51, 60, 61, 65, 70, 71, 73, 78, 92–100, 104–105, *106*, 117, 130, 173–174, 215, 256
carbon removal 6, 13, 17, 22, 27–28, 199, 208; certification system 27, 28; land-based 27
Carbon Removal Certification Framework 208, 210
carbon sinks 9, 27, *201*, 201–203, 205
carbon taxes 60, 95, 107
CDP Equity (CDPE) 245
Chernobyl disaster 23
Chicago Convention (1944) 112, 114, 118, 119
China: building sustainable finance 242; CORSIA and 118–119; ETS 96; greenhouse gas emissions 38; Industrial Policy programme 221; national emissions trading systems 107; taxonomy 242; United States (US) relationship with 40
chlorofluorocarbons (CFCs) 188
circular economy 24, 50, 236, 245
Circular Economy Action Plan 209
Clean Development Mechanism (CDM) 17, 37, 64, 107, 108, 142, 146

clean hydrogen 223, 231
'Clean Planet for All' Communication (2018) 216, 223
climate adaptation 29–30, 46, 60, 98, 160, 190, 201, 211, 236
Climate Bank Roadmap (2021–2025) 249
climate change 3–6, 35, 36, 43; adverse effects of 46–47; anthropogenic 44; impact of 4, 5, 13
Climate Change Committee 73
Climate Club 50, 98
Climate Law 12, 17, 18, 147, 157, 158, 160, 162, 203
climate mitigation 190, 205, 236, 243
climate neutrality 12–14, 18, *19*, 27, 28, 62, 88, 160, 199
climate neutral materials 215, 233n3
climate resilience 30, 46–47
Climate Resilience Dialogues 30
climate smart measures 198
climate targets 12, 13, 22, 28, 53, 109, 215, 239
climate tipping points 4
Club of Rome 14
CO_2 emissions 6, 9, 20; from aviation 109; decoupling economic growth from *10*; fossil *39*; reduction 71, 186
Coal and Carbon-Intensive Regions in Transition Initiative 26
coal mining 26, 33n25
coal use 9, 23, 31
Cohesion Fund (CF) 230, 244, 245, *246*
Commission Implementing Act 87
Committee on Implementation and Compliance 46
Common Agricultural Policy (CAP) 27, 145, 190, 205, 209–211, 243, 244, 248
Common But Differentiated Responsibilities (CBDR) 97, 98, 109
Conference of the Parties (COP) 36; COP9 12; COP15 40; COP16 41; COP27 47; COP28 22, 23, 44–47, 255; COP30 22, 45
Connecting Europe Facility 30
contracts for difference (CfDs) 173
Convention on International Civil Aviation 111
Copenhagen Accord (2009) 38, 40–42
COPERNICUS earth observation programme 50

Corporate Sustainability Reporting Directive (CSRD) 29, 238, 239, 253n18
cost-effectiveness 20, 22, 23, 25, 26, 161, 214
cost-efficiency 53, 143, 147, 149, 162, 168, 187, 225, 257
Council of Europe Development Bank (CEB) 245
COVID-19 pandemic 13, 62, 64, 118, 129, 154, 175, 179, 216
Crimea, annexation of 9
Critical Raw Materials Act 24, 227, 229–230, 231
cross-border trade 173
customs duties 93
Customs Nomenclature codes 92

decarbonisation 45, 71, 77, 88, 125, 130, 173, 174, 177, 178, 215, 216, 221
deforestation 6, 50, 199
Deforestation-free supply chains Regulation 210
deindustrialisation 24
desertification 4, 201
Digital Europe programme 230
direct emissions approach 9
disasters policies 30
Doha Amendment (2012–2020) 41
do-no-significant-harm (DNSH) principle 28, 29, 243–245, 251
double-counting 27, 120
"double-dividend" 78, 79
Draghi, Mario 24

Earth Summit (1972) 35
Eco-design Directive 177
Eco-design measures 145
Eco-design Regulation 177, 216
Eco-design Working Plan (2020–2024) 177
eco-innovations 183
Economic Commission for Europe (2023) 197n74
economic crisis *see* banking crisis (2008)
economic development 4, 5, 9, 10, 26, 31, 48
economic incentives 13, 28, 31, 61, 116, 117, 256
economies in transition 36, 37

Effort Sharing 2013–2020 142–143, 145–147; emissions in Effort Sharing sectors 145; flexible provisions *145*, 145–147; re-distributional elements 142–143, *144*; target setting 142, *143*
Effort Sharing 2021–2030 147, 149, 151–154, 156–158; continuation of differentiated target approach 147, *148*, 149; flexibility related to EU ETS 154, 156; land use, land use change, and forestry (LULUCF) Regulation 156–157, **157**; Member States over-achieved their targets 157–158; more convergence among member states 151, **151**, *152*; more differentiation among member states 149, *150*, 151; starting point and trajectories 152–154, *153*, *155*; 2030 targets 158, *159*
Effort-Sharing Decision 139, 142, 145
Effort Sharing Regulation (ESR) 16, 20, 22, 25, 27, 70, 71, 161, 162, 190, 193, 198, 202, 203, 205, 212; emissions from effort sharing sectors 139–141, *140*
electricity and gas market regulation and climate policy 171–174; challenge of integrating energy 171–173; electricity market reform in combination with carbon pricing 173–174; role for consumers 174
electricity market reform 171, 173–174
Electricity Market Regulation 172–173
emissions accounting system 20
energy crisis 23, 167, 168, 174, 175, 244
energy efficiency 50, 175–179; bottom-up approach 176–177; of buildings 178–179; energy dependence 175–176, *176*; energy use regulation and labelling 177; EU Energy Efficiency Directive 176–177; import bill and barriers 175–176, *176*
Energy Efficiency Design Index (EEDI) 128
Energy Efficiency Directive 71, 88, 176–177, 178
"Energy Efficiency First" principle 175
Energy Labelling Directive 177
Energy Performance of Buildings Directive 145, 177, 178
Energy Tax Directive 16

Energy Union Governance Regulation, European Union 46
Enforcement Branch, of Compliance Committee 37
environmental, social and governance (ESG) 29, 235
environmental degradation 35, 236
environmental pollution 6
environmental taxes 78
ETS2 15–17, 20, 66–68, 70–73, 75, 81n30, 83, 88–90, 99, 112, 119, 126, 141, 162, 180, 218; cap trajectory 71; implementation and safeguards 72–73; Market Stability Reserve for 71–73
EU4Health programme 230
EU allowances (EUAs) 15, 61, 62, 64, 73
EU Biodiversity Strategy (2030) 209
EU climate mainstreaming 243–245, 247–248
EU climate policy 3–32, 145, 166, 256; climate change, consequences of 3–7; designing and impact analysis 18, 20, 22–23; endorsement at highest political levels of long-term policy vision 11–14; explicit price on carbon 14–18; geopolitical EU strategy 23–30; greenhouse gas emissions reduction (1990–2022) 7, 9–10; international cooperation on 36; structure of *21*
EU Climate Transition Benchmarks Regulation 240
EU Emissions Trading System (EU ETS) 15–18, 20, 23, 25, 27, 31, 38, 53, 59–79, 99, 179, 212, 218, 256; ETS2 for road transport, buildings, and smaller industry 70–73; functions 59–61; Market Stability Reserve 64–67, *65*; price and emissions development 61–62, *62, 63*, 64; revenues (*see* EU ETS revenues); strengthening of emissions cap (2024–2030) 67–68, *69*
EU Energy Policy 166, 209
EU Energy Taxation Directive 114
EU ETS, international dimension of 104–130; aviation emissions (*see* aviation emissions); carbon credits 108–109; carbon market 104–105, 107–108; maritime emissions (*see* maritime emissions and EU ETS extension)

EU ETS revenues 73–77; raising through auctioning of allowances 73–75, *74*; Social Climate Fund 77; solidarity and use 75–76
EU geopolitical industrial strategy: adaptation 29–30; climate transition as part of 23–25; investing in carbon removals 27–28; social and regional cohesion investments 25–27; sustainable finance 28–29
EU Green Bond Standard (EUGBS) 239–240
EU industry, greening of 214–216, 218–232; EU-level auctioning under Innovation Fund 224–226, *227*; European Battery Alliance 221–222; Hydrogen Bank 224–226; Innovation Fund 218–221, *219*; net-zero industry 227–231; policy instruments development 214–216, *217*, 218; role of State aid 223–224; Temporary Crisis and Transition Framework 223–224
EU Member States 3, 11, 16–18, 20, 22, 23, 25–28, 31, 35; auction revenue to climate purposes 74–75, 77, 78; cancelling allowances 68, 125; contribution to global public climate finance 51; granting State aid 91; Modernisation Fund to 75–76; re-distributional elements for 143; submitting voluntary 2020 emission reduction pledges 41; using ETS revenues for climate change 125
EU Methane Strategy 190, *191*, 192
EU Mobile Air Conditioning (MAC) Directive (2006) 188, 189
European Atomic Energy Community (EURATOM) 166
European Bank for Reconstruction and Development (EBRD) 245
European Battery Alliance 221–222
European Bauhaus 211
European Central Bank (ECB) 17, 241, 242, 252
European Climate, Infrastructure and Environment Agency (CINEA) 233n14
European Climate Risk Assessment 30
European Coal and Steel Community (ECSC) 166
European Commission 16, 22, 26, 52, 85, 95–97, 99, 114, 121, 125, 127,

161, 167, 173, 174, 190, 219, 220, 223, 232, 235, 236
European Council 12, 115–117, 125, 219
European Court of Auditors (ECA) 243
European Court of Justice (ECJ) 112
European Defence Fund 230
European Economic Area 92, 105, 111, 112, 223
European Energy Exchange (EEX) auction platform 74
European Environment Agency 30
European Financial Reporting Advisory Group (EFRAG) 239
European Green Bond Standard 29
European Green Deal 3, 7, 12, 28, 31, 59, 62, 84, 92, 114, 116, 121, 125, 166, 190, 193, 209, 224, 227, 231, 249
European Green Deal, international dimensions of 49–52; sharing experiences on climate and energy transition 50; sustainable finance 51–52; trade-related climate measures 50–51
European Hydrogen Bank 224–226
European Innovation Council 232
European Investment Bank (EIB) as climate bank 30, 233n14, 249, *250*, 251, 252
European Parliament 115–117, 125, 219; Directive 2014/95/EU 238
European Regional Development Fund (ERDF) 244, 245, *246*
European Scientific Advisory Board on Climate Change 160
European Securities and Market Authority (ESMA) 73, 240
European Semester 161
European Social Fund (ESF+) 248
European Sustainability Reporting Standards (ESRS) 239
European University Institute 107
Eurovignette Directive (2022) 186
EU Strategy on Adaptation to Climate Change 209
EU Sustainable Finance Strategy 235–236, *237*, 238–243; benchmarks and green bonds 239–240; disclosure rules 238–239; international approach 240–242; Taxonomy Regulation 236, 238
EU Taxonomy Regulation (2020) 29, 210, 236, 238–240, 251, 252

EU Treaty 14, 75, 83
EU-UK Trade and Cooperation Agreement 114
EU/US Open Skies Agreement 112

fairness 22, 23, 25, 27, 31
Farm to Fork strategy 22, 209
F-gases *see* fluorinated gases (F-gases)
F-gas Regulation (2014) 189
first-generation biofuels 181
Florence Process 17, 107
fluorinated gases (F-gases) 188–189; hole in ozone layer 188; Kigali Amendment 188–189; Montreal Protocol 188–189
forest degradation 50
forest management 170, 201, 202, 208, 210
Forest Monitoring Law 210
Forest Strategy 209
fossil fuel: emissions 124; taxation 116, 117; use 5–7, 9, 23, 31, 70, 71, 75, 114
fossil kerosene 116, 117
Fourth IMO Greenhouse Gas Study (2020) 124
free allocation 15, 31–32, 84–85, 87–91, 98, 99, 115; carbon leakage list 88–89; correction factor 90–91; New Entrants Reserve 91; seizing technological progress benefit 89–90; share of *85*; State aid provisions 91; technological benchmarks 85, **86–87**, 87–88
Free Allocation Regulation 90
fuel consumption monitoring device 184
FuelEU maritime 127
fuel switching 9, 10, 64, 147, 174, 256
fuel taxes/excises 95, 114
fugitive methane emissions 190, 192
Fukushima disaster 23
funding gap 223

G20 countries 13
G20 Financial Stability Board 241
gas market reform 173
geological cycle 6
gilets jaunes protest movement 26
Global Gateway initiative 51
Global Memorandum of Understanding (MoU) on Zero-Emission

Medium- and Heavy-Duty
Vehicles 187
Global Methane Pledge (2021) 192
Global MTTC Network (GMN) 128
global surface temperature *4, 5, 6,
7,* 43
global warming 4–6, 27, 43–45, 190
Gothenburg Protocol 192
green bond catalogue 242
green bonds 239–240
Green Claims Regulation 29
Green Climate Fund 40
green commodities 15
Green Deal Industrial Plan (2023) 24,
215, 218, 227, 231
green finance standard system 242
greenhouse gas (GHG) emissions: from
aviation 111; from human activities
5, 7; land use sector in 199, *200,* 201;
per capita 10, *11,* 49; reduction 5–7,
8, 9–10, 12, 43–44, 60, 141, 145,
168; stabilisation 36
green hydrogen 25, 215
Green Industrial Policy 216, 231
green premium 215, 225–227
green transition 227, 235, 242, 251
greenwashing practices 27, 236
Guarantee Agreements 245
Gulf Stream system 4
Guterres, António 111

Heat Pump Reserve 189
heavy-duty vehicles (HDV) emissions
184, 186–188
Holocene 6, *7*
Horizon Europe 30, 211, 218, 230,
244, 247
hydrochlorofluorocarbons (HCFCs) 188
hydrofluorocarbons (HFCs) 188, 189;
HFC134a 188
Hydrogen Strategy 224

IATA 112
IEA-(Emissions Database for Global
Atmospheric Research) EDGAR
CO2 54n5
impact assessment 18, 22, 67, 143
Important Projects of Common European
Interest (IPCEI) 222, 225
Inclusive Forum on Climate Mitigation
Approaches 50
Indirect Land Use Change (ILUC)
180, 181
industrial decarbonisation 219

Industrial Emissions Directive 192
industrialisation 5, 23
Industrial Revolution 6, 7, 23
Innovation Fund 24, 25, 28, 68, 76, 77,
81n32, 84, 115–116, 124, 125, 127,
130, 218–221, *219,* 224–226, 230–232
Instrument for Pre-Accession Assistance
(IPA III) 247
integrated energy and climate
governance system 20, 22, 158–161;
and Climate Law 158, 160; national
plans 160–162
Intergovernmental Panel on Climate
Change (IPCC) 4–6, 109
International Carbon Action
Partnership 107
International Civil Aviation Organisation
(ICAO) 16, 44, 109, 111, 114, 115,
120; *see also* Carbon Offsetting and
Reduction Scheme for International
(Civil) Aviation (CORSIA) and ICAO
International Energy Agency (IEA) 49
International Maritime Organisation
(IMO) 44, 111, 121, 126–129
International Monetary Fund 17
International Panel on Climate Change
(IPCC) 43
international trade 32, 36, 50
InvestEU 30, 218, 230, 232, 244, 245
IPCC Guidelines for National
Greenhouse Gas Inventories (2006)
81n30

Joint Implementation (JI) 108
Just Energy Transition Plans (JETPs) 51
Just Transition Fund 26

Kerry-Boxer bill 130n3
Kigali Amendment 188–189
Kyoto Protocol 3, 14, 35–38, 40–42, 45,
53, 61, 64, 65, 104, 105, 107–109,
111, 112, 129,
141, 142, 158, 182, 202–203, *204*

Landfill Directive 192
Land Use, Land Use Change and
Forestry (LULUCF) 20, 27, 28, 198,
199; *see also* LULUCF carbon sink
in EU
Land Use, Land-Use Change and
Forestry (LULUCF) Regulation 156–
158, **157,** 170, 198, 202, 203, 205,
206–207; Decision No 529/2013/EU
203; EU 2018/241 203

land use sector: carbon removals and credibility 208; climate action in forestry and agriculture 208–211; LULUCF carbon sink in EU *201, 201–203*, 205; in mitigating and removing greenhouse gas emissions 199, *200,* 201

Least Developed Countries (LDCs) 45, 47, 97, 98

Letta, Enrico 24

LIFE programme 211, 244, 247

linear reduction factor 67, 68, 71, 78, 80n20, 91, 115

low-carbon economy 29, 51, 53

low-carbon electricity 24

low-carbon investments 18, 23

low-carbon technology 6, 10, 13, 24, 26, 32, 48, 51, 60, 83, 145, 256–257

low-carbon transition 25, 193, 239, 251, 252

low-emission vehicles (LEV) 183, 187

LULUCF carbon sink in EU *201, 201–203*, 205; evolution 202–203, *204;* Kyoto Protocol 202–203, *204;* LULUCF Regulation (2018) 203, 205, **206–207**; targets 202–203, *204*

Marine Environment Protection Committee (MEPC) 121

maritime emissions and EU ETS extension 121, 123–128; domestic and international *122;* geographical scope 123–124; IMO developments 127–128; international governance of 121; monitoring, reporting, and verification 126; multilateral action 126–127; phase-in approach and use of revenues 124–125; responsibility between shipowner and charterer 126

Market Stability Reserve (MSR) 16–17, 62, 64–68, *65,* 71–74, 78, 91, 112

market volatility 17

MARPOL Convention 121; Annex VI 128

McCain-Lieberman bill (2003) 130n3

Medical Dose Inhalers 189

methane: anthropogenic 190; emissions of 6, 9, 124, 125; natural 190; sources of 190

Modernisation Fund 26, 75–77, 81n32, 125, 230

monitoring, reporting, and verification (MRV) 61, 93, 96, 120, 121, 123, 126

Monitoring, Reporting and Verification (MRV) Regulation (2015) 121, 123, 124, 126

Monitoring Mechanism Regulation 158

Montreal Protocol 188–189

Multi-Annual Financial Framework (MFF) 232, 235, 244, 252

multilateralism 16, 42, 43, 52, 53, 114, 120, 126, 249

mutual agreement 119

National Communication, European Union 36

National Energy and Climate Plans (NECPs) 205

Nationally Determined Contributions (NDCs) 6, 7, 22, 42–45, 48, 49, 52, 111, 257

natural gas 9, 10, 18, 25, 124, 166, 168, 190, 224, 225, 256

natural methane 190

Nature Protection Law 22

Nature Restoration Law 210

Neighbourhood, Development and International Cooperation Instrument (NDICI) 244, 247

NER300 fund 76, 218

net carbon sequestration 198

Network of Central Banks and Supervisors for Greening the Financial System (NGFS). 241

Network of Maritime Technologies Cooperation Centres (MTCCs) 128

net zero emissions 49, 54n13, 78

Net-Zero Industry Act (NZIA) 24, 216, 227–229, **228,** 231

New Entrant Reserve (NER) 76, 91

New European Driving Cycle (NEDC) 183–184

New Zealand, national emissions trading system in 107

NextGenerationEU (NGEU) 244

nitrous oxide (N_2O) emissions 9, 92, 121, 124, 125

Non-Annex I Parties 36, 40

non-biological renewable fuels 181

Nordic Investment Bank (NIB) 245

Obama, Barack 41

open markets 32, 257

open strategic autonomy 218, 231, 232n2

OPEX support 24

Organisation for Economic Cooperation and Development (OECD) 36, 50, 95

Paris Agreement (2015) 3, 5–7, 9, 10, 13, 29, 31, 35–38, 40–53, 61, 97, 104, 105, 123, 141, 160, 162, 170, 198, 203, 240, 241, 243, 249, 255; applicable to all parties 42–43; Article 2(1) (c) 51; Under Article 2(1) (c) 235; Article 4(4) 111; Article 6 17, 32, 95, 104, 109, 256; Article 6(4) 119; climate resilience and adverse effects of climate change 46–47; collective goals 43–44; Copenhagen Accord (2009) failure and 38, 40–42; dynamic five year ambition cycles 44–45; European Green Deal, international dimensions of 49–52; fostering cooperation and financial flows 47–48; global emissions increase 48–49; Kyoto Protocol 35–38; success 38, 40–42; transparency and accountability 45–46; UN Framework Convention on Climate Change 35–38
Paris UNFCCC Conference (2015) 12
passenger duties 114
perfluorocarbons (PFCs) 189
polluter-pays principle 75, 78, 83, 93, 116, 126
Power Purchasing Agreements 173
priority dispatch 171, 172
Protocol to Abate Acidification, Eutrophication and Ground-level Ozone (2012) 197n74
PV technology 214–216

Q-Cells 214, 215
quota system 189

Recovery and Resilience Facility (RRF) 244–245, 248, 251, 252
Recovery and Resilience Fund 13, 22, 179
Recovery and Resilience Plans 230
reforestation 28, 208
ReFuelEU aviation 117
Regional Greenhouse Gas Initiative (RGGI) 107
Regulation on the Governance of the Energy Union and Climate Action 160–162, 177
renewable electricity 25, 76, 168, 169, 173, 181, 215, 219, 224
renewable energy and climate-related regulations 9, 10, 12, 13, 17, 18, 25, 145, 166–170; binding target for Member States 167–169, *169*; biomass as fuel 169–170; EU policies on 50; technologies 50
Renewable Energy Directive 71, 117, 194n7, 218, 226; 2009 167, 170; 2023 178
RePowerEU Plan 68, 81n32, 216, 220, 224, 235, 244, 245, 251
RES Directive 209
resource shuffling 96
RFNBO hydrogen 226
Roadmap to Sustainable Investing (2021) 242
road transport emissions and climate-related regulations *179*, 179–184, 186–188; biofuels and renewable energy 180–182; heavy-duty vehicles (HDV) 184, 186–188; regulating zero CO_2 emissions by 2035 182–184, *185*
rulebook 45–46
Russia 9, 13, 23; invasion of Ukraine 9, 13, 18, 23, 67, 68, 75, 79, 167, 169, 172, 175, 193, 220, 235, 236, 244, 256; and Kyoto Protocol 37

Small Island Developing States (SIDS) 45, 47
Smart Finance for Smart Buildings Initiative 178
Social Climate Fund (SCF) 15, 26, 27, 70, 77, 81n32, 84, 179
social tariffs 173
Soil and Forest Monitoring Laws 210
"A Soil Deal for Europe" 211
soil organic matter 201
solar feed-in tariffs 215
South Korea, national emissions trading system in 107
Sovereignty Seal 230
Standards and Recommended Practices (SARPs) 118, 119
Strategic Action Plan for Batteries (2018) 222
Strategic Technologies for Europe Platform (STEP) 227–228, 230–232
subsidies 171, 172, 182, 214
super credits 183, 186
sustainable agriculture 201, 208
Sustainable and Smart Mobility Strategy 180
sustainable aviation fuels 116–117

Sustainable Banking Network (SBN) 241
Sustainable Europe Investment Plan
  (2020) 51, 249
sustainable finance 51–52, 210,
  235, 242
Sustainable Finance Disclosure
  Regulation (SFDR) 29, 238, 239
sustainable forest management 170
sustainable land management 201
sustainable supply chains 50
Swiss emissions trading system 104
synthetic fuels 181

Task Force on Climate-related Financial
  Disclosures (TFCFD) 241, 242
Technical Expert Group on Sustainable
  Finance 240
Technical Support Instrument (TSI) 248
Temporary Crisis and Transition
  Framework (TCTF)
  223–224, 232
TESLA 221
total number of allowances in circulation
  (TNAC) 112
trade-related climate measures
  50–51
transition risks 252n6
Transmissions System Operators 171
Treaty of Rome (2009) 166
Trump, Donald 41, 53
type-approval procedure 183,
  184, 186

UN 2030 Sustainable Development
  Agenda 51, 235
UN Environment Programme
  (UNEP) 111
UN Framework Convention on Climate
  Change (UNFCCC) 5, 7, 9, 11,
  35–38, 41, 42, 45, 52, 97, 104, 108,
  109, 141, 158, 160, 255; Annex II of
  36; Annex I of 36, 40, 48, 111

United Kingdom, national emissions
  trading system in 105, 107
United Nations Conference on
  Environment and Development 35
United Nations Economic Committee for
  Europe (UNECE) 183
United States (US): CORSIA application
  119; emissions trading system 107;
  and Kyoto Protocol 37; and Paris
  Agreement 41–42; relationship with
  China 40
Urban Wastewater Treatment
  Directive 192
US Federal Aviation Authority 120
US Inflation Reduction Act (US IRA,
  2022) 24, 116, 130n3, 216, 222, 223,
  230, 231
US Securities and Exchange Commission
  (US SEC) 242

value chain 24, 97, 216, 222, 225, 229,
  232, 239
VAT 93, 114, 128
Vehicle Energy Consumption Calculation
  Tool (VECTO) 186
Voluntary Carbon Markets
  (VCM) 17

Waste Framework Directive 192
waste recycling 24, 181
Waxman-Markey bill (2009) 130n3
World Bank 17, 38
World Harmonised Light Vehicles Test
  Procedure (WLTP) 183
World Meteorological Organisation
  (WMO) 3
World War II 35

zero-carbon technology 83
zero CO_2 emissions 182–184, *185*
zero-emission vehicles (ZEV) 77, 183,
  186, 187

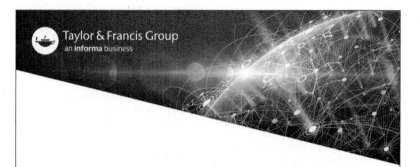